ING OF DARTMOUTH COLLEGE.

removed his family and school from Lebanon, Conn. and
college in a forest. In the open air with his numerous fa-
and evening prayer, and the surrounding forest re... led
of supplication and praise.
15

177

...u-Hall, with a Front View of the Presidents House in New Jersey.

UNIVERSITY OF VIRGINIA, CHARLOTTESVILLE.

The

College Years

Edited by A. C. SPECTORSKY

HAWTHORN BOOKS, INC · PUBLISHERS · NEW YORK

Library of Congress Catalogue Card Number 58-11466

FIRST EDITION, OCTOBER, 1958

ACKNOWLEDGMENTS

The editor and his publisher wish to express their gratitude for permission to reprint selections from the works of the authors and publishers listed:

How the Student Should Behave: from "Morale scolarium of John of Garland," in *Memoirs of the University of California,* University of California Press, 1927, L. J. Paetow, translator and editor.

A Clerke of Oxenford: from *The Book of English Classic Poetry,* © 1934 by Wm. H. Wise & Co., Inc.; by permission.

A Plan for the Education of the Youth of Pennsylvania: from *The Benjamin Franklin Reader,* edited by Nathan G. Goodman; by permission of Thomas Y. Crowell Company.

Shelley Expelled from Oxford: from *The Life of Percy Bysshe Shelley* by Thomas Jefferson Hogg, edited by Humbert Wolfe, published by E. P. Dutton & Co., Inc., and J. M. Dent & Sons, Ltd.; by permission of the publishers.

Harvard College, 1815: from *A Chilmark Miscellany* by Van Wyck Brooks, © 1948 by Van Wyck Brooks, published by E. P. Dutton & Co., Inc.; by permission of the publisher.

Cadets: from *West Point* by Sidney Forman, © 1950 by Columbia University Press; by permission of the United States Military Academy and the publisher.

Semester at Heidelberg: from *The Autobiography of Lincoln Steffens,* © 1931 by Harcourt, Brace and Company, Inc.

The Chair of Philanthromathematics: from *The Gentle Grafter* by O. Henry, © 1907 by Sarah Coleman Porter; by permission of Doubleday and Company, Inc.

How Good Were the Good Old Times?: from "The Good Old Times," © 1929 by Curtis Publishing Co.

Syrian Sophomores: from *Philosopher's Holiday* by Irwin Edman, © 1938 by Irwin Edman; by permission of The Viking Press, Inc.

Let's Away With Study: from *Carmina Burana,* translated by Helen Waddell; by permission of Constable & Company, Ltd., London.

Freshman Adviser: from *Harper's Magazine,* © 1930 by Harper & Brothers; by permission of the author.

A Student in Economics: from *No More Trumpets,* © 1933 by Harcourt, Brace and Company, Inc.; by permission of Paul R. Reynolds & Son.

How a Writer Is Made: from *The Barefoot Boy With Cheek* by Max Shulman, © 1943 by Max Shulman; by permission of Doubleday and Company, Inc.

A Lonely Year: from *Look Homeward, Angel,* © 1929 by Charles Scribner's Sons, © 1957 by Edward C. Aswell, administrator C.T.A. of the Estate of Thomas Wolfe and/or Fred W. Wolfe; by permission of the publisher.

A Sophomore's Soul: from *The Patient Observer* by Simeon Strunsky, © 1911 by Dodd, Mead & Company, Inc.; by permission of the publisher.

Flowers for a Professor's Garden of Verses: from *Innocent Merriment* by F. P. Adams; by permission of Mrs. Lester Markel.

Propaganda: from *The Yale Record;* by permission.

The Life and Work of Professor Roy Millen: from *Circus In The Attic And Other Stories* by Robert Penn Warren, © 1943 by Robert Penn Warren; by permission of Harcourt, Brace and Company, Inc.

Contents

2 CLASS

3 CAMPUS

4 REFLECTIONS AND INQUIRIES

5 AND FOND RECALL

Preface

FOR the past eleven centuries, throughout the civilized world, in times of war and peace, of enlightenment and of intellectual and spiritual darkness, in prosperity and in poverty, the idea of the university has survived and flourished.

Like many of the most profoundly important ideas which have influenced the evolution of thinking man, the idea of the university is, essentially, simple: a convocation of people whose primary purpose is the accumulation, the sharing, and the extension of knowledge. This is the unifying notion which makes it possible to consider the smallest medieval university—with its pauper-poor scholars, its few teachers, its meager store of books—and the largest and most magnificently equipped university of today, as more alike than they are different. It is the unifying notion which makes it accurate to say that, at any given instant in those thousand-odd years, there have been unique and essentially similar communities throughout the world whose inhabitants—however disparate they might be, however benighted or wrong-minded we might think some of them to have been—knew a common motivation and a common aim: the desire to follow the light of knowledge to the ever-beckoning, never-attainable goal of universal understanding.

The history of the university idea may be likened to a fluctuating current, now swelling and flowing strong and straight, then twisting and turbulent; or narrowed to a trickle, or in flood; here misdirected, there eddied and almost stagnant. But always it has been there, a river, if you will, whose droplets are the individual minds and spirits of the faculties and students, a river seeking to meet the sea of universal knowledge and enlightenment.

It was Alfred Korzybski, founding father of General Semantics, who isolated what he considered the one most significant characteristic of human beings which advantageously distinguishes them from other forms of life. He called it "time binding," the capacity to transmit knowledge from generation to generation so that, in a sense, each generation could "begin"

17

where the preceding one left off. Language is the means of time binding; great books and great minds are its reservoirs; the institution of the university is its most potent instrument.

Your editor asks your indulgence for having voiced these thoughts and musings, evoked by the exacting but engrossing task of poring over some thousand years of writings about college and university life. It was an edifying assignment from which some further, more specific thoughts emerged.

From a literary point of view, this body of writing stands out as partaking of the freshness and vigor which animate collegiate life and thought itself. From the reader's point of view, it is gratifyingly nonhomogeneous: in variety, it rivals the diverse interests and activities which lie behind the dry verbiage of college catalogues and curricula. And even its most casual sampler can't fail to be impressed with its atmosphere of vivid aliveness—which is not surprising. For this is a collection of writing by and about those men and women who have enjoyed the university experience, a unique adventure which, in each generation, brings together the cream of the crop to spend unforgettable years between the end of adolescence and the attainment of full maturity, in a place of its own, where each day spells growth, excitement, interaction of people and ideas, stimulation—and downright good fun.

The attempt in this volume has been to hold the literary mirror to college life in all its aspects. These are glimpses, some profound, some perhaps a bit rosy with sentimental recall, others jaundiced and bitter, still others ebulliently young and carefree—but each and all contributing, it is hoped, to a view in the round of the university world.

As is usual with all books, but most typically with collections having the scope of this one, a very liberal sharing of credit must be accorded those without whom—as the cliché has it—publication of this volume would have been impossible. The degree to which the editor has been helped cannot be measured by the order in which his gratitude is extended.

Kenneth Giniger, of Hawthorn Books, employed Socratic means to implant in the editor's mind the idea for this book. When it was firmly set, he gracefully retired and it remained to get the project launched.

How does one go about searching the memory—and the libraries—for the best writings about university life? Not alone, for one thing. With some trepidation, the help of English and Literature professors in some hundred American colleges and universities was solicited. They were told the scope and aim of the book to be, were given a partial list of initial selections, and were asked to make nominations. One of the most heartwarming experiences a man can have then befell the editor. For these teachers—busy men with work (and books) of their own to be done—responded so generously that the editor's task became more one of culling than of searching. The following is a list of some of those whose recommendations proved most valuable:

Cecilia A. Hotchner, Hunter College; Robert G. Davis, Columbia University; George A. Peck, Brooklyn College; George B. Parks, Queens College; Warner G. Rice and Arno L. Bader, University of Michigan; Willard Thorp, Princeton University; Frederic E. Faverty, Northwestern University; C. A. Robertson, University of Florida; Norman Weyand, S.J., Loyola University; Weller Embler, The Cooper Union; Francis E. Mineka, Cornell University; Stanley Hyman, Bennington College; Walter Blair, University of Chicago; Judson Jerome, Antioch College; Herschel Baker, Harvard University; William Peden, University of Missouri; Charles A. Fenton, Yale University; Henry Nash Smith and James D. Hart, University of California; Lyall H. Powers, University of Wisconsin; E. L. McAdam, Jr., New York University; Irvin Stock, Rollins College; Fred L. Bergmann, DePauw University; Dorothy Bethurum, Connecticut College; Edgar Johnson, City College; Patrick F. Quinn, Wellesley College. Special thanks, too, are due Maxwell Geismar, literary critic and essayist, and Edward H. Styles, perennial student of "Eng. Lit."

Even an editor must have an editor: to Fred Kerner, of Hawthorn Books, fell the task of keeping the over-enthusiastic compiler from making an impossibly large and unwieldy tome, and of pulling together words and pictures into a cohesive whole. J. Stewart Johnson's practiced eye and grasp of graphics deserve special credit for the pictorial content of this book. Last to be named, but perhaps most owed the editor's gratitude, is that tireless scholar and literary detective, Louis Lerman: his help has made the assembling of this collection a far happier job of work than it otherwise would have been.

Grateful thanks, too, are due the reader of this volume. His taking it in hand is an act of faith: he is saying, in effect, "I will accord you my attention, on which there are so many claims, until I tire." The editor's fervent wish is that when and if the reader tires, he will have found enough to please him so that, refreshed and time permitting, he will return for more. Because, this book is not meant to be read at a sitting, or continuously; though it was planned to have continuity and unity, as well as variety, it was principally designed for browsing, for visiting with, for pleasure and, perhaps, a few surprises. If the planning was carried out successfully, then some of the joy and excitement, some of the fun and enlightenment which characterize the college years will emerge from these pages—thus justifying the book's title, the editor's efforts, and the reader's act of faith.

A. C. SPECTORSKY

Halls of Ivy

1

"AFTER God had carried us safe to New England, and we had builded our houses, provided necessaries for our liveli-hood, rear'd convenient places for God's worship, and setled the Civill Government; One of the next things we longed for, and looked after was to advance Learning and perpetuate it to Posterity."

And so they voted £400, these earliest newcomers to America, to found "a schoale or colledge"—the beginnings of the Harvard of today. Into the brick and mortar they built a venerable tradition. They planted ivy to grace the walls with seeds carried from Salerno —where the first university in the western world had been founded in the ninth century—from Paris, Salamanca, Oxford, wherever students and teachers and books and ideas had been gathered in one place.

The earliest universities had no buildings, no campuses, few books. But where there was a teacher, there were students. They studied and sang and caroused and fought and debated, as have students since. They paid dearly at times (and have since) for the right they claimed to free inquiry and to explore the unknowns of man and his world. But through these thousand years from that first school at Salerno to the great universities of our day, through all the hazards of time, place and circumstance, their purpose has remained unaltered—"to advance Learning and perpetuate it to Posterity."

In whatever scholars' Olympus the founders of the university tradition may now dwell, they must be gratified with how well they sowed their seed. For it is a fact that from the colleges and universities with long years of tradition upon them have come, in each generation, leaders and movers into new knowledge, shedders of light into what had been darkness. This, too, is part of the tradition.

From past and present, from history and song and story, those writings have been chosen which seem best to convey the sense and feel and sweep of this great tradition.

ANONYMOUS

Gaudeamus Igitur

FROM Carmina Burana

The mellow "Gaudeamus Igitur," so universally sung at academic festivities, has a venerable if somewhat alcoholic tradition. It is the most famous of the drinking songs of the medieval Wandering Students, with sentiments more pagan than clerical.

They were a purse-free, heart-free lot, these medieval scholars, "more capable," says one historian, "of pronouncing judgment upon wine and women than upon problems of divinity or logic."

"Gaudeamus Igitur," and other such scholarly songs, was preserved for later generations of university students in a richly illuminated thirteenth-century manuscript, Carmina Burana, *found in a Bavarian monastery.*

LET us live then and be glad
  While young life's before us!
    After youthful pastime had,
    After old age hard and sad,
  Earth will slumber o'er us.

Where are they who in this world,
  Ere we kept, were keeping?
    Go ye to the gods above;
    Go to hell; inquire thereof:
  They are not; they're sleeping.

Brief is life, and brevity
  Briefly shall be ended:
    Death comes like a whirlwind strong,
    Bears us with his blast along;
  None shall be defended.

Live this university,
　Men that learning nourish;
　　Live each member of the same,
　　Long live all that bear its name;
　Let them ever flourish!

Live the commonwealth also,
　And the men that guide it!
　　Live our town in strength and health,
　　Founders, patrons, by whose wealth
　We are here provided!

Live all girls!　A health to you,
　Melting maids and beauteous!
　　Live the wives and women too,
　　Gentle, loving, tender, true,
　Good, industrious, duteous!

Perish cares that pule and pine!
　Perish envious blamers!
　　Die the Devil, thine and mine!
　　Die the starch-necked Philistine!
　Scoffers and defamers!

[Tr. John Addington Symonds]

Riot at Oxford

FROM *History and Antiquities of University of Oxford*

There was no love lost between the medieval university scholars and the townspeople. The universities were self-governing communities with special grants and privileges bitterly resented by the towns. It needed no more than a few "snappish words" for violent and bloody rioting to begin and spread.

In the great riot of Saint Scholastica's Day, 1354, Town and Gown fought each other for three days and nights. Sixty scholars were killed; the number of town casualties is unreported.

Anthony Wood was a seventeenth-century graduate of Merton College. He spent years collecting the material for his History and Antiquities of the University of Oxford, *from which this hardly dispassionate account is taken.*

HOWBEIT seeing that divers Chronicles do remember a very grievous discord to have hapned this year between the Scholars and Townsmen, and that divers were wounded and some slain, which they deliver very briefly or unsatisfactorily; I shall therefore give the Reader a full account of it and its proceedings, as I find it from a multitude of writings, that so truth might take place, and inquisitive persons understand the whole story of the matter. Such an unheard of outrage it was, that though the Clerks or Scholars were worsted by the Townsmen, assisted with Rustics; yet it proved at length a glorious day, and advantageous to them in respect of Liberties, as it shall be shewed in due time. Furthermore though the Townsmen were the first abettors of, and fought all occasions to promote, the quarrel; yet by so doing, with the sad events that followed, their Privileges were laid at stake, and worthily forfeited to the King, and by him bestowed for the most part on the University. But to the relation of the matter.

On Tuesday 10 Feb. (being the feast of S. Scholastica the Virgin) came

Walter de Springheuse, Roger de Chesterfield, and other Clerks, to the
Tavern called Swyndlestock (being now the Meermaid Tavern at Quatervois, stiled at this day in leases Swynstock) and there calling for wine,
John de Croydon the Vintner brought them some, but they disliking it, as
it should seem, and he avouching it to be good, several snappish words
passed between them. At length the Vintner giving them stubborn and
saucy language, they threw the wine and vessel at his head. The Vintner
therefore receding with great passion, and aggravating the abuse to those
of his family and neighbourhood, several came in, encouraged him not to
put up the abuse, and withal told him they would faithfully stand by him.
Among these were John de Bereford (owner of the said Tavern by a
lease from the Town) Richard Forester and Robert Lardiner, who out of
propensed malice seeking all occasions of conflict with the Scholars, and
taking this abuse for a ground to proceed upon, caused the Town Bell at
St. Martin's to be rung, that the Commonalty might be summoned together
in a body. Which being begun they in an instant were in arms, some
with bows and arrows, others with divers sorts of weapons. And then
they without any more ado did in a furious and hostile manner, suddenly
set upon divers Scholars, who at that time had not any offensive arms, no
not so much as any thing to defend themselves.

They shot also at the Chancellor of the University and would have killed
him, though he endeavoured to pacify them and appease the tumult. Further also though the Scholars at the command of the Chancellor did presently withdraw themselves from the fray, yet the Townsmen thereupon
did more fiercely pursue him and the Scholars, and would by no means
persist from the conflict. The Chancellor perceiving what great danger
they were in, caused the University Bell at St. Mary's to be rung out,
whereupon the Scholars got bows and arrows, and maintained the fight
with the Townsmen till dark night, at which time the fray ceased, no one
Scholar or Townsman being killed or mortally wounded or maimed.

On the next day being wednesday, albeit the Chancellor of the University caused public proclamation to be made in the morning both at St.
Mary's church in the presence of the Scholars there assembled in a great
multitude, and also at Quatervois among the Townsmen, that no Scholar
or Townsman should wear or bear any offensive weapons or assault any
man, or otherwise disturb the peace (upon which the Scholars did in
humble obedience to that proclamation, repaired to the Schools, and de-
meaned themselves peaceably till after dinner) yet the very same morning
'circa horam ordinariam' (as I find it exprest) the Townsmen came with
their bows and arrows, and drave away a certain Master in Divinity and
his auditors, who was then determining in the Augustine Schools. The
Ballives of the Town also had given particular warning to every Townsman

at his respective house in the morning that they should make themselves
ready to fight with the Scholars against the time when the Town bell
should ring out, and also given notice before to the country round about,
and had hired people to come in and assist the Townsmen in their intended
conflict with the Scholars. In dinner time the Townsmen subtilly and
secretly sent about fourscore men armed with bows and arrows, and other
manner of weapons into the parish of St. Giles in the north suburb; who,
after a little expectation, having discovered certain Scholars walking after
dinner in Beaumont (being the same place we now call St. Giles's fields)
issued out of St. Giles's church, shooting at the said Scholars for the space
of three furlongs: some of them they drove into the Augustine Priory,
and others into the Town. One Scholar they killed without the walls, some
they wounded mortally, others grievously and used the rest basely. All
which being done without any mercy, caused an horrible outcry in the
Town: whereupon the Town bell being rung out first and after that the
University bell, divers Scholars issued out armed with bows and arrows
in their own defence and of their companions, and having first shut and
blocked up some of the Gates of the Town (least the country people who
were then gathered together in innumerable multitudes might suddenly
break in upon their rear in an hostile manner and assist the Townsmen
who were now ready prepared in battle array, and armed with their targets
also) they fought with them and defended themselves till after Vesper tide;
a little after which time, entered into the Town by the west gate about two
thousand countrymen with a black dismal flag, erect and displayed. Of
which the Scholars having notice, and being unable to resist so great
and fierce a company, they withdrew themselves to their lodgings. . . .

But the Townsmen finding no Scholars in the streets to make any opposition, pursued them, and that day they broke open five Inns, or Hostles
of Scholars with fire and sword. . . .

Such Scholars as they found in the said Halls or Inns they killed or
maimed, or grievously wounded. Their books and all their goods which
they could find, they spoiled, plundered and carried away. All their victuals,
wine, and other drink they poured out; their bread, fish &c. they trod
under foot. After this the night came on and the conflict ceased for that
day, and the same even public proclamation was made in Oxon in the
King's name, "that no man should injure the Scholars or their goods under
pain of forfeiture."

The next day being Thursday (after the Chancellor and some principal
persons of the University were set out towards Woodstock to the King,
who had sent for them thither) no one Scholar or Scholar's servant so
much as appearing out of their Houses with any intention to harm the
Townsmen, or offer any injury to them (as they themselves confessed) yet

the said Townsmen about sun rising, having rung out their bell, assembled themselves together in a numberless multitude, desiring to heap mischief upon mischief, and to perfect by a more terrible conclusion that wicked enterprise which they had began. This being done they with hideous noises and clamours came and invaded the Scholars' Houses in a wretchless fort, which they forced open with iron bars and other engines; and entring into them, those that resisted and stood upon their defence (particularly some Chaplains) they killed or else in a grievous sort maimed. Some innocent wretches, after they had killed, they scornfully cast into houses of easment, others they buried in dunghills, and some they let lie above ground. The crowns of some Chaplains, viz. all the skin so far as the tonsure went, these diabolical imps flayed off in scorn of their Clergy. Divers others whom they had mortally wounded, they haled to prison, carrying their entrails in their hands in a most lamentable manner. They plundred and carried away all the goods out of fourteen Inns or Halls, which they spoiled that Thursday. They broke open and dashed to pieces the Scholars' Chests and left not any moveable thing which might stand them in any stead; and which was yet more horrid, some poor innocents that were flying with all speed to the Body of Christ for succour (then honorably carried in procession by the Brethren through the Town for the appeasing of this slaughter) and striving to embrace and come as near as they could to the repository wherein the glorious Body was with great devotion put, these confounded sons of Satan knocked them down, beat and most cruelly wounded. The Crosses also of certain Brethren (the Fryers) which were erected on the ground for the present time with a *procul hinc ite profani,* they overthrew and laid flat with the cheynell. This wickedness and outrage continuing the said day from the rising of the sun till noon tide and a little after without any ceasing, and thereupon all the Scholars (besides those of the Colleges) being fled divers ways, our mother the University of Oxon, which had but two days [before] many sons is now almost forsaken and left forlorn. The names of the Clerks or Scholars that were killed which were the next day or two days after known and told to the Bishop of Lincoln were

Thomas Mestologie, Robert Morbogard, Priests, of Ireland, as I suppose.
Roger Grenham, Henry Havecate, Scholars.
John Walleys, Servitor, Philip Beauchampe, Clerk.

The names of the wounded Clerks, whose lives were then despaired of, were

Malachie Murbanan, Priest	Charles Ogormulyn
Malachie Magnigir	Dionysius Ohagagan, Priest
Patrick Magbradardie	Maurice Odeorogean

All Irish men, as I conceive.

The last of which was wounded to death in the head in procession with the Brethren.

Gilbert Osserir   William Deerley
John Salton   Mr. Hugh de Breynton M. of A.
Hugh Middleham   and Priest
Barthelm. Wellyngton   John Harald, Priest
Roger Blaby   Roger of Wales, a Deacon
William Godeshale   Richard Haryngton.

Which last (Haryngton) fled to the body of our Lord and was thence dragged, grievously wounded and imprisoned. Then

Roger Bourgh;   -------Cote of St. Mary Hall.
Salamon Tirie, Priest,   Gilbert Harmach.

With divers others who were run into the country and could not be as yet known whether they were dead or alive. Some died in their flight, or rather creeping away, into the country; and others not yet known that were wounded, killed, cast into privies and buried in dunghills.

The slaughter being thus finished (albeit a thirst continued still after blood on the Town part) the Sages or the chief Magistrates with the company of Regents that were remaining, gathered privately together, and drawing up a diary of these proceedings (such mostly that I have already repeated) inclosed it in a Latin Epistle written by them, and dated 16 Febr; which being done they sent it to the Bishop of Lincoln by the hands of Mr. John de Staunton, M. of A. who on the 18 of the said month wherein this conflict fell out, arriving at Buckden in Huntingdonshire, the seat belonging to the said Bishop, delivered it into his own hands with the diary inclosed, attested by the subscriptions of such that were spectators of the said outrage: the former beginneth thus *Reverendo in Christo patri, D. Johanni Episcopo Lyncolniæ &c.* the other thus—*Die Martis in sesto S. Scholasticæ Virginis proxima prædicta &c.* The particulars of all which, the Bishop hearing, not without grief and astonishment, caused forthwith letters of excommunication to be drawn up. In which, in the first place, praising the University of Oxford with this elogie—*super omnia Studia per cuncta mundi climata landabilis &c.* and others, and then inserting the chief particulars of the said Conflict, he interdicted the Town, and caused the same letters of excommunication to be read in each parish church in Oxon for several (both Lord's and Festival) days, with ringing of bells, crosses erected, lighted and extinguished candles, by the Priests or Chaplains of the said churches in their sacerdotal vestments and robes. So that the Townsmen being utterly deprived of all ecclesiastical benefit in hearing Service, receiving the Sacraments, Burial, Marriage, &c. caused such good people that made a conscience of religion (such I mean that were not accessary to the conflict) to be full of grief and sorrow, especially when they considered if death in the mean time should arrest them.

How the Student Should Behave

FROM *Morale Scholarium*

These rules of decorous behavior for the medieval university student were set down by John of Garland, a professor at the University of Paris in the thirteenth century. From the professor's admonitions about how not to behave, one gathers that our academic forebears must have paid considerable attention to the somewhat less scholarly pursuits. The thirteenth-century scholars were a riotous crew who seem to have proportioned their time between taverns and breaking heads—preferably those of townspeople— and chapel and theology.

Be NOT a fornicator, O student, a robber, a murderer, a deceitful merchant, a champion at dice. In the choirstalls a cleric should chant without noise and commotion. I advocate that the ordinary layman, who does not sing, be kept out of the choir. A student, who is a churchman, is expected to follow good custom, to be willing to serve, to fee the notary who has drawn up a charter for him, to gladden the giver. Do not constantly urge your horse on with the spur, which should be used only on rare occasions. Give your horse the reins when he mounts an incline; fearing a serious accident, avoid crossing swollen rivers, or the Rhine. If a bridge is not safe, you should dismount and let the horse pick his way over the smooth parts. Mount gently on the left stirrup. Select beautiful equestrian trappings suitable to your clerical station. Ride erect unless you are bent by age. If you are of the elect you should have a rich saddle cloth. The cross should be exalted, the voice be raised in prayer, Christ should be worshipped, the foot should be taken out of the stirrup. The horseman will descend from his horse and say his prayers; no matter how far he then will travel, he will ride in safety. He who wishes to serve should be quick, not go to sleep, and not give way to anger against his lord. Avoid drunkards, those who indulge in secret sin, those who like to beat and strike, those who love lewdness, evil games, and quarrels. Passing a cemetery, if you are well-bred, and if you hope for salvation, you pause to pray that the dead may rest in peace. Have nothing to do with the prostitute, but love your wife; all wives should be honoured but especially those who are distinguished by virtue. A person who is well should not recline at table in the fashion of the ancients. When you walk after dinner keep on frequented streets. Avoid insincere speeches. Unless you wish to be considered a fool learn to keep your mouth shut in season. Stand and sit upright, do not scratch yourself. . . .

Exhibit a good deportment in deeds, and in words; learn the custom of the country in which you happen to be. Do not be noisy, rash in your actions, odious because of your insulting words, wrathful about little annoyances. You should never despair if you suffer on account of sin; you will bear all the bitterness of poverty, knowing that you are an heir of the eternal Prince. Be peaceful among peaceful citizens, be like a rich patron among the poor. You should disassociate yourself from the rich, for, a celibate on earth, you will dwell with Christ, the celibate, in heaven. Hasten to help a needy friend, give him money if you can. Be a good debtor and hasten to pay your debts lest you be condemned by your burden of sin and by the peasant bewailing his losses. You should take good care of your horse, give him enough water, clean straw when he is worn out, and enough of the kind of food he likes to eat. There are more such precepts for him who wishes to know all the rules of politeness; as such, make it your ambition, by careful study, to learn them.

[*Tr. L. J. Paetow*]

GEOFFREY CHAUCER

A Clerke of Oxenforde

FROM *The Canterbury Tales*

Geoffrey Chaucer's *"A Clerke of Oxenforde"* is one of the earliest characterizations of a college student. Chaucer had a seeing eye for character, an
absorbing curiosity about his world and the people in it, and his writing's
blend of humor, grace and vigor make his Canterbury pilgrims come alive
for us today.

Chaucer was a soldier and diplomat. His writing was largely avocational.
He was obviously a man of considerable education, and scholars speculate
that he may have studied either at Oxford or Cambridge. The Middle
English dialect in which he wrote (that of London) became the basis of
our modern English.

A CLERK there was of Oxenford also,
Who unto logic had gone long ago.
As skinny was his horse as is a rake;
And the clerk was not right fat, I undertake.
For he had got him yet no benefice,
Nor was so worldly as to have office;
For he would rather have at his bed's head
A twenty bookës, clad in black or red,
Of Aristotle and his philosophy,
Than robës rich or fiddle or psaltéry.
But all be that he was a philosópher,
Yet had but little riches in his coffer,
And all that might be by his friendës lent,
On bookës and on learning he it spent;
And busily began for souls to pray
Of them that gave him wherewith to studý.
Of study took he mostë care and heed:

Not a word spoke he morë than was need;
And that was said in form and reverence,
And short and quick, and full of high senténce.
Sounding in moral virtue was his speech
And gladly would he learn, and gladly teach.

Research Projects

FROM *Gulliver's Travels*

The vitriolic fury of Swiftian satire stemmed from outraged conscience and hatred of stupidity. Although Gulliver's Travels, *through time's ironic erosion, has become a children's book, it remains the outstanding satiric work in our language. In the following selection from Swift's writings, his savage pen is aimed at what we would call higher education today.*

Swift received his B.A. from Trinity College, Dublin, "by special grace." With unequal grace, he characterized his college years as wasted time. Swift was the editor of a Tory newspaper, Dean of St. Patrick's, and a potent pamphleteer, hated and feared by many of his peers and acclaimed by the poor and downtrodden. His period of greatest power was during the reign of Queen Anne. In the final years of his life he was insane.

I HAD hitherto seen only one side of the academy, the other being appropriated to the advancers of speculative learning; of whom I shall say something when I have mentioned one illustrious person more, who is called among them, "The universal artist." He told us, he had been thirty years employing his thoughts for the improvement of human life. He had two large rooms full of wonderful curiosities, and fifty men at work: some were condensing air into a dry tangible substance, by extracting the nitre, and letting the aqueous or fluid particles percolate: others softening marble for pillows and pincushions; others petrifying the hoofs of a living horse, to preserve them from foundering. The artist himself was at that time busy upon two great designs: the first, to sow land with chaff, wherein he affirmed the true seminal virtue to be contained, as he demonstrated by several experiments which I was not skilful enough to comprehend. The other was, by a certain composition of gums, minerals, and vegetables outwardly applied, to prevent the growth of wool upon two young lambs; and he hoped in a reasonable time to propagate the breed of naked sheep all over the kingdom.

We crossed a walk to the other part of the academy, where, as I have already said, the projectors in speculative learning resided.

The first professor I saw was in a very large room, with forty pupils about him. After salutation, observing me to look earnestly upon a frame, which took up the greatest part of both the length and breadth of the room, he said, perhaps I might wonder to see him employed in a project for improving speculative knowledge by practical and mechanical operations. But the world would soon be sensible of its usefulness; and he flattered himself, that a more noble exalted thought never sprang in any other man's head. Every one knew how laborious the usual method is of attaining to arts and sciences; whereas by his contrivance, the most ignorant person at a reasonable charge, and with a little bodily labour, may write books in philosophy, poetry, politicks, law, mathematicks and theology, without the least assistance from genius or study. He then led me to the frame, about the sides whereof all his pupils stood in ranks. It was twenty foot square, placed in the middle of the room. The superficies was composed of several bits of wood, about the bigness of a dye, but some larger than others. They were all linked together by slender wires. These bits of wood were covered on every square with paper pasted on them; and, on these papers were written all the words of their language in their several moods, tenses, and declensions, but without any order. The professor then desired me to observe, for he was going to set his engine at work. The pupils at his command took each of them hold of an iron handle, whereof there were forty fixed round the edges of the frame; and giving them a sudden turn, the whole disposition of the words was entirely changed. He then commanded six and thirty of the lads to read the several lines softly as they appeared upon the frame; and where they found three or four words together that might make part of a sentence, they dictated to the four remaining boys who were scribes. This work was repeated three or four times, and at every turn the engine was so contrived, that the words shifted into new places, as the square bits of wood moved upside down.

Six hours a day the young students were employed in this labour; and the professor shewed me several volumes in large folio already collected, of broken sentences, which he intended to piece together; and out of those rich materials to give the world a compleat body of all arts and sciences; which, however might be still improved, and much expedited, if the publick would raise a fund for making and employing five hundred such frames in Lagado, and oblige the managers to contribute in common their several collections.

He assured me, that this invention had employed all his thoughts from his youth; that he had emptied the whole vocabulary into his frame, and made the strictest computation of the general proportion there is in books between the numbers of particles, nouns, and verbs, and other parts of speech.

I made my humblest acknowledgments to this illustrious person for his great communicativeness; and promised, if ever I had the good fortune to return to my native country, that I would do him justice, as the sole inventor of this wonderful machine; the form and contrivance of which I desired leave to delineate upon paper as in the figure here annexed. I told him, although it were the custom of our learned in Europe to steal inventions from each other, who had thereby at least this advantage, that it became a controversy which was the right owner; yet I would take such caution, that he should have the honour entire without a rival.

We next went to the school of languages, where three professors sat in consultation upon improving that of their own country.

The first project was to shorten discourse by cutting polysyllables into one, and leaving out verbs and participles, because in reality all things imaginable are but nouns.

The other, was a scheme for entirely abolishing all words whatsoever: and this was urged as a great advantage in point of health as well as brevity. For, it is plain, that every word we speak is in some degree a diminution of our lungs by corrosion; and consequently contributes to the shortning of our lives. An expedient was therefore offered, that since words are only names for *things,* it would be more convenient for all men to carry about them, such *things* as were necessary to express the particular business they are to discourse on. And this invention would certainly have taken place, to the great ease as well as health of the subject, if the women in conjunction with the vulgar and illiterate had not threatned to raise a rebellion, unless they might be allowed the liberty to speak with their tongues, after the manner of their forefathers: such constant irreconcileable enemies to science are the common people. However, many of the most learned and wise adhere to the new scheme of expressing themselves by *things;* which hath only this inconvenience attending it; that if a man's business be very great, and of various kinds, he must be obliged in proportion to carry a greater bundle of *things* upon his back, unless he can afford one or two strong servants to attend him. I have often beheld two of those sages almost sinking under the weight of their packs, like pedlars among us; who, when they met in the streets would lay down their loads, open their sacks, and hold conversation for an hour together; then put up their implements, help each other to resume their burthens, and take their leave.

But, for short conversations, a man may carry implements in his pockets and under his arms, enough to supply him, and in his house he cannot be at a loss; therefore the room where company meet who practise this art, is full of all things ready at hand, requisite to furnish matter for this kind of artificial converse.

Another great advantage proposed by this invention, was, that it would serve as an universal language to be understood in all civilized nations, whose goods and utensils are generally of the same kind, or nearly resembling, so that their uses might easily be comprehended. And thus, embassadors would be qualified to treat with foreign princes or ministers of State, to whose tongues they were utter strangers.

BENJAMIN FRANKLIN

A Plan for the Education of
Youth in Pennsylvania

FROM *The Benjamin Franklin Reader*

The academy later to become the University of Pennsylvania was only one of the many public undertakings which Benjamin Franklin fathered. He founded the Pennsylvania hospital, the first free library in America, the first volunteer fire company, and the "Junto," the famous club, where he reported his first scientific experiments. He was as close to the ideal of the roundly educated man as colonial America produced. His own formal schooling ended at ten, after a year and a half of reading, writing and arithmetic.

Advertisement to the Reader

IT HAS long been regretted as a misfortune to the youth of this province that we have no *academy*, in which they might receive the accomplishments of a regular education. The following paper of hints toward forming a plan for that purpose is so far approved by some public-spirited gentlemen, to whom it has been privately communicated, that they have directed a number of copies to be made by the press, and properly distributed, in order to obtain the sentiments and advice of men of learning, understanding, and experience in these matters; and have determined to use their interest and best endeavors to have the scheme, when completed, carried gradually into execution; in which they have reason to believe they shall have the hearty concurrence and assistance of many who are wellwishers to their country. Those who incline to favour the design with their advice, either as to the parts of learning to be taught, the order of study, the method of teaching, the economy of the school, or any other matter of importance to the success of the undertaking, are desired to communicate their sentiments as soon as may be, by letter directed to B. FRANKLIN, *Printer,* in PHILADELPHIA.

Proposals

The good education of youth has been esteemed by wise men in all ages as the surest foundation of the happiness both of private families and of commonwealths. Almost all governments have therefore made it a principal object of their attention to establish and endow with proper revenues such seminaries of learning, as might supply the succeeding age with men qualified to serve the public with honor to themselves and to their country.

Many of the first settlers of these provinces were men who had received a good education in Europe, and to their wisdom and good management we owe much of our present prosperity. But their hands were full, and they could not do all things. The present race are not thought to be generally of equal ability: For though the American youth are allowed not to want capacity; yet the best capacities require cultivation, it being truly with them, as with the best ground, which, unless well tilled and sowed with profitable seed, produces only ranker weeds.

That we may obtain the advantages arising from an increase of knowledge, and prevent as much as may be the mischievous consequences that would attend a general ignorance among us, the following hints are offered toward forming a plan for the education of the youth of Pennsylvania, viz.:

It is proposed,

That some persons of leisure and public spirit apply for a charter, by which they may be incorporated, with power to erect an *academy* for the education of youth, to govern the same, provide masters, make rules, receive donations, purchase lands, etc., and to add to their number, from time to time, such other persons as they shall judge suitable.

That the members of the corporation make it their pleasure, and in some degree their business, to visit the academy often, encourage and countenance the youth, countenance and assist the masters, and by all means in their power advance the usefulness and reputation of the design; that they look on the students as in some sort their children, treat them with familiarity and affection, and, when they have behaved well, and gone through their studies, and are to enter the world, zealously unite, and make all the interest that can be made to establish them, whether in business, offices, marriages, or any other thing for their advantage, preferably to all other persons whatsoever even of equal merit.

And if men may, and frequently do, catch such a taste for cultivating flowers, for planting, grafting, inoculating, and the like, as to despise all other amusements for their sake, why may not we expect they should acquire a relish for that more useful culture of young minds. Thompson says,

'Tis Joy to see the human Blossoms blow,
When infant Reason grows apace, and calls
For the kind Hand of an assiduous Care.
Delightful Task! to rear the tender Thought,
To teach the young Idea how to shoot;
To pour the fresh Instruction o'er the Mind,
To breathe th' enliv'ning Spirit, and to fix
The generous Purpose in the glowing Breast.

That a house be provided for the academy, if not in the town, not many miles from it; the situation high and dry, and if it may be, not far from a river, having a garden, orchard, meadow, and a field or two.

That the house be furnished with a library (if in the country; if in the town, the town Libraries may serve) with maps of all countries, globes, some mathematical instruments, an apparatus for experiments in natural philosophy, and for mechanics; prints, of all kinds, prospects, buildings, machines, etc.

That the rector be a man of good understanding, good morals, diligent and patient, learned in the languages and sciences, and a correct pure speaker and writer of the English tongue; to have such tutors under him as shall be necessary.

That the boarding scholars diet together, plainly, temperately, and frugally.

That, to keep them in health, and to strengthen and render active their bodies, they be frequently exercised in running, leaping, wrestling, and swimming, etc.

That they have peculiar habits to distinguish them from other youth, if the academy be in or near the town; for this, among other reasons, that their behavior may be the better observed.

As to their *studies,* it would be well if they could be taught everything that is useful, and everything that is ornamental. But art is long, and their time is short. It is therefore proposed that they learn those things that are likely to be most useful and most ornamental, regard being had to the several professions for which they are intended.

All should be taught to *write* a fair hand, and swift, as that is useful to all. And with it may be learnt something of *drawing,* by imitation of prints, and some of the first principles of perspective.

Arithmetic, accounts, and some of the first principles of *geometry* and *astronomy.*

The English language might be taught by *grammar;* in which some of our best writers, as Tillotson, Addison, Pope, Algernon Sidney, Cato's Letters, etc., should be classics: the styles principally to be cultivated, being the clear and the concise. Reading should also be taught, and pronouncing, properly, distinctly, emphatically; not with an even tone, which under-does, nor a theatrical, which over-does nature.

To form their style they should be put on writing letters to each other, making abstracts of what they read; or writing the same things in their own words; telling or writing stories lately read, in their own expressions. All to be revised and corrected by the tutor, who should give his reasons, and explain the force and import of words, etc.

To form their pronunciation, they may be put on making declamations, repeating speeches, delivering orations, etc.; the tutor assisting at the rehearsals, teaching, advising, correcting their accent, etc.

But if *history* be made a constant part of their reading, such as the translations of the Greek and Roman historians, and the modern histories of ancient Greece and Rome, etc., may not almost all kinds of useful knowledge be that way introduced to advantage, and with pleasure to the student? As:

Geography, by reading with maps and being required to point out the places where the greatest actions were done, to give their old and new names, with the bounds, situation, extent of the countries concerned, etc.

Chronology, by the help of Helvicus or some other writer of the kind, who will enable them to tell when those events happened; what princes were contemporaries, what states or famous men flourished about that time, etc. The several principal epochs to be first well fixed in their memories.

Ancient Customs, religious and civil, being frequently mentioned in history, will give occasion for explaining them; in which the prints of medals, bas-reliefs, and ancient monuments will greatly exist.

Morality, by descanting and making continual observations on the causes of the rise or fall of any man's character, fortune, power, etc., mentioned in history; the advantages of temperance, order, frugality, industry, perseverance, etc., etc. Indeed, the general natural tendency of reading good history must be to fix in the minds of youth deep impressions of the beauty and usefulness of virtue of all kinds, public spirit, fortitude, etc.

History will show the wonderful effects of *oratory,* in governing, turning and leading great bodies of mankind, armies, cities, nations. When the minds of youth are struck with admiration at this, then is the time to give them the principles of that art, which they will study with taste and application. Then they may be made acquainted with the best models among the ancients, their beauties being particularly pointed out to them. Modern political oratory being chiefly performed by the pen and press, its advantages over the ancient in some respects are to be shown; as that its effects are more extensive, more lasting, etc.

History will also afford frequent opportunities of showing the necessity of a public religion, from its usefulness to the public; the advantage of a religious character among private persons; the mischiefs of superstition, etc., and the excellency of the *Christian religion* above all others ancient or modern.

History will also give occasion to expatiate on the advantage of civil orders and constitutions; how men and their properties are protected by joining in societies and establishing government; their industry encouraged and rewarded, arts invented, and life made more comfortable: The advantages of liberty, mischiefs of licentiousness, benefits arising from good laws and a due execution of justice, etc. Thus may the first principles of sound politics be fixed in the minds of youth.

On historical occasions, questions of right and wrong, justice and injustice, will naturally arise, and may be put to youth, which they may debate in conversation and in writing. When they ardently desire victory, for the sake of the praise attending it, they will begin to feel the want, and be sensible of the use of *logic,* or the art of reasoning to discover truth, and of arguing to defend it, and convince adversaries. This would be the time to acquaint them with the principles of that art. Grotius, Puffendorff, and some other writers of the same kind, may be used on these occasions to decide their disputes. Public disputes warm the imagination, whet the industry, and strengthen the natural abilities.

When youth are told that the great men whose lives and actions they read in history spoke two of the best *languages* that ever were, the most expressive, copious, beautiful; and that the finest writings, the most correct compositions, the most perfect productions of human wit and wisdom, are in those languages, which have endured ages, and will endure while there are men; that no translation can do them justice, or give the pleasure found in reading the originals; that those languages contain all science; that one of them is become almost universal, being the language of learned men in all countries; that to understand them is a distinguishing ornament, etc., they may be thereby made desirous of learning those languages, and their industry sharpened in the acquisition of them. All intended for divinity should be taught the Latin and Greek; for physick, the Latin, Greek, and French; for law, the Latin and French; merchants, the French, German, and Spanish: And though all should not be compelled to learn Latin, Greek, or the modern foreign languages; yet none that have an ardent desire to learn them should be refused; their English, arithmetic and other studies absolutely necessary, being at the same time not neglected.

If the new *universal history* were also read, it would give a connected idea of human affairs, so far as it goes, which should be followed by the best modern histories, particularly of our mother country; then of these colonies; which should be accompanied with observations on their rise, increase, use to Great Britain, encouragements, discouragements, etc., the means to make them flourish, secure their liberties, etc.

With the history of men, times, and nations, should be read at proper hours or days, some of the best *histories of nature,* which would not only be delightful to youth, and furnish them with matter for their letters, etc., as well as other history; but afterwards of great use to them, whether they are merchants, handicrafts, or divines; enabling the first the better to understand many commodities, drugs, etc., the second to improve his trade or handicraft by new mixtures, materials, etc., and the last to adorn his discourses by beautiful comparisons and strengthen them by new proofs of Divine Providence. The conversation of all will be improved by it, as occasions frequently occur of making natural observations, which are instructive, agreeable, and entertaining in almost all companies. Natural history will also afford opportunities of introducing many observations relating to the preservation of health, which may be afterwards of great use. Arbuthnot on Air and Aliment, Sanctorius on perspiration, Lemery on foods, and some others, may now be read, and a very little explanation will make them sufficiently intelligible to youth.

While they are reading natural history, might not a little gardening, planting, grafting, inoculating, etc., be taught and practiced; and now and then excursions made to the neighboring plantations of the best farmers, their methods observed and reasoned upon for the information of youth? The improvement of agriculture being useful to all, and skill in it no disparagement to any.

The *history of commerce,* of the invention of arts, rise of manufactures, progress of trade, change of its seats, with the reasons, causes, etc., may also be made entertaining to youth and will be useful to all. And this, with the accounts in other history of the prodigious force and effect of engines and machines used in war, will naturally introduce a desire to be instructed in *mechanics,* and to be informed of the principles of that art by which weak men perform such wonders, labor is saved, manufactures expedited, etc. This will be the time to show them prints of ancient and modern machines, to explain them, to let them be copied, and to give lectures in mechanical philosophy.

With the whole should be constantly inculcated and cultivated that *benignity of mind* which shows itself in searching for and seizing every opportunity to serve and to oblige; and is the foundation of what is called *good breeding,* highly useful to the possessor, and most agreeable to all.

The idea of what is *true merit* should also be often presented to youth, explained and impressed on their minds, as consisting in an inclination joined with an ability to serve mankind, one's country, friends, and family; which ability is (with the blessing of God) to be acquired or greatly increased by true learning; and should indeed be the great aim and end of all learning.

[Philadelphia, 1749]

THOMAS JEFFERSON HOGG

Shelley Expelled from Oxford

FROM *The Life of Percy Bysshe Shelley*

For whatever small comfort we may take from the thought, ours is only one of many periods that punishes unpopular thinking. In our time it is dangerous political thinking that is suspect. In Percy Bysshe Shelley's nineteenth-century England it was dangerous religious thinking. In whatever case, non-conformism is always a dearly bought commodity.

In 1811, Shelley, poet and rebel, then in his second year at University College, Oxford, wrote a pamphlet on "The Necessity of Atheism," published anonymously by a local bookseller. Called to account by the university authorities, he proudly admitted and defended authorship. The interview is described in this selection by his friend, classmate and biographer, Thomas Jefferson Hogg.

WE HAD read together attentively several of the metaphyiscal works that were most in vogue at that time, as *Locke concerning Human Understanding,* and Hume's *Essays,* particularly the latter, of which we had made a very careful analysis, as was customary with those who read the *Ethics* and the other treatises of Aristotle for their degrees. Shelley had the custody of these papers, which were chiefly in his handwriting, although they were the joint production of both in our common daily studies. From these, and from a small part of them only, he made up a little book, and had it printed, I believe, in the country, certainly not at Oxford. . . .

It was a fine spring morning on Lady Day, in the year 1811, when I went to Shelley's rooms: he was absent; but before I had collected our books he rushed in. He was terribly agitated. I anxiously inquired what had happened.

"I am expelled," he said, as soon as he had recovered himself a little, "I am expelled! I was sent for suddenly a few minutes ago; I went to the common room, where I found our master and two or three of the fellows.

46

The master produced a copy of the little syllabus, and asked me if I were the author of it. He spoke in a rude, abrupt, and insolent tone. I begged to be informed for what purpose he put the question. No answer was given; but the master loudly and angrily repeated, 'Are you the author of this book?' If I can judge from your manner, I said, you are resolved to punish me, if I should acknowledge that it is my work. If you can prove that it is, produce your evidence; it is neither just nor lawful to interrogate me in such a case and for such a purpose. Such proceedings would become a court of inquisitors, but not free men in a free country. 'Do you choose to deny that this is your composition?' the master reiterated in the same rude and angry voice." Shelley complained much of his violent and ungentlemanlike deportment, saying, "I have experienced tyranny and injustice before, and I well know what vulgar violence is; but I never met with such unworthy treatment. I told him calmly, but firmly, that I was determined not to answer any questions respecting the publication on the table. He immediately repeated his demand; I persisted in my refusal; and he said furiously, 'Then you are expelled; and I desire you will quit the college early to-morrow morning at the latest'. One of the fellows took up two papers, and handed one of them to me; here it is." He produced a regular sentence of expulsion, drawn up in due form, under the seal of the college.

Shelley was full of spirit and courage, frank and fearless; but he was likewise shy, unpresuming, and eminently sensitive. I have been with him in many trying situations of his after-life, but I never saw him so deeply shocked and so cruelly agitated as on this occasion. A nice sense of honour shrinks from the most distant touch of disgrace—even from the insults of those men whose contumely can bring no shame. He sat on the sofa, repeating, with convulsive vehemence, the words, "Expelled, expelled!" his head shaking with emotion, and his whole frame quivering. The atrocious injustice and its cruel consequences roused the indignation, and moved the compassion, of a friend, who then stood by Shelley. He has given the following account of his interference:

"So monstrous and so illegal did the outrage seem, that I held it to be impossible that any man, or any body of men, would dare to adhere to it; but, whatever the issue might be, it was a duty to endeavour to the utmost to assist him. I at once stepped forward, therefore, as the advocate of Shelley; such an advocate, perhaps, with respect to judgment, as might be expected at the age of eighteen, but certainly not inferior to the most practised defenders in good will and devotion. I wrote a short note to the master and fellows, in which, as far as I can remember a very hasty composition after a long interval, I briefly expressed my sorrow at the treatment my friend had experienced, and my hope that they would reconsider their sentence; since, by the same course of proceeding, myself, or any other person, might be subjected to the same penalty, and to the imputation of equal guilt. The note was dispatched; the conclave was still sitting; and in an instant the porter came to summon me to attend, bearing in his countenance a promise of the reception which I was about to find. The angry and troubled air of men, assembled to commit injustice according to established forms, was then new to me; but a native instinct told me, as soon as I entered the room, that it was an affair of party; that whatever could conciliate the favour of patrons was to be done without scruple; and whatever could tend to impede preferment was to be brushed away without remorse. The glowing master produced my poor note. I acknowledged it; and he forthwith put into my hand, not less abruptly, the little syllabus. 'Did you write this?' he asked, as fiercely as if I alone stood between him and the rich see of Durham. I attempted, submissively, to point out to him the extreme unfairness of the question; the injustice of punishing Shelley for refusing to answer it; that if it were urged upon me I must offer the like refusal, as I had no doubt every man in college would—every gentleman, indeed, in the university; which, if such a course were adopted with all—and there could not be any reason why it should be used with one and not with the rest—would thus be stripped of every member. I soon perceived that arguments were thrown away upon a man possessing no more intellect or erudition, and far less renown, than that famous ram, since translated to the stars, through grasping whose tail less firmly than was expedient, the sister of Phryxus formerly found a watery grave, and gave her name to the broad Hellespont.

"The other persons present took no part in the conversation: they presumed not to speak, scarcely to breathe, but looked mute subserviency. The few resident fellows, indeed, were but so many incarnations of the spirit of the master, whatever that spirit might be. When I was silent, the master told me to retire, and to consider whether I was resolved to persist in my refusal. The proposal was fair enough. The next day, or the next week, I might have given my final answer—a deliberate answer; having in the meantime consulted with older and more experienced persons, as to what course was best for myself and for others. I had scarcely passed the door, however, when I was recalled. The master again showed me the book, and hastily demanded whether I admitted, or denied, that I was the author of it. I answered that I was fully sensible of the many and great inconveniences of being dismissed with disgrace from the university, and I specified some of them, and expressed a humble hope that they would not impose such a mark of discredit upon me without any cause. I lamented that it was impossible either to admit, or to deny, the publication—no man of spirit could submit to do so— and that a sense of duty compelled me respectfully to refuse to answer the question which had been proposed. 'Then you are expelled,' said the master angrily, in a loud, great voice. A formal sentence, duly signed and sealed, was instantly put into my hand: in what interval the instrument had been drawn up I cannot imagine. The alleged offence was a contumacious refusal to disavow the imputed publication. My eye glanced over it, and observing the word *contumaciously,* I said calmly that I did not think that term was justified by my behaviour. Before I had concluded the remark, the master, lifting up the little syllabus, and then dashing it on the table, and looking sternly at me, said, 'Am I to understand, sir, that you adopt the principles contained in this work?' or some such words; for, like one red with the suffusion of college port and college ale, the intense heat of anger seemed to deprive him of the power of articulation; by reason of a rude provincial dialect and thickness of utterance, his speech being at all times indistinct. 'The last question is still more improper than the former,' I replied—for I felt that the imputation was an insult; 'and since, by your own act, you have renounced all authority over me, our communication is at an end.' 'I command you to quit my college to-morrow at an early hour.' I bowed and withdrew."

Harvard College 1815

FROM *A Chilmark Miscellany*

In a series of thoughtful and finely wrought books, Van Wyck Brooks has recreated the cultural life of nineteenth-century America. Harvard College was a seminal influence, perhaps the most significant of the period. In this essay we see the Harvard of 1815, focus for all the orbiting intellectual currents of the time.

Van Wyck Brooks was Harvard '08. He has been honored with degrees by many universities for his major contributions to American cultural history.

Harvard COLLEGE was the heart of Cambridge. Seven generations before, every New England household had given the college twelvepence, or a peck of corn, or its value in unadulterated wampum peag. But those were the good old days when the Orthodox faith reigned in every mind. Established now on a Unitarian basis,—for the founding of the Divinity School, with Dr. Henry Ware as its chief professor, settled the character of the new regime,—the college was considered, in the country districts, dangerously lax and liberal. West of Worcester, and up the Connecticut Valley, the clergy, Calvinist almost to a man, united in condemning the Cambridge collegians, in the very words of Whitefield, as "close Pharisees, resting on head knowledge,"—the same collegians who had called Whitefield "low." But as for this "head knowledge," no one denied that they possessed it. More than a few of the Orthodox admitted that it was what collegians ought to possess. Harvard still had an exalted prestige. The patrician families of Boston and Cambridge regarded it as more than a family affair. It was a family responsibility. They sent their sons to the college, as a matter of course. But they considered it a public duty, not only to endow and foster it, in the interests of the meritorious poor, but to maintain its standards and oversee it. They founded chairs that bore their names, the Boylston chair,

50

the Eliot chair, the Smith professorship. They watched and brooded over its progress and welfare. Who would have respected wealth in Boston if wealth had not, in turn, respected learning? And, if the professors' salaries were very small, everyone knew they were partly paid in honour.

It was true that the standard of learning was not too lofty. In this, as in certain other respects, the well-known "Harvard indifference" resembled that of Oxford and Madrid. Intellectual things took second place. The object of study was to form the mind, but this was to form the character; and Massachusetts knew what its character was and took a certain satisfaction in it. Everyone was aware of the best Boston and Cambridge type, the type that Josiah Quincy represented, or the late Chief Justice Dana, formed on the classic models. A clear, distinct mentality, a strong distaste for nonsense, steady composure, a calm and gentle demeanour, stability, good principles, intelligence, a habit of understatement, a slow and cautious way of reasoning, contempt for extravagance, vanity and affectation, kindness of heart, purity, decorum, profound affections, filial and paternal. A noble type, severely limited, which Boston celebrated in its marble busts. Comparing it, trait for trait, with half of Plutarch's characters, one might have felt that Boston deserved its busts. Moreover, beneath its cold and tranquil surface, burned, though the fires were low, the passions and convictions of the Revolution, ready to flame forth on a fresh occasion. But would the occasion ever recur? That was what a stranger might have asked, face to face with the marble busts. The surface, at least, seemed somewhat tame, suited for the merchant and the lawyer, and the man of God after the Boston fashion.

This was the type, and almost the only type, the curriculum of Harvard contemplated. Whatever studies favoured its formation, whatever were the best ways to form it, these were the ways and the studies that Harvard knew. Whatever studies did not favour it, or favoured the formation of other types that Boston did not like or had never heard of, these were no concern of Harvard, or its concern only to oppose them. Josiah Quincy was not enthusiastic. Why should Harvard be? Mr. Dana was eminently decorous. He had caused the arrest, for contempt of court, of a butcher who, appearing at the bar, had left his coat behind him. Decorum was a Harvard characteristic. Neither Mr. Quincy nor Mr. Dana cared a button for the German language, which had been spoken by the Hessian troops, a half-barbarous tribe of Europeans who had been hired out to the British king. German, from the point of view of Harvard, always excepting John Quincy Adams, who, as everyone knew, was a little queer,—German was an outlandish dialect; and, while it was not improper to speak French, the language of Lafayette, which it was quite improper not to know, more than a few felt that Bonaparte had destroyed its respectability. Greek was esteemed as the tongue of a group of ancient republics that possessed some of the virtues of New England. Greece had produced a number of orators who were more eloquent even than Samuel Adams. Search as one might, however, in Massachusetts, one could not find a play of Euripides; besides, compared with Latin, which everyone drank in with his mother's milk, Greek was a little questionable. The Roman word "convivium" meant "living together." "Symposium" had a similar sense in Greek, but what did "symposium" imply? "Drinking together." Was not this alone enough to prove that the Romans were more respectable than the Greeks? Cicero had made the point, and everyone knew that Cicero must be right.

These were the days of the genial President Kirkland, who, after conducting an examination, regaled the boys with a fine dish of pears. He was an easy-going man, a Unitarian minister, like most of the professors, sympathetic and of the gentlest temper, naturally frank and cordial, with all the delicate feeling for human behaviour that characterized the best New Englanders. It was said that he threw his sermons into a barrel, as the farmers threw their corn into the silo, and that on Sunday morning he fished out enough for a discourse and patched the leaves together. The story had a symbolic truth, at least. It signified the president's "Harvard indifference," which was accompanied by the best intentions and a notably warm heart. He never took the narrow view. Hearing that the flip at the Porter House had proved to be too attractive to the students, he dropped in to see the proprietor. "And so, Mr. Porter," he said, "the young gentlemen come to drink your flip, do they?"—"Yes, sir," said Mr. Porter, "sometimes."—"Well, I should think they would," the president said. "Good day, Mr. Porter." Any sort of illumination, physical or spiritual, might have taken place under his eye. He was kind to the rich young men whose fathers, at their graduation, gave them dinners in a great marquee, with five hundred guests and dancing in the Yard. He was kinder to the poor young men whose black coats were turning green. He was not a man to oppose any important change in the system of studies; and before the end of his long reign, in fact, certain changes were to occur that were eventually to transform the college. But he could not see why changes should occur. He thought the old ways were good enough, and he played into the hands of firmer men who thought that all other ways were bad. Four hours a day for study and recitation were quite enough for anyone. A library of twenty thousand books was certainly large enough. In fact, the Harvard library was a wonder. No other American library was larger, except perhaps one. A young man with literary tastes could find Hakluyt's *Voyages* there, Cotton's Montaigne and Dodsley's *Old Plays*, as well as the books that he ought to have at home; and the window-sills were broad enough to sit on, if he was too fidgety to keep his chair. What more, in reason, could one ask for? For the rest, the teaching consisted of recitations. No nonsense on the part of the professors,

no lectures, no unnecessary comments, no flowery illustrations. One ground
in one's Latin and mathematics, under a pair of candles, and the next day
one ground them out again. Professors were not nurses, neither were they
dancing-masters. One did not go to Harvard to stimulate a dubious fancy.
One went to learn to deserve a marble bust.

A few imaginative persons had their doubts. The college was dying of
antiquated notions,—so, at least, they thought. Twenty years before, one of
the students, who was known later as a writer, had printed certain strictures
on the college. He had called it "the death-bed of genius." How many immortals, he asked, had Harvard educated?—and how could it expect to produce immortals? The delicate muse of belles-lettres could never be induced
to visit Harvard. "No, she would recoil at the sight of our walls." And very
properly, the professors thought. The college was not for ladies, neither was
it meant for men of genius, or any other sort of extravagant creature. For a
thorough Boston lawyer, a merchant who desired a well-trained mind, a
minister who did not indulge in raptures, Harvard had proved to be an
adequate nest. It fostered polite, if not beautiful letters, it sent one back to
Plutarch for one's models, it sharpened the reasoning faculties, it settled
one's grounds for accepting a Christian faith that always knew where to
draw the line.

In short, the college was a little realm as fixed and final as a checkerboard. The squares of the various studies were plainly marked, with straight
lines and indisputable corners. All one had to do was to play the game. Dr.
Popkin, "Pop," was Professor of Greek. Over his cocked hat he carried a
circular canopy that Cambridge learned to know as an umbrella. The doctor
was a sound grammarian. He found his poetry in the Greek roots; he did
not need to seek it in the flowers. A second umbrella appeared in the Cambridge streets, in the hands of Professor Hedge, who had written a famous
Logic. He had spent seventeen years composing this work, with the aid of
the other members of his household. No Logic could have been better, and
he hoped his students would learn it word for word. For logic was important. Unless one knew logic, one could not read Locke; and who that had
not read Locke could ever be certain that his Christian faith had a solid
bottom? Logic was the Golden Calf of Cambridge, the muse of Theology,
the muse of Law. For Hebrew, one went to Professor Willard; for Latin, to
Brazer or Otis; for Natural Religion, to Professor Frisbie, whose taste for
the ethically severe was modified by his love of graceful ease. He enjoyed
Maria Edgeworth as well as the rigours of Tacitus. Dr. Ware presided over
Divinity. Dr. Ware's favourite phrase was "on the one hand, on the other
hand." He knew he possessed the truth, but he did not wish to slight its
minor aspects. He was famous for the accuracy of his definitions. No one
could distinguish better than he between "genuineness" and "authenticity";

and, although he had nineteen children, he never used the rod. He punished infractions of the household law by the hydropathic treatment.

Towering modestly over the other professors, Andrews Norton symbolized the *zeitgeist,* a word that he would have deprecated. It savoured of those antic tricks which the young men were beginning to play with language (or were so soon to begin to play),—German barbarisms, exclamations, inversions, coarse and violent metaphors, innovations which, to Mr. Norton, seemed both *outré* and *bizarre,* much as he would have disliked to use two foreign words in a single sentence. His own greatest days had not arrived, but Cambridge was prepared for his fortunate marriage. The heir of John Norton, who had proclaimed his line a "royal priesthood," not himself ordained, was yet a potent theologian, the Dexter Professor of Sacred Literature. He was more than a match for the daughter of a Boston merchant who kept a variety-store on Dock Square and who, after sending his son to Europe, to make the grand tour in his own carriage, wished his daughter to live in becoming style. Mr. Norton's father-in-law purchased Shady Hill for the promising couple, made a gentleman's house of it and bought the fifty acres of Norton's Woods, as the domain was henceforth to be called, an elegant park, unrivalled in homely Cambridge, where, in time, were to blossom, along with little Charles Eliot Norton, the handsome daughters whom the college knew as the "Evidences of Christianity," a reference to their father's famous book. Shady Hill was to have a notable history long after its first lord, the "Unitarian Pope," as Carlyle was to call him, who, for a generation, was to fight, on behalf of Harvard and common sense, against the Germanizing radicals, the Transcendentalists and their noxious crew, metaphysicians of the wilder sort,—long after the great Andrews Norton had laid his cold head in the colder tomb.

These days were still remote. Professor Norton was not married yet. He was not yet the "tyrant of the Cambridge Parnassus," nor was there an Emerson to call him so. He had not yet edited Mrs. Hemans, although he had written his own devotional poems. He had not visited his English readers; nor had he produced his commanding work, the *Evidences of the Genuineness of the Gospels,* which proved, to the satisfaction of honest men,— whatever the Germans might say, in their so-called higher criticism,—that Matthew, Mark, Luke and John had really written the books that bore their names, a demonstration as clear as Hedge's *Logic.* The four great volumes were still unborn, but Mr. Norton had won his spurs already. His head was long, his head was firm, his mind never wavered or misgave him. In Cambridge, chiaroscuro, a word unknown, would have been thought to savour of corruption; and the man who had put the Calvinists to rout, by sheer force of reasoning, was not the man to be upset by any other appeal to the vulgar "feelings," that of the pantheist Schleiermacher, for instance, with his notion that the verities of religion rested, not on the letter of the Scriptures, but on "the soul's sense of things divine." Odious phrase, how German! Mr. Norton's lectures had spread his fame. There was not a lawyer in Boston or Cambridge who could find a crack in his chain of logic. No one could prove that he was mistaken; and, inasmuch as a lawyer-proof religion was exactly what Boston wished for, Mr. Norton's eminence was uncontested. Was he a little petulant and vain? That was beside the point. And if he was called a Pharisee by certain ill-bred persons, that was wholly a matter of definition. Mr. Norton, like Professor Ware, was a master of definition. He was benevolent, he was conscientious. Moreover, he was the only professor,—or he was soon to be,—who had his private carriage. One saw it every Sunday, drawn up beside the president's carriage at the entrance of the college chapel.

Such was Harvard College, as it might have appeared in the eyes of a travelling Persian. It resembled Paley's watch. One found the watch on the seashore and instantly inferred that some intelligent mind must have designed it. One found Harvard College in the village of Cambridge: the evidences of design were also there, the wheels and all the parts in perfect order. The mainspring was useful common sense, based on a thrifty view of Christian ethics; and, if it resembled the watch in other ways, if it was small, cold and mechanical, was it more mechanical than Oxford, where they also put the Apostles in the witness-box and drowsed over their bottles of port? Oxford was torpid also, droning along in its eighteenth-century grooves, waiting for its great awakening. Harvard was only a more provincial Oxford, as the travelling Persian would have seen at once. A sympathetic stranger, an aspiring student, especially one who had been born in Cambridge, would have seen it in a rosier light. The Cambridge boy would have known the "Cambridge elm," with its suggestions of the Revolution, the old houses with their charming customs, the gracious lawns, the birds, the luxuriant flowers, stuff for a dozen poets, especially when the naturalist Thomas Nuttall became curator of the Botanic Garden and wrote his books on botany and ornithology, drawn from observations on the local scene. The Cambridge folk were intelligent and kind; and, if it was one of their foibles to put other people in their places, this was an indication, after all, that other people's places were not Cambridge. They were serious, devout, cultivated, stable. They were not given to excesses, even on the side of righteousness. The "ministers' sons" who became proverbial were the sons of the brimstone God of the inland regions. The ministers' sons of Cambridge never knew repression and therefore had no wild oats to sow. Neither in its action nor in its reaction was the Cambridge mind marked by a waste of force. Its only danger was a certain smugness. Its only excess was an excess of caution.

Harvard, moreover, was on the brink of change. Woe to the student, woe to the youthful tutor who counted overmuch on the signs of the times, who interlarded his speech with foreign phrases, sported embroidered waistcoats or even thought that modern languages ought to be included in the course of studies. Harvard was intellectually sound, and the sound intellect makes its changes slowly. But the changes were plainly imminent. President Kirkland might have been indifferent, but he was also liberal in temper. The ethics that Professor Frisbie taught might have been cold and dry, but the warmth with which he taught them,—he was a poet himself, in a modest way,—gave his pupils an impulse to study ethics instead of accepting them on authority. The Harvard philosophy was not exciting,—Locke, Paley, Reid,—but one became excited over it. One acquired a taste for philosophy. One acquired a sceptical attitude that opened the way for other points of view. Even Andrews Norton promoted this sceptical attitude. He had no sympathy with the new ideas that were dawning in people's minds, but he had demolished the old ideas. One could not, after hearing Mr. Norton, revert to the Calvinist view; and if one had disposed of Nortonism, to one's own satisfaction, at least, one was obliged to go forward to something else. And Mr. Norton's positive tone aroused the desire for combat in his pupils. They learned to fight, in the world of the mind. Their intellectual life was filled with zest.

In a word, the students learned to think. Moreover, they learned to write. Whatever might have been said of the Harvard professors, their taste could not have been impugned. Their taste was as refined as their ethical instincts. Their standards were severe. Their students might have certain limitations, but certain others they could hardly have. Their style was almost sure to be marked by grace and, as often as not, by force. Their scholarship was sure to be exacting, especially when Edward Tyrrel Channing, the younger brother of Dr. Channing, became professor of Rhetoric,—two years after the birth of a Concord boy, Henry Thoreau by name, who was to acknowledge, in later years, that he had learned to write as Channing's pupil. In fact, the whole New England "renaissance" was to spring so largely from Channing's pupils, Emerson, Holmes, Dana, Motley, Parkman, to name only a few, that the question might have been asked, Did Channing cause it?—

> *Channing, with his bland, superior look,*
> *Cold as a moonbeam on a frozen brook,*
> *While the pale student, shivering in his shoes,*
> *Sees from his theme the turgid rhetoric ooze.*

That the rhetoric oozed from his pupils' themes, under his bland eye,—that is to say, the "turgid" rhetoric,—was one of the secrets of his influence; for turgid rhetoric was the bane of letters in the days of the Boston orators, the orators whom every boy adored. He had a remorseless eye for the high-falutin, the swelling period, the emphatic word, morbid tissue to this ruthless surgeon whose Puritan instincts had been clarified by a sensible classical culture. None of his pupils grew the sort of feathers that required the ministrations of Artemus Ward.

One of these pupils kept his college themes, and a list of some of the subjects that Channing set might go as far as any other fact to explain why his pupils were to go so far. Bearing in mind the careers of his pupils, poets, historians, essayists or whatever, one asks oneself what must have been the effect, on adolescent minds, prepared and eager, of questions like the following,—on which they were obliged to write, and to write with perspicuity, whether they shivered in their shoes or not: on keeping a private journal, the anxieties and delights of a discoverer, the cultivation of the imagination, the pleasures and privileges of a literary man, the duty and dangers of conformity, the superior and the common man. These were the subjects that Channing discussed and urged his little classes to discuss, these and the topics of his brilliant *Lectures,* a writer's preparation, a writer's habits, permanent literary fame. The literary life, as he described it, seemed very important and very exciting. Moreover, he spoke of its problems in a way that brought it home to the rising generation. He referred to the confident freedom of thought and style that comes from a writer's pride in his own people and gives him a fine "bravery and indifference to foreign doubts and censure." He showed how the world in general values most the writers who bear the unmistakable stamp, the pungency and native sincerity, of their own time and place. The early Roman writers,—like the American writers of the past,—depended on foreign examples and supplies. In Rome, at least, this question had found an answer in the praise the Romans bestowed upon their writers for turning home at last for their themes and their style.

Judging by the fruits of his instruction, one might almost say that Channing sowed more of the seeds that make a man of letters,—when the seeds fall on a fortunate soil,—than all the other teachers of composition and all the writers of ingenious text-books that have ever taught a much-taught country. A Harvard student of his generation had certain advantages of an inward kind that were not likely to be soon repeated. One of them was that, reading Plutarch, in this sympathetic atmosphere, he might have understood Cicero's youth,—how, consulting the Delphic oracle, he listened to the pythoness who advised him not to regard the opinion of other people, but to make his own genius the guide of his life.

Cadets

FROM *West Point*

🏛 *In the history of our country and of its national heroes, the names of Annapolis and West Point—the naval and military academies of the United States—have been prominent. Behind their walls, on their drill fields, and in their classrooms, the fortunes of sea and land war were prefigured in the training of their undergraduates. Soldier-statesmen are a regular product of "The Point's" education.*

But for a candid, revelatory look at cadet life, the memoirs of famous graduates offer none of the riches to be found in the letters and diaries of unsung undergraduates. These natural, immediate glimpses—uninfluenced alike by fond recall and by awareness of possible publication and a potential audience of strangers—have a fresh, unselfconscious intimacy which is at once endearing and convincing. The following extracts are by cadets of the classes of the 1820s, '30s, and '40s, pre-Civil War snapshots of student life as it was in the years when Grant, Lee, Jackson and Sherman were being trained as lieutenants in the Army of the United States. The prevailing sentiments of cadets toward their alma mater then (and possibly since) is summed up in the comment of one of the letter-writers, William Dutton, USMA 1846: "It is terrible but I like the whole of it."

West Point, the history of the Academy from which this selection comes, was written for the 150th anniversary of the academy's founding, commemorated in 1952.

Plebe

*A*BNER R. HETZEL, USMA 1827, to his father, John Hetzel, June 28, 1823: The Point & Country adjoining it far exceeds the most Sanguine expectations I had formed of it. I had anticipated entering a wilderness where there was nothing to gratify the optical sense but a few old Buildings used as habitations for the Cadets, but instead of that I find 7 or 8 large brick buildings occupied by professors & officers. Two very large Stone Buildings 2 Story High, one used as the Hotel & mess-hall for the Cadets, the other as a Library, Chapel & Examination Hall, & two very large Stone buildings one 3 & the other 4 Story High, used as barracks for the Cadets. There being but two, sometimes, three in a Room, at the most, & well calculated for Study. There are also a great many buildings of Inferior note, 2 Stores— Wash women, Suttlers, Doctors, Shoemaker, Taylors, Barbers, Shoe Blacks & a large framed building for the Musicians & Regular Soldiers.

Abner R. Hetzel, USMA 1827, to his father, John Hetzel, June 17, 1823: The first day after my arrival I was taken out to drill & sure you never saw a more awkward creature in your life than I was or appeared to be. Indeed every new Cadet appeared to have gyves on. To display the Chest, draw in the Corporation, draw the Chin in perpendicular to the Chest, hold the hands down so as to touch the seam of the Pantaloons, & take care dont bend the elbows, keep the Shoulders drawn back & always be sure to keep the feet in an angle of 45° etc., etc. Indeed I had so many things to learn that I almost despaired of ever being a Soldier. . . .

Encampment

Marsena R. Patrick, USMA 1835, to Mr. Oliver Baker, July 9, 1831: After our Examination, we (that is the 4th Class "Plebs," as we were termed) were marched into camp from our Quarters. Here, we shall be kept until the First of September, Studying Tacticks of all kinds, Infantry, heavy and light, Rifle, Artillery, etc., etc., etc.

John Pope, USMA 1842, to his mother, Mrs. Lucretia Pope, July 7, 1838: I was obliged to stand Guard 4 hours in the Day & 4 hours in the night. I tell you about 3 O'clock at night walking Post both Cold & Dark and raining I thought of my Dear Mother & home & wished that I were with them but as the old saying is, Whatever is, is right, and with that I console myself, although it is but poor consolation.

James W. Burbridge, USMA ex-1831, to a friend, June 10, 1827: We have the best band of musick in the United States which keeps a fellows spirits up.

William Dutton, USMA 1846, to his uncle, John W. Mathews, July 31, 1842: You may think I do not like it here—if so you are mistaken—However I would like to see Mecklenburg—& a field of corn—or wheat or some such thing & would above all things like to get into Aunt Dorcas's cupboard a moment.

John Pope, USMA 1842, to his mother, Mrs. Lucretia Pope, July 7, 1838: The skin is coming off my face up to my nose on account of standing Guard yesterday for four hours during the most intense heat and we are obliged to wear those tall bell crowned leather Caps which with the brass trimmings weigh about 5 Pounds and hurt my head extremely and the rim also coming just to the nose.

William Davidson Frazer, USMA 1834, to the Rev. James P. Wilson, December 1, 1852: When at first us new Cadets stood post the old cadets used to come round at nights and try to fool us in trying to cross our post, and to frighten us at night, but some of our fellows run at some of them and came very near running some through. Immediately after guard mounting we had Artillery drill, we had six large brass field pieces, at first it used to almost deafen me, it would have astonished you I think to see little boys not 5 feet high touching off a large cannon, and performing all the different duties necessary to man a piece.

William Dutton, USMA 1846, to his cousin, Lucy J. Mathews, February 18, 1843: Many a time I have seen the "Guard turned out" & some man being missed—find him, snoring on the ground without a blanket just like a hog— I never had sweeter sleep than I have had—in that way— But our duties are so arduous together with walking one hour in 3 for the 24—that exhaustion is the result— All I want of those Editors who say—that "that lily fingered cadets, lounge on their velvet lawns—attend their brilliant balls & take pay for it" as I saw in a paper yesterday—is that they may go through but one "plebe" encampment.

William Dutton, USMA 1846, to his uncle, J. W. Mathews, July 12, 1842: Since we pitched our tents the Point has been thronged with visitors of every rank and description from "Boz"[1] who was here sometime since.

George W. Cullum, USMA 1833, to Alfred Huidekoper, July 30, 1832: It is rather a dry business dancing without ladies, however we cannot complain for the want of them in the evening. The Cholera in New York has driven legions of girls here who generally, if they are not true orthodox or cripples, attend our cotillion parties very willingly.

Jacob W. Bailey, USMA 1832, to his brother, William M. Bailey, August 21, 1829: We shall go into Barracks next week, the day before we move we are to have a Grand Fancy Ball, all Cadets who will wear fancy dresses will be allowed to attend, the others will see the fun. The objections which exist against Fancy Balls in cities, do not exist here. In the city any ragamuffin can obtain admittance, here all the actors are Cadets. It really seems like "old times" to get into a room with men, women, girls and boys, dressed as they used to when we were in the World.

Barracks

William Dutton, USMA 1846, to his cousin, Miss Lucy J. Mathews, February 18, 1843: I believe I have never given you a description of our

---

[1] A pseudonym assumed by Charles Dickens in his *Sketches by Boz* first published as a collection in 1836.

room—etc. If not it may not be uninteresting to give you an "Order" posted on every door—"Bedstead—against door—Trunks—under iron bedsteads— Lamps—clean on mantel—Dress Caps—Neatly arranged behind door— Looking Glass—between washstand & door—Books—neatly arranged on shelf farthest from door—Broom—Hanging behind door—Drawing books—under shelf farthest from door—Muskets—in gun rack and locks sprung—Bayonets in scabbards—Accoutrements—Hanging over muskets—Sabres—Cutlasses & swords—hanging over muskets—Candle Box—for scrubbing utensils—Against wall under shelf nearest door, & fire place—clothes—neatly hung on pegs over—bedsteads—Mattress & Blankets neatly folded—Orderly Board—over mantel—chairs—when not used under tables—Orderlies of rooms are held responsible for the observance of the above mentioned arrangement. By order of Lieut. E. J. Steptoe—1st Lieut. 1st Art. & commd't A compy.

William Dutton, USMA 1846, to his brother, C. Dutton, June 19, 1842: We have five in our room, which you know is but about 10 by 12. At 5 A. M. which is ½ an hour after the morning gun, the drums are beat by the barracks, & the cry grows—"fall in there," when we all have to be in the ranks or be reported. The roll is then called, we go to our rooms & have 15 minutes to roll up our blankets put them up, wash, clean the room etc., when every thing must be in order. We have no mattresses & only 2 blankets to lay on the floor and cover ourselves with, & when we all five spread our-selves out we just cover the floor—(In camp, we have no more.) We then remain in our rooms until the drums beat for breakfast, again if missing we are reported. We then march to the mess hall, & if one speaks, raises his hand, looks to the right or left (which is the case on all parade) we are reported indeed we are reported for everything. I have been so fortunate as to escape as yet. When we arrive at the tables, the command is given "take seats," & then such a scrambling you never saw. For breakfast we have the remains of the meat of the former days dinner, cut up with potato with considerable gravy—& not more than two thirds of them get a bit.—bread cut in chunks, butter and coffee. We have to eat as fast as we can, & before we get enough, the command is given "Squad rise," at dinner we have "Roast Beef," & boiled potato, & bread—no butter, At Tea, bread & butter & tea. We have to drill twice a day, & a good many faint away. It is terrible, but I like the whole of it, after we have marched from tea, we stay in our room till ½ hour past 9 when we can go to bed if we choose, & at taps at 10 every light must be out & after that the inspector happens in all times of night.

MS Journal of Samuel Peter Heintzelman, USMA, February 18, 1825: Last evening I fixed up a blanket so that I might keep a light after taps.

George W. Cullum, USMA 1833, to Alfred Huidekoper, September 9, 1830: Fortunately I live with a Cadet Professor who is entitled to a light after taps (10 O'clock) by which I am very glad to profit until about 12, as it requires all of that time for me to get my lessons.

William Dutton, USMA 1846, to his brother, C. Dutton, June 19, 1842: There are about a dozen or 15 of splendid talent who have been about through the course, a graduate of Yale, & if I take a place near the head it must be by tremendous exertion.

George W. Cullum, USMA 1833, to his sister, Miss Catherine Cullum, April 24, 1831: Monday morning April 25th.—I have just returned from a hard morning's work, of surveying. I have been taking a plan of the point, for the sake of a little practice and still more for some fresh air. It is delightful working on the field instead of on the blackboard, particularly as we sometimes have a peep at some of the fair sex, when taking the positions of their dwellings.

William Dutton, USMA 1846, to his cousin, Miss Lucy J. Mathews, March 11, 1843: It is truly a lovely day & as our arms glittered in the sun at morning inspection I could not help contrasting in my mind the difference between a Sunday morning at home and here. There all is peace and quiet. Here accoutrements must be in their best order, & then ¾ of an hour spent in evolutions. But then from Inspection till the Church Drum, one can call home his thoughts or let them rove on home if he chooses without interruption, as there's no visiting on the sabbath.

George W. Cullum, USMA 1833, to Alfred Huidekoper, November 22, 1829: I have just got back from church, after hearing rather a dry sermon. Going to church is very different from what it used to be at good old Meadville. If I had not there the pleasure of hearing a good sermon, I had at least the pleasure of seeing all my young friends, particularly my female acquaintances; but when I got to church here, I am obliged to sit for two hours on a bench without a back, squeesed up among a parcel of Cadets, and squeesed up more with my belts, as we have all to wear our side arms to church.

William D. Frazer, USMA 1834, to his brother Reah Frazer, April 24, 1833: We have finished our course for this year and are now reviewing, we went as far as Spherical Projections in Descriptive Geometry, it is a study which is studied no other place but here, the object is to represent all Geometrical Problems on planes, the objects are given in space, we have to find the Projections of them on planes. I drew yesterday the intersections of two cylinders. I will send them to you just to show you what it is like, may be Mr. Findley can explain it to you.

James W. Schureman, USMA 1842, to his sister Mary, February 14, 1840 (in the Library of Congress): Every moment is nearer than the preceding to that happy time known as furlough time, it is a period ever welcome to a cadet, its joys constitute his dreams by night, his thoughts by day. It is the climax of his wishes and the boundary of his imagination, it is a period calculated to awaken the strongest idea of human happiness, it is liberty sweetened by confinement, and ease enhanced by previous labours. Long and ardently have I wished for that happy moment to arrive when I can say farewell O West Point with all thy grandeur and thy halls of science and to say mind rest for a season from thy laborious occupation, home and friends are far more endearing than you all.

Examination

George W. Cullum, USMA 1833, to Alfred Huidekoper, January 21 [1832]: Attendant upon a West Point Inquisition. In preparing for this last, I believe for two weeks previous, that I scarcely lifted my eyes from my book except to eat and sleep my six hours, and even then after such close application I shuddered to obey the call of "turn out first section second class." This however was not the trying time, although my heart palpitated strong enough to have shaken the Alleghenies had they been placed upon it.

William Dutton, USMA 1846, to his cousin, Miss Lucy J. Mathews, June 22, 1843: The long agony is at length over, & it may well be called "The agony": for I have never seen more anguish depicted in the countenances of any than the U.S. Corps of Cadets have manifested.

William Dutton, USMA 1846, to his brother, C. Dutton, June 19, 1842: The closing up of the Examination was signalized by a display of fire works etc. In the PM. horses were attached to all the cannon on both sides of the plain & the way the cannon balls & bombs flew about was like hail. It seemed as if the earth would open, & the echoing from hill to hill produced an effect. Astonishing. In the evening they sent up rockets from every quarter & the air was full of them, while every now and then large fire bombs were fired from the mortars shaking the earth, & lighting the vale as far up as Newburg & when several hundred feet from the ground would burst & those fragments would again burst with a noise. They then placed candles around a hollow square and danced.

Recreation

James W. Schureman, USMA 1842, to his sister, January 24, 1841 (in the Library of Congress): But nevertheless we do once in a while have something to break this monotony. On Saturday we have the sweet sound of music from our well organized band headed by Mr. Kendall a brother of the celebrated bugler, and how sweet after poring for a week over a dry mechanics or optics does it fall upon the ear.

Jerome N. Bonaparte, Jr., USMA 1852, to his parents, February 3, 1850

(Maryland Hist. Soc.): The concert last night was delightful—it consisted almost entirely of stringed instruments, and Appelles played one or two solos on the violin beautifully. The Cadets behaved better than usual, although they talked pretty loudly during the solos.

MS Journal of Samuel P. Heintzelman, USMA 1826, February 5, 1825: Temp. 4¾ below zero Went skating . . . I broke in several times, once up to my middle there were over a dozen broke in. It was on the flats where the water is not deep. I played chess this evening the first time for a long time and beat a man six or seven times in succession.

MS Journal of Samuel P. Heintzelman, USMA 1826, July 29, 1825: A bear and three cubs were seen in the mountains and about a half dozen cadets took their muskets and went after them but did not see them.

MS Journal of Samuel P. Heintzelman, USMA 1826, November 5, 1825: The Cadets played Foot-Ball to day.

Jacob W. Bailey, USMA 1832, to his brother, William M. Bailey, April [25], 1832: I went up to Crow's nest last Saturday and found a party of 10 or a dozen Cadets already on the top. When they started to come down, I appointed myself pilot and for my own amusement led them home by one of the most frightful ways which I knew, there is in reality not much danger in the path I chose, but it would make one not used to climbing feel somewhat queer. I pretended to lose my way and led them to the brink of a precipice some hundred feet high.

MS Journal of Samuel P. Heintzelman, USMA 1826, May 7, 1825: Our barber has finished the addition to his shop, he has his soda fountain playing.

Jacob W. Bailey, USMA 1832, to his brother, William M. Bailey, March 11, 1844: We have had some fun here last week in a course of lectures by a Prof Grimes on Animal Magnetism and Phrenology I was delighted to witness such a transparent piece of humbuggery, for I expected to be perhaps puzzled to account for the results, but to convince one that miracles are performed I must see something that I can only account for by a miracle. The most that this fellow could do, was to get a man who was unknown to any of the audience into a state in which he would do what Grimes told him to do, Oh wonderful—The magic of money would easily effect this— Grimes told some good stories, and we got our moneys worth of laughter, to say nothing of being confirmed in ones previous opinions concerning Animal Magnetism and Phrenology.

George W. Cullum, USMA 1833, to his sister, Miss Catherine Cullum, February 11, 1833: I believe I never told you that our class was called the Carroll class. Every Saturday evening we have a meeting for the purpose of literary improvement as our course of education here is almost purely scientific, which does not fit one very well to palaver in the world. We have regular debates and recitations. Many voluntary compositions are made by a reader selected by the society. The pieces are handed to him so that nobody but him knows the authors. You would be surprised to hear so many stories, essays etc., etc., serious and comic written in one week besides attending to our other studies. There are scarcely ever less than ten or twelve good compositions. Our debates are very interesting and instructing: perhaps you would not judge so from the one I have just been on. That was chosen as a kind of relief as we had had a very long run of serious ones before.

In addition to this we have another society, called the United Carroll Club: its object is to keep up the present generous and noble feeling, which characterizes our class, by having a grand meeting of the whole class once in four years in Baltimore, on the anniversary of our graduating day.[2]

MS Journal of Samuel P. Heintzelman, USMA 1826, February 22, 1825: To day it was proposed by the Corps to illuminate, we obtained permission from the Superintendent to do it. We prepared a transparency with the name of Washington. At 9 o'clock the signal was given to light candles, in the South Barrack we closed the window shutters and lighted the candles before the time, so that at the instant that signal was given we threw open the window shutters.

MS Journal of Samuel P. Heintzelman, USMA 1826, July 4, 1825: At 11 o'clock we marched to the chapel where the Declaration of Independence was read by Cadet Allen, and an oration delivered by Cadet Henderson (B. N.) it was a very eloquent one, at 3 o'clock we marched to the mess-hall to an excellent dinner served up by Mr. Cozzens, many patriotic toasts were drunk & many would have been drunk but the new-cadets became very noisy so that we retired (at half past 5 o'clock) much sooner than is usual on such occasions & before all the toasts were drunk (if I can obtain them I will record them) some few got tipsy.[3]

William D. Frazer, USMA 1834, to his brother, Reah Frazer, July 9, 1833: We had splendid celebration here on the 4th. Just as the sun began to peep over the mountain we fired a salute of 13 guns from the Cadets battery, at eleven oclock the procession began, it was in the following order, 1st colours and escort, 2d cadets of the 4th class 3d Cadets of the 3d class, 4th cadets of the 2d and 1st class, 5th invited guests, 6th citizens. We

---

[2] Many classes took or received names. The Class of 1833 was designated "The Carrolls" in honor of Charles Carroll, then the sole surviving signer of the Declaration of Independence.

[3] "The celebrations of the 4th of July by a Public dinner, with wine having been sometimes permitted, and having nearly as often, led to much inebriety and disorder among Cadets, it was, with their cheerful acquiescence, omitted in 1838, and may now be considered as permanently discontinued at the Military Academy." Excerpt from Opinion of a Court of Inquiry, General Winfield Scott, President, July 6, 1840, in Engineer Department Orders, February 1838 to April 1842, p. 64. Whisky was a regular part of Army rations until November 2, 1832.

marched to the chapel where a very fine address was delivered by Cadet Pope of Kentucky. In the afternoon at 4 oclock we had a splendid dinner, all the Officers were there and also General Scott, there was a great many elegant toasts drank, among them the following struck me the most. Poland the land where justice sleeps and liberty lies bleeding. The spirit of 76, 9 cheers, tune Yankee doodle. The Union esto perpetua, tune a hymn. We had claret and champagne but not a drop of it touched my lips, and may God grant that it never will.

Pledge signed by 49 Cadets, dated February, 1824: We the undersigned conscious of the alarming degree to which the drinking of spiritous liquor has been carried in the Corps, and knowing full well that if continued it must prove the destruction of the most valuable Institution, do set our countenances against it, and do pledge our word and honor that we will not in any wise use Wine or Spiritous liquor so long as we remain members of the Institution except when sanctioned by the Superintendent.[4]

First Classman

George W. Cullum, USMA 1833, to Alfred Huidekoper, June 21, 1832: One year more and my pilgrimage will be completed. When I think of the three last and particularly of the past year, all seems a dream. It appears but as a month since I was receiving the warm greetings of relatives and friends at my own beloved home. It is astonishing how constant employment gives wings to time. I can hardly realize the fact that we are first class-men, lords of the land, independent as journey-men shoe-blacks, under half pay, turning neither to the right or left for favour from Uncle Sam or any of his numerous progeny, and fearing not even Black Hawk and his thousand warriors.

Edward L. Hartz, USMA 1855, to his father, September 7, 1854 (in the Library of Congress): I have learned to throw off that feeling of humbleness which the treatment ones superiors give to him when a "plebe" imbues him with. Having no longer any superior class to bow to, while all others at the academy grant our supremacy. We acquire that air of importance, that show of dignity and condescension to our inferiors, which forms the great characteristic of first class men.

Jacob W. Bailey, USMA 1832, to his mother, Mrs. Jane Keeley, January 13, 1832: I thought when I entered the first class that we should have a comparatively easy time, but the contrary was the case, we have been obliged to study this year, almost as hard as when Lacroix' Algebra was our trouble. I have had so much writing to do, that I am heartily tired out. Memoir

---

[4] The custom of an entire class taking a pledge to refrain from committing some act of delinquency in order to save guilty classmates from dismissal lasted for about a hundred years. Other schools followed the same procedure.

after memoir, and note after note, have been required of us, ever since last September. . . .

We shall [have] a very busy time between now and next June, it will take about a week to examine my class, next June we shall have so many subjects to be called upon, Civil engineering is the most important of them, and the one to which I shall pay the most attention. The number of Rail-roads constructing in all parts of our country will furnish employment for many engineers, and if I do not get stationed at West Point, I think I should try to get employed on some one of them for a while.

James W. Burbridge, USMA ex-1831, to W. G. Hawkins, March 18, 1828: I am well aware that engineering at this time is one of the most lucrative & honorable proffessions that a young man can get in to but on the other hand it takes a man of superior tallents to get into that body, there is not more than 10 out of 100 of the graduates of this place who immediately get into that Corps.

MS Journal of Samuel P. Heintzelman, USMA 1826, February 1, 1825: This evening there was read out an order from the Secretary at War that the vacancies in the Marine Corps should be filled from the Military Academy and that the Marine Corps should be put on the same footing with the other Corps composing the army.

Henry W. Halleck, USMA 1839, to Theodore Miller, July 6, 1838: The new army bill will give me a better situation when graduating than under the old one provided that the President does not fill up the present vacancies with citizens. It is hard for us to be placed under citizens who have spent no time in preparation for their commissions, while we have spent four or five years here at hard toil fitting ourselves for the various duties of our stations.

From the diary of John Bratt, USMA 1837, April 7, 1837: My class has given orders, measurements, etc. for a class ring—a heavy gold, a red carnelian stone with a sunken design—a book with a sword passed thro', the owner's named engraved enmity to "Artillery," *vide* "Notes on Artillery," a book of much trouble and sorrow to many a West Pointer.

Jacob W. Bailey, USMA 1832, to his mother, Mrs. Jane Keeley, June 1, 1832: The examination is over and I have graduated at last. I am 5th this year which is as high as I wished, and higher than I expected. I suppose you expect me in Waterville soon, there is a chance however of your being disappointed. The Indians in the west have been making bad work and General Scott, has orders to proceed immediately to the scene of action and he wishes to take my class with him. If he concludes to do so, I shall be informed of it in a few days. The Indians will probably be put down long before the expedition under General Scott, can get to the seat of war, So that you need not dream of tomahawks and scalps.

Jacob W. Bailey, USMA 1832, to his brother, William M. Bailey, April [25], *1832:* It would take a fortune almost to furnish a graduate with his dress etc. if he purchased it here for instance, the price of boots here is $7.00, of leather trunks $20.00 Which I'd be shot before I'd pay. Coat $30.00 to $34.00 I shall buy as little here as possible I have spoken for a coat in New York.

MS Journal of Samuel P. Heintzelman, USMA 1826, August 2, 1826: I received my appointment as Lieutenant. It came from the Post Adj at West Point. My station is at Belle Fontaine Missouri. I belong to the 3rd Reg. of Inf. I am Furloughed to the 31st of Oct.

LINCOLN STEFFENS

Semester at Heidelberg

FROM *The Autobiography of Lincoln Steffens*

The Heidelberg that Lincoln Steffens knew in the 1890s is two world wars and—in feeling—centuries away. It was a younger and quieter world of beer drinking, dancing and lovemaking, of endless talk of philosophy and art, of exploration of a universe which seemed stable and permanent.

It was beginning to die even then, when young Lincoln Steffens was looking for an education and an ethics by which he could live. He returned from three years at Berlin, Heidelberg and the Sorbonne to look at his native America with the sharp and penetrating eye of a talented reporter. His was the most powerful voice among the muckrakers of the early 1900s, and his autobiography, from which this selection comes, is a brilliant analysis of his time.

WITH the Black Forest behind it and the Neckar River running through it to the Rhine, Heidelberg is a place of temptation and pleasure, and this wise old university was no spoilsport. All the lectures were on the four working days of the week, Tuesday, Wednesday, Thursday, and Friday, leaving the week-end long and clear for play. Many students go there for fun. I met an American corps student who had been fighting and drinking and idling so long there that he could hardly rally his English to talk with me.

"I must quit this, go to some other university and work," he said when we parted. I had reminded him of some old drowned purpose.

I went to Heidelberg to hear Kuno Fischer, the most eloquent if not the most apostolic of the professors of Hegel's philosophy, and I studied hard with him. Other subjects also I took, continuing my Berlin courses in art history and economics. My semester at Heidelberg was a fruitful season, but it bore flowers too. I made some friends there, and together we had all the fun that was going, in the town, on the river, in the Forest—

beer-drinking, dancing, swimming and boating, walking, talking, and exploring the world and one another.

My room was up on the *Anlage,* just above the city park in a little house kept by a Viennese woman who in turn was kept by a local merchant. Her gay days were over; she was a good old mother to her two children and altogether contented with her condition of dependence upon the honor of the gentleman who had "married a lady" and was devoted to her, his proper wife. He only paid, but he paid regularly for his past sins. His old mistress did not regret hers; she loved to talk about them. She took me in as her one lodger to make a little extra money out of the front room, which her small family did not need. An expressive woman with a common story, lived and seen from her Viennese point of view, she served lively entertainment and some light upon ethics with all the meals that I took in my room. These were not many.

Kuno Fischer gave his first lecture, logic, at seven o'clock in the morning; no time for more than a hot cup of coffee at home with a piece of bread, which I finished often as I finished dressing on the way down to the university. Other students also showed signs of haste at 7:15, when, on the dot, the professor began his lecture with a smile for the breathless state of his hearers and the imperfect arrangement of collars and ties. I saw some fellows in slippers, pajamas, and overcoats, looking up with admiration at the professor, neat, composed, and logical. And eloquent; I missed taking many a note to sit and listen to Kuno Fischer's poetical prose. Few Germans can either speak or write German—well. Their language is too rich, variable, and unripe for them. Only the masters can master it, and Kuno Fischer, handsome and intelligent, was a master of German as he was of his own thinking in it. I asked him once how it came that he spoke German so well.

He had a habit which I had of going from his first lecture to the river for a swim. Sometimes we walked together down to the floating bath-house, and many a pleasant talk we had on the way. He chatted as he lectured, in short, clear, incisive sentences, and he liked it that I liked his style. It was by way of a jesting compliment that I put to him my question: "Herr Geheimrat, wie kommt es dass Sie so schön deutsch sprechen?"

"It's because I speak English," he answered in English, and, laughing, he reminded me that Goethe, asked once the same question, replied that his best German was written in the period when he was soaking in French.

After the swim I had breakfast in some café or beer hall, where I completed my notes; then more lectures till one o'clock. The noon meal was usually with some crowd of students in a restaurant, under the stiff forms of the student ritual, the gossip, the controversies, the plans for excursions or fights. Once a week I had an art history course which took us up to the castle to examine the stones and trace their periods, or off to the excavations near by, as far as Wiesbaden. Other days there were other lectures or library work or home study till along about four, when I went forth either to the Schloss or to some other café for coffee or to the river for a paddle. The boatman had several canoes, "left by the English," he said.

Just above the bridge the river is artificially narrowed and deepened, making a rapid, called the Hart Teufel, for about an eighth of a mile, and it's a struggle to paddle up it. I used to do it for exercise and then drive the little craft on up the easy, broad river to some one of the many garden restaurants along shore. After a bath out in the stream, I had an appetite which made the good cooking seem perfect, and a thirst which took beer as the Hart Teufel took water. There was always some other loose student to join for a long, slow supper and a long, highbrow conversation. When the darkness fell, there was the canoe to lie in and the river to float me effortlessly back to town. I could philosophize in the dark; if there was a moon I could romance. Pleasant days, those lonely Heidelberg days. Pleasanter still the friendly days that followed.

Once, when the art history professor had his class out for field work on some ruin or other, a tall young German came up to me, struck his heels together, saluted stiffly, and said: "My name is Johann Friedrich Krudewolf. I am a German; I take you for an American. I want to learn English. I propose to exchange with you lessons in German for lessons in English."

I closed the foolish bargain, and we shook hands on it. There was one lesson in English, one in German, and no more. I did not have to study German; I was learning it fast enough by absorption, and I think now that while he did want to learn English, he was really seeking a friend. Anyhow we became so interested in each other that the conversation, even at the first and last lesson, ran away from the purpose and, of course, ran into the language easiest for both of us to understand. Bad as my German was then, it was so much better than his school English that we always spoke German and soon forgot lessons. His specialty was art history, and I was glad of that; Hegel's history of art gave a philosophic meaning to the subject, and my friend's interest in the details filled in beautifully my efforts to feel art both in itself and as a border of flowers along the course of our civilization.

Our excursions with the class to churches, castles, and ruins were pleasant recreations for me, so pleasant that we made study trips by ourselves for fun. We foot-toured the Black Forest three days at a time, always to see things Krudewolf wished to examine for art history reasons, but his notes told by the way and the ruined castles illustrated vividly the history of the rise of great German families from robbers to robber knights, to military and social power, to riches, position, and honors. That was the way it was done of old, and I made notes on morals as studiously as my companion did on art.

The best excursion we made, however, was for its own sake. The Neckar River was navigable up to Heilbron, and a curious kind of boat-train operated on it, the *Schlepper*. There was a cable laid in the middle of the stream. The power boat picked up this cable, pulled itself up on it, and passed it out over the stern. By this means the tuglike *Schlepper* schlepped a string of cargo boats up the Neckar to Heilbron and back down to the Rhine. Johann hired a rowboat and sent it on the *Schlepper* up to Heilbron, whither we went by train to meet it. A day and a night in funny old Heilbron, with its old, old stories, and we set out in the rowboat to row (or float) home to Heidelberg. We started early one morning, meaning to go far that day, but by ten o'clock we were passing such tempting restaurants in river gardens that we yielded, stopped and had breakfast, which we thought would do for lunch, too. But we could not pass by the resorts that called to us; we had to see some of them. We chose one for luncheon, a long luncheon, and when we embarked again, chose others here, there, everywhere for beer, coffee, or—something. We could not row; it was a waste, and—even drifting was too fast.

The Neckar, from Heilbron to Heidelberg, is one of the most beautiful stretches of country that I have ever seen—or it seemed so to me then. We stayed our first night at a village inn on the river bank, and while we dined made two important discoveries. This was a *Schaumwein* (champagne) country, with the "fizz" at seventy-five cents the bottle; and this season was a church festival at which everybody drank, danced, and made love. We danced till midnight that night and then took some peasant girls out rowing in our boat. We got away late the next morning and were stopped everywhere by pretty places for coffee or wine or meals or historical sights that Johann had to investigate. We didn't make five miles the second day. That night we danced—every night we danced, and we began to get away later and later in the mornings. We were ten days making a distance that one might have rowed in three or four, and then felt and wondered that we had done so beautiful a journey so fast. And I wonder now that I have never gone back, as I declared and have always been sure that I would "some day," to do the Neckar over again in a rowboat slowly—two or three weeks of it.

Toward the end of the semester a friend of mine, Carlos J. Hittell, came over from Munich to visit me. He was an art student from California. I had known well his brother Franklin at Berkeley; his father, Theodore H. Hittell, the historian, had had more to do with my education than many a teacher. A retired attorney, he had turned to the writing of history, especially of California. He used to work on the dining-room table after dinner while I, his children and their friends, talked as youth will, finally and positively, of all sorts of things. Once he kept me when the others left, and he went into my mind and broke all the idols he found there. He was rough.

"You can't learn if you know everything already," he said. "You can't have a free mind if it's full of superstitions." And he whanged away. I took it pretty well, and because I came back for more, he continued to destroy my images. Every time I went to the house, whether to dinner, to call on his daughter, Catherine, or to sing songs with his sons, he lay for me and drew me into talk and some reading in his good library. A great service this fine old man rendered me. And his son, Carlos, did me another.

When Carlos joined me at Heidelberg, he completed our trio, one student of art history, one of ethics and philosophy, and one of the real thing, art. We played, walking, rowing, swimming, and touring, but also we talked, and the artist, without knowing or meaning it, spoke as one having authority. Johann and I listened to the man who was doing what we were merely reading and thinking about. We saw what the artist had told me at Berkeley, that we were getting scholarship about art, not art. But, like that other artist, Carlos Hittell could not express in our medium, words, what he was doing or trying to do when he was painting. We must go and be with art students when they were at work in their studios and see if we could—not hear, but see what art is. When the semester was over, therefore, we all went to Munich to study art instead of art history. No more Heidelberg for either of us.

And no more philosophy for me. There was no ethics in it. I had gone through Hegel with Kuno Fischer, hoping to find a basis for an ethics; and the professor thought he had one. I had been reading in the original the other philosophers whom I had read also in Berkeley, and they, too, thought they had it all settled. They did not have anything settled. Like the disputing professors at Berkeley, they could not agree upon what was knowledge, nor upon what was good and what evil, nor why. The philosophers were all prophets, their philosophies beliefs, their logic a justification of their—religions. And as for their ethics, it was without foundation. The only reasons they had to give for not lying or stealing were not so reasonable as the stupidest English gentleman's: "It isn't done."

This was my reluctant, disappointed conclusion, arrived at after a waste of a couple of good years of conscientious work. I must leave the philosophers and go to the scientists for my science of ethics as I must go to the artists for art. I said good-by to the good kept woman who had kept me so comfortable. She accepted my departure as she accepted everything.

"Men come and men go," she said cheerfully.

"Always?" I asked.

"They don't always come," she laughed, "but always they go, always."

"And that's all there is of it?"

"All? Nay," she protested, pointing to her two. "For me there are always the children, thank God."

O . HENRY

The Chair of
Philanthromathematics

FROM *The Gentle Grafter*

O. Henry's acquaintance with colleges may have been remote, but his familiarity with shady characters was large and personal, as this story bears witness. He left school at fifteen to work as a drug clerk, bookkeeper, draftsman, and, unhappily, as bank teller: he served a three-year prison sentence for embezzlement, a technical embezzlement, his biographers say.

It was in prison that he began writing the sentimental, homey surprise-ending stories so closely associated with his name. Of these, he wrote some six hundred—most of them at the rate of one a week and a hundred dollars each, for a newspaper—before he died at forty-eight of tuberculosis complicated by the daily consumption of two quarts of whisky.

I SEE that the cause of Education has received the princely gift of more than fifty millions of dollars," said I.

I was gleaning the stray items from the evening papers while Jeff Peters packed his briar pipe with plug cut.

"Which same," said Jeff, "calls for a new deck, and a recitation by the entire class in philanthromathematics."

"Is that an allusion?" I asked.

"It is," said Jeff. "I never told you about the time when me and Andy Tucker was philanthropists, did I? It was eight years ago in Arizona. Andy and me was out in the Gila mountains with a two-horse wagon prospecting for silver. We struck it, and sold out to parties in Tucson for $25,000. They paid our check at the bank in silver—a thousand dollars in a sack. We loaded it in our wagon and drove east a hundred miles before we recovered our presence of intellect. Twenty-five thousand dollars don't

75

sound like so much when you're reading the annual report of the Pennsylvania Railroad or listening to an actor talking about his salary; but when
you can raise up a wagon sheet and kick around with your bootheel and
hear every one of 'em ring against another it makes you feel like you
was a night-and-day bank with the clock striking twelve.

"The third day out we drove into one of the most specious and tidy
little towns that Nature or Rand and McNally ever turned out. It was in the
foothills, and mitigated with trees and flowers and about 2,000 head of
cordial and dilatory inhabitants. The town seemed to be called Floresville,
and Nature had not contaminated it with many railroads, fleas or Eastern
tourists.

"Me and Andy deposited our money to the credit of Peters and Tucker
in the Esperanza Savings Bank, and got rooms at the Skyview Hotel. After
supper we lit up, and sat out on the gallery and smoked. Then was when
the philanthropy idea struck me. I suppose every grafter gets it sometime.

"When a man swindles the public out of a certain amount he begins
to get scared and wants to return part of it. And if you'll watch close and
notice the way his charity runs you'll see that he tries to restore it to the
same people he got it from. As a hydrostatical case, take, let's say, A. A made
his millions selling oil to poor students who sit up nights studying political
economy and methods for regulating the trusts. So, back to the universities
and colleges goes his conscience dollars.

"There's B got his from the common laboring man that works with
his hands and tools. How's he to get some of the remorse fund back into
their overalls?

" 'Aha!' says B, 'I'll do it in the name of Education. I've skinned the
laboring man,' says he to himself, 'but, according to the old proverb,
"Charity covers a multitude of skins." '

"So he puts up eighty million dollars' worth of libraries; and the boys
with the dinner pail that builds 'em gets the benefit.

" 'Where's the books?' asks the reading public.

" 'I dinna ken,' says B. 'I offered ye libraries; and there they are. I suppose if I'd given ye preferred steel trust stock instead ye'd have wanted the
water in it set out in cut glass decanters. Hoot, for ye!'

"But, as I said, the owning of so much money was beginning to give me
philanthropitis. It was the first time me and Andy had ever made a pile
big enough to make us stop and think how we got it.

" 'Andy,' says I, 'we're wealthy—not beyond the dreams of average; but
in our humble way we are comparatively as rich as Greasers. I feel as if
I'd like to do something for as well as to humanity.'

" 'I was thinking the same thing, Jeff,' says he. 'We've been gouging the
public for a long time with all kinds of little schemes from selling self-

igniting celluloid collars to flooding Georgia with Hoke Smith presidential campaign buttons. I'd like, myself, to hedge a bet or two in the graft game if I could do it without actually banging the cymbalines in the Salvation Army or teaching a bible class by the Bertillon system.'

" 'What'll we do?' says Andy. 'Give free grub to the poor or send a couple of thousand to George Cortelyou?'

" 'Neither,' says I. 'We've got too much money to be implicated in plain charity; and we haven't got enough to make restitution. So, we'll look about for something that's about half way between the two.'

"The next day in walking around Floresville we see on a hill a big red brick building that appears to be disinhabited. The citizens speak up and tell us that it was begun for a residence several years before by a mine owner. After running up the house he finds he only had $2.80 left to furnish it with, so he invests that in whisky and jumps off the roof on a spot where he now requiescats in pieces.

"As soon as me and Andy saw that building the same idea struck both of us. We would fix it up with lights and pen wipers and professors, and put an iron dog and statues of Hercules and Father John on the lawn, and start one of the finest free educational institutions in the world right there.

"So we talks it over to the prominent citizens of Floresville, who falls in fine with the idea. They give a banquet in the engine house to us, and we make our bow for the first time as benefactors to the cause of progress and enlightenment. Andy makes an hour-and-a-half speech on the subject of irrigation in Lower Egypt, and we have a moral tune on the phonograph and pineapple sherbet.

"Andy and me didn't lose any time in philanthropping. We put every man in town that could tell a hammer from a step ladder to work on the building, dividing it up into class rooms and lecture halls. We wire to Frisco for a car load of desks, footballs, arithmetics, penholders, dictionaries, chairs for the professors, slates, skeletons, sponges, twenty-even cravenetted gowns and caps for the senior class, and an open order for all the truck that goes with a first-class university. I took it on myself to put a campus and a curriculum on the list; but the telegraph operator must have got the words wrong, being an ignorant man, for when the goods come we found a can of peas and a curry-comb among 'em.

"While the weekly paper was having chalk-plate cuts of me and Andy we wired an employment agency in Chicago to express us f. o. b., six professors immediately—one English literature, one up-to-date dead languages, one chemistry, one political economy—democrat preferred—one logic, and one wise to painting, Italian and music, with union card. The Esperanza bank guaranteed salaries, which was to run between $800 and $800.50.

"Well, sir, we finally got in shape. Over the front door was carved the words: 'The World's University; Peters & Tucker, Patrons and Proprietors.' And when September the first got a cross-mark on the calendar, the come-ons begun to roll in. First the faculty got off the tri-weekly express from Tucson. They was mostly young, spectacled and red-headed, with sentiments divided between ambition and food. Andy and me got 'em billeted on the Floresvillians and then laid for the students.

"They came in bunches. We had advertised the University in all the state papers, and it did us good to see how quick the country responded. Two hundred and nineteen husky lads aging along from 18 up to chin whiskers answered the clarion call of free education. They ripped open that town, sponged the seams, turned it, lined it with new mohair; and you couldn't have told it from Harvard or Goldfields at the March term of court.

"They marched up and down the streets waving flags with the World's University colors—ultramarine and blue—and they certainly made a lively place of Floresville. Andy made 'em a speech from the balcony of the Skyview Hotel, and the whole town was out celebrating.

"In about two weeks the professors got the students disarmed and herded into classes. I don't believe there's any pleasure equal to being a philanthropist. Me and Andy bought high silk hats and pretended to dodge the two reporters of the Floresville Gazette. The paper had a man to kodak us whenever we appeared on the street, and ran our pictures every week over the column headed 'Educational Notes.' Andy lectured twice a week at the University; and afterward I would rise and tell a humorous story. Once the Gazette printed my picture with Abe Lincoln on one side and Marshall P. Wilder on the other.

"Andy was as interested in philanthropy as I was. We used to wake up of nights and tell each other new ideas for booming the University.

" 'Andy,' says I to him one day, 'there's something we overlooked. The boys ought to have dromedaries.'

" 'What's that?' Andy asks.

" 'Why, something to sleep in, of course,' says I. 'All colleges have 'em.'

" 'Oh, you mean pajamas,' says Andy.

" 'I do not,' says I. 'I mean dromedaries.' But I never could make Andy understand; so we never ordered 'em. Of course, I meant them long bedrooms in colleges where the scholars sleep in a row.

"Well, sir, the World's University was a success. We had scholars from five States and territories, and Floresville had a boom. A new shooting gallery and a pawn shop and two more saloons started; and the boys got up a college yell that went this way:

" 'Raw, raw, raw,
   Done, done, done,
Peters, Tucker,
   Lots of fun.
Bow-wow-wow,
   Haw-hee-haw,
World University,
   Hip, hurrah!'

"The scholars was a fine lot of young men, and me and Andy was as proud of 'em as if they belonged to our own family.

"But one day about the last of October Andy comes to me and asks if I have any idea how much money we had left in the bank. I guesses about sixteen thousand. 'Our balance,' says Andy, 'is $821.62.'

" 'What!' says I, with a kind of a yell. 'Do you mean to tell me that them infernal clod-hopping, dough-headed, pup-faced, goose-brained, gate-stealing, rabbit-eared sons of horse thieves have soaked us for that much?'

" 'No less,' says Andy.

" 'Then, to Helvetia with philanthropy,' says I.

" 'Not necessarily,' says Andy. 'Philanthropy,' says he, 'when run on a good business basis is of the best grafts going. I'll look into the matter and see if it can't be straightened out.'

"The next week I am looking over the payroll of our faculty when I run across a new name—Professor James Darnley McCorkle, chair of mathematics; salary $100 per week. I yells so loud that Andy runs in quick.

" 'What's this,' says I. 'A professor of mathematics at more than $5,000 a year? How did this happen? Did he get in through the window and appoint himself?'

" 'I wired to Frisco for him a week ago,' says Andy. 'In ordering the faculty we seemed to have overlooked the chair of mathematics.'

" 'A good thing we did,' says I. 'We can pay his salary two weeks, and then our philanthropy will look like the ninth hole on the Skibo golf links.'

" 'Wait a while,' says Andy, 'and see how things turn out. We have taken up too noble a cause to draw out now. Besides, the further I gaze into the retail philanthropy business the better it looks to me. I never thought about investigating it before. Come to think of it now,' goes on Andy, 'all the philanthropists I ever knew had plenty of money. I ought to have looked into that matter long ago, and located which was the cause and which was the effect.'

"I had confidence in Andy's chicanery in financial affairs, so I left the whole thing in his hands. The University was flourishing fine, and me and

Andy kept our silk hats shined up, and Floresville kept on heaping honors on us like we was millionaires instead of almost busted philanthropists.

"The students kept the town lively and prosperous. Some stranger came to town and started a faro bank over the Red Front livery stable, and began to amass money in quantities. Me and Andy strolled up one night and piked a dollar or two for sociability. There were about fifty of our students there drinking rum punches and shoving high stacks of blues and reds about the table as the dealer turned the cards up.

" 'Why, dang it, Andy,' says I, 'these free-school-hunting, gander-headed, silk-socked little sons of sapsuckers have got more money than you and me ever had. Look at the rolls they're pulling out of their pistol pockets!'

" 'Yes,' says Andy, 'a good many of them are sons of wealthy miners and stockmen. It's very sad to see 'em wasting their opportunities this way.'

"At Christmas all the students went home to spend the holidays. We had a farewell blowout at the University, and Andy lectured on 'Modern Music and Prehistoric Literature of the Archipelagos.' Each one of the faculty answered to toasts, and compared me and Andy to Rockefeller and the Emperor Marcus Autolycus. I pounded on the table and yelled for Professor McCorkle; but it seems he wasn't present on the occasion. I wanted a look at the man that Andy thought could earn $100 a week in philanthropy that was on the point of making an assignment.

"The students all left on the night train; and the town sounded as quiet as the campus of a correspondence school at midnight. When I went to the hotel I saw a light in Andy's room, and I opened the door and walked in.

"There sat Andy and the faro dealer at a table dividing a two-foot high stack of currency in thousand-dollar packages.

" 'Correct,' says Andy. 'Thirty-one thousand apiece. Come in, Jeff,' says he. 'This is our share of the profits of the first half of the scholastic term of the World's University, incorporated and philanthropated. Are you convinced now,' says Andy, 'that philanthropy when practiced in a business way is an art that blesses him who gives as well as him who receives?'

" 'Great!' says I, feeling fine. 'I'll admit you are the doctor this time.'

" 'We'll be leaving on the morning train,' says Andy. 'You'd better get your collars and cuffs and press clippings together.'

" 'Great!' says I. 'I'll be ready. But, Andy,' says I, 'I wish I could have met that Professor James Darnley McCorkle before we went. I had a curiosity to know that man.'

" 'That'll be easy,' says Andy, turning around to the faro dealer.

" 'Jim,' says Andy, 'shake hands with Mr. Peters.' "

CHRISTIAN GAUSS

How Good
Were the Good Old Times?

FROM *The Good Old Times*

How good were they indeed, the good old times? A pertinent question. In this dissenting opinion, Christian Gauss, Dean of Princeton University for a quarter of a century, goes back to earlier college life in America to answer the plaintive cry of old graduates that the times have degenerated and the undergraduate with them.

History, says Dean Gauss, quoting chapter and verse, has a way of taking the gilt off the golden age that more sentimental and more forgetful old grads remember as their college years. True, the undergraduate of past decades was a hardier soul, but then, he had to be.

EVERY professor who has reached middle age in any of the older colleges has in recent years received quite regularly, by word of mouth or by letter, complaints from older alumni against the changes which have been taking place upon the campus and in the undergraduate. These alumni assume that things have been steadily degenerating and that somewhere in the past, as in the Greek mythology, there lies a golden age of the colleges. Through all their grievances one recurrent note sounds like a bourdon: "The good old times—the good old times." It has been repeated so frequently that we have come to believe the phrase, and it is worth while to inquire how good these good old times actually were.

In the Town, But Not of It

In the rather harum-scarum throng of nearly a million undergraduates now in the colleges, there are, of course, all sorts. They represent all social

81

strata in our country, though the sons of the professional and economically more prosperous classes still predominate. In many ways they are like their predecessors. There are, therefore, certain constant factors which must be considered. Undergraduates today, as undergraduates of fifty years ago, are all young. Some of their troubles may spring from this source. The average age of the freshman classes remains about what it was fifty years ago—eighteen or nineteen. Students were slightly younger in the eighteenth century. At Brown the average age at graduation was 20.43 years, before the Revolution, and 21 years after it. None of these young men was born on the campus. They have already spent eighteen years at home, if, in this flibbertigibbet age, they are still fortunate enough to have one. All their sins and all their peculiarities should not, therefore, be charged against their alma mater. We call them "collegiate" when they respond over-enthusiastically to the extremes of manner and custom which are prevalent in the colleges. Whether there were good old times or not, one thing has happened which no faculty or board of trustees could have prevented. In former days the campuses were isolated communities on the outskirts of towns, as Harvard was to Boston, or Yale to New Haven, or sometimes, like Princeton, they were deliberately set down in the country. Even where the college was in the city proper, like Brown at Providence, the under-graduate made his home almost exclusively within college walls. Tristram Burgess, a graduate of Brown in 1796, could write that he knew little of Providence until after graduation: "For though I had resided in the town more than three years, my residence was at the college, nor was I in the street more than once a week, and then on the Sabbath."

The Business of a Student

The experience of Burgess was not unusual. The rules of the older colleges prevented that free coming and going, that week-ending now prevalent everywhere, but particularly deplored where the residential tradition is strong, as, for instance, at Yale and Princeton. At such colleges the rule prescribed that from sundown on Saturday to Monday morning the student must remain in his room and receive no visitors. He could leave only for necessary errands and to attend religious exercises.

The manner in which the student was to spend his ordinary working day was likewise prescribed, and it looks as if colleges here also took their cue one from another, since Harvard, Princeton and Brown are all sub-stantially in agreement and their old rule reads:

> That the scholars may furnish themselves with useful learning, they shall keep in their respective chambers, and diligently follow their stud-ies; except half an hour at breakfast; at dinner from twelve to two; and

after evening prayers till nine of the clock. To that end, the Tutors shall frequently visit their chambers after nine o'clock in the evening and at other studying times, to quicken them to their business.

Isolated communities of this sort could have their way with students. In them the collegiate atmosphere could, therefore, be more concentrated than it is now. With the changes in modern life, there are no such isolated communities anywhere. The entire country, including the colleges, is being reduced to pretty much a common denominator of social custom, of which this newer habit of week-ending is only one. It would be normal to expect, therefore, that with this absorption of the college by the modern city there would be a less distinctively college life, and so we find it.

If anyone is curious and will take the trouble to look through a volume like Yale Yesterdays, he will soon come upon what may at first strike him as an amusing picture of Yale Men of the Seventies around the Pump. Now the only funny thing about that picture is that it was not intended to be funny. The Yale undergraduates had not the slightest idea of being amusing; they are, in fact, a bit solemn and self-conscious. This matter of standing around the pump was a grim business. Some of them are wearing stovepipe hats. They must have been upper classmen.

The College of Hard Knocks

Could it be that there was a touch of the collegiate even in those far-off days of the giant killers? And what were they doing with those pitchers, huddled together under the spout of the pump? In the '70s they no longer hewed their own wood, but they did draw their own water, for there were no spigots in any of the old dormitories, and long after the beginnings of modern conveniences every man was, in this regard, his own chambermaid.

If he will look through the records of other colleges they will tell pretty much the same story. Ten years later, Princeton was no better. Here is a "Sophomore Eating Club of the Eighties." Sophomores today are usually a bit class-conscious. This is not because we live in degenerate days; it is because they are sophomores. If anything, they were more so then. Notice those deliberately careless postures. They are almost posed. Every man jack of them knows that he is having his picture taken; it is quite an occasion. They do not even group themselves around the door as sophomores of today would gather around an entrance to Commons. Even in the '80s, these young gentlemen already felt their academic oats. They sit on the roof of the porch, they are the second-story men and they dangle their feet over the edge in insolent sophomoric libertarianism.

The observer will notice also that they all wear curiously foreshortened hats. They must have been prescribed by some tyrannical college custom even then, for certainly no one but a sophomore could ever have chosen one on the unsupported dictates of his love for the good, the true and the beautiful. In these pictures, and any others of that robustious time, it will be noticed that a great many of these young men, probably all who could, wore mutton-chop whiskers. To them it was an index of the larger freedom and of that grown-up masculinity which sophomores have always affected. They, too, in their way, treated themselves like men and, college custom for college custom, the reader of the present will probably conclude that it is a mercy that the tides of today have set in other directions.

If in our search for the good old times we go back to the very beginning of college life in America, we meet with disappointments. Six years after the settlement of Boston the first action toward establishing the first college in America was taken, in 1636. When, in the year of its opening, 1638, John Harvard, a young Nonconformist minister, died and left about £800 and a library, everything seemed promising. The woes of undergraduates, however, began at once. The Reverend Nathaniel Eaton was appointed head of the college and, in the opinion of the Harvard historian, proved himself particularly unfit—"dishonest and violent." His wife, who was housekeeper and stewardess, abetted him in his evil courses, and with her connivance he cheated the students and "with his own hands he ill-used them." Educational malpractice, which was to have a long history in America, seems to have begun with the first head of the first college. Eaton quarreled with his usher, Nathaniel Briscoe, had two men hold him, then beat him over the head and shoulders with a club. Briscoe, fearing he was to be murdered, began to pray; "whereupon Eaton gave him some extra blows for taking the name of God in vain." If we were headed toward the good old times, the start was inauspicious.

There were several fairly serious disabilities which those early students accepted with praiseworthy heroism. Their first building, according to Arthur Stanwood Pier, was primitive, poorly constructed and far from weatherproof. The rooms were dingy and cold, as only a portion of each sash was glazed, and oiled paper was used in the rest. When, in New England's winter, their small dark studies were frigid, the boys carried their books to the hall, where a fire was maintained at the expense of those who used it. This probably meant that those who could not contribute were not allowed to have places near it. On these bitter nights the boys read by the flickering flame of the "public candle."

From this semicircle of light and warmth they must have slunk away shivering to the icy little cubicles where they slept. It will be readily granted that it was heroic to begin higher education in America under these Spartan conditions. One of the most striking facts, however, in the history of our colleges has been quite generally overlooked. For nearly 250 years—

certainly until 1850—living quarters and the meals provided for American students were pitifully inadequate. This was an important factor in creating that restive and rebellious spirit which, in spite of the common belief, was considerably more frequent and more serious in the old colleges than it is today.

Corporal and Spiritual Guidance

Corporal punishment, often in the presence of the student body, continued at Harvard until the middle of the eighteenth century, though to the receiver it may have been mitigated by the thought that its infliction had been preceded and followed by prayers from the president. As late as this period, breakfast was still two "sizings" of bread and a cue—half pint —of beer, and "evening Commons were a Pye." It was still necessary, in the second half of that century, for the student to carry his own knife and fork to the dining room, and when he had dined he wiped them on the table-cloth. At Yale as late as 1815, students at meals drank cider out of a common pewter pitcher, since the university could not afford tumblers.

At Bowdoin, and probably in America generally, blackboards were used for the first time in 1824. Before that date, at Bowdoin and probably at most other American colleges, college men did much of their work on slates.

Libraries and library facilities were pitiful. After Harvard had been in existence for one hundred years the first catalogue of the library showed that it contained 3500 volumes, two-thirds of which were theological, and though Dryden, Johnson, Pope and Swift had done their work, their names were conspicuously absent. In the ten years from 1743 to 1753, the total accessions to the Yale Library numbered thirty-one volumes, "mostly sermons." At Hampden-Sidney, in the South—founded 1776—by 1821 the library consisted of only 500 volumes. It was estimated in 1782 that at Rhode Island College, later Brown University, the number of books was between two and three hundred, mostly theological and not well chosen, as the president wistfully adds, "being such as our friends could best spare." Because of this inadequacy of library facilities, college students there had to be denied access to English classics like Chaucer, Shakspere, Pope and Dryden. There was no library building, and for lack of attendants it was possible to keep the room open only one day a week, from one to three o'clock in the afternoon.

The Cream of Existence

The alumnus of today who complains so bitterly about the continual solicitation for funds on the part of his university should take heart and not imagine that he is witnessing a new phenomenon. All the way back the records of the colleges show that they were constantly detaching some member of their small staff to solicit funds, and usually with little success. On the whole, it may be said that the country was poor and private benefactions scantier even than they should have been. Nothing proves this better than the account of how Brown University at Providence came into its present name. It had been founded in 1764 as The College of Rhode Island. After thirty years of highly successful operation, the corporation of this already well-known institution passed a resolution that if any person would give the college $6000 he should have the right to name it. Even at that, there were no takers. Six thousand dollars was too much to expect from any donor of those times, and after waiting eight years, in 1803 the corporation was forced to cut the price to $5000. In 1804, Nicholas Brown came forward with this sum and Rhode Island College became Brown University. It is only fair to Nicholas Brown to say that he was later to prove a generous patron.

There was, of course, no gymnasium, no facilities whatever for social life or recreation, except the debating societies or halls, which in part explains their great pristine popularity and their present decline. In many cases we find a lack of what would be called not only the comforts but the decencies of life. The trustees' report on conditions at the University of Georgia—Franklin College—made in 1826, reads as follows:

> The charge of the want of cleanliness is universal and may be well maintained against every room in both buildings, as well those occupied by students as those reserved for purposes of recitation. In many instances this want of cleanliness is extended to a want of decency, and filth is found to have accumulated of such sort in such quantities as to be offensive and doubtless injurious to health.

Cows were generally pastured upon most of the college campuses until 1850, and pigs kept on the spot disposed of the garbage of Commons. A dawning consciousness that these conditions were not what they should be appears in the votes of the Dartmouth faculty in the 1840s. They recommended that "the college back yard be immediately cleaned" and that a fence be put up "such as shall keep out the entrance of cows." When we find them urging naïvely that "the experiment of scouring be made upon the windows of the recitation rooms," it seems fair to assume that the practice of washing had not previously been resorted to.

A considerable part of the revenue of the struggling colleges came to them from the rental of dormitory rooms. A student who chose to live in town had to pay the college an equivalent tax. At Dartmouth, dormitory rooms had become so dilapidated that Professor Sanborn reported there, in 1845, that "during the past year more than twenty rooms had been unoccupied. Some of them are positively untenantable, and others are soiled, shattered and defaced. The neglect to occupy these rooms brings a heavy tax upon those who room in the village." He adds, naïvely, that this "seems to annoy and irritate those who pay for it." They showed this irritation by breaking windows in the dormitories and causing damage at least to the amount of the tax imposed. . . .

If housing conditions were inadequate, the situation was possibly even worse with regard to the meals provided. Here the records are unanimous and repeat the same dismal story. We hear complaints from the farthest Western institution of that time, Illinois College at Jacksonville, founded 1829. The historian of this frontier outpost of learning reminds us that "Among the petty difficulties of the time [the mid-nineteenth century] there were many that arose out of the management of the College Commons." This is the case at Hampden-Sidney in the South, at Dartmouth, at Middlebury, at Brown, at Williams, at Yale, at Princeton, at Harvard. The undergraduate ate without relish and was forever in protest. Yet he does not seem to have been over-exacting. The food was scant, poorly cooked, and the service primitive. We have had an inkling of conditions at Harvard in the eighteenth century. In the early nineteenth they had not greatly improved. Sidney Willard, a Harvard professor who had been graduated in 1798, reports that students who boarded in Commons were obliged to go to the kitchen door with their own bowls or pitchers for their suppers. There "they received their modicum of milk or chocolate in their vessel held in one hand and their piece of bread in the other." After Josiah Quincy became president in 1829 breakfast consisted solely of coffee, hot rolls and butter. The evening meal was plain as the breakfast, "with tea instead of coffee, and cold bread of the consistency of wool." This is not a description by a disgruntled undergraduate. It is the statement of Dr. Andrew P. Peabody, then tutor at Harvard. Necessity, the mother of invention, drove these often underfed boys to "pin to the under surfaces of the table by a two-pronged fork some slices of meat from the previous day's dinner." This practice of forking meat to the underside of the pine tables seems to have been almost general college custom, for we find it reported in accounts of life at Princeton, where, the historian, Varnum Lansing Collins, tells us that ownership of these dividends from yesterday's dinner was "strictly respected, stray dogs alone excepted."

At Yale "the breakfast consisted of ollapodrida hashed up from the remains of yesterday's dinner and fried into a consistency that baffled digestion. This compound was known as slum. To these accommodations a senior or a tutor would prefix and suffix a grace, during the telling of which two forks were sometimes observed sticking into each potato on the table."

That perfect gentleman, the late President James B. Angell of Michigan, a graduate of Brown in 1849, confesses, "I cannot say that usages in Commons Hall were conducive to elegant manners." Plain living and high thinking would still have constituted an admirable ideal for the American college of 1850, but the whole scale was too low. It was below the level of comfort and the amenities prevalent in the country generally. The food was not only plain; it was scant, and the service hugger-mugger.

How this impressed representative undergraduates we may judge from the *Reminiscences* of the late Cyrus Northrup, for many years president of the University of Minnesota, a self-made man and a distinguished graduate of Yale in the class of 1857.

> No impression of Yale College is more deeply impressed upon me than the inadequate provision for the comfort of students. The freshman recitation rooms were furnished with three rows of benches, were lighted by oil lamps, were occupied by a needy student as his room when not used by the class for recitation, and were cheerless and uncomfortable. The unseemly hour for chapel services and for morning recitation, both before breakfast and daylight, was an abomination.

At Princeton the situation was no better. The late Prof. Basil Gildersleeve, one of America's most distinguished Greek scholars, who died in 1924, was graduated there in 1849. He tells us that refuse was disposed of by the direct method—it was thrown out of the windows! "Waste water of all kinds was projected from the upper floors, so that the lower floors smelt to heaven." He concludes, without enthusiasm, "It was a Spartan life in those days, and for me a somewhat joyless one."

Syrian Sophomores

FROM *Philosopher's Holiday*

Irwin Edman was hardly suited by nature, inclination or avocation, to sit
for the traditional portrait of either philosopher or professor. He was both
—and much more—in a highly unorthodox combination. As Johnsonian
Professor of Philosophy he taught at Columbia, and he was an accomplished
essayist, critic, and writer of captivating light verse.

Edman traveled widely as a Fulbright Scholar and visiting professor,
meeting a wide and unusual assortment of students in the process, among
them these Syrian sophomores at the American University at Beirut.

AFTER a certain number of years of teaching one awaits no surprises
or perhaps becomes incapacitated for having any. The academic pattern
has become familiar, and one is prepared to believe that in this educational
place, at this academic time, things will always be about the same. One
cherishes, however, the illusion that the pattern is not the same everywhere,
that if, for example, one were lecturing in Timbuktu, or conducting a
seminar in Somaliland, students would be different and perhaps one would
think of new things to say, or even think of new things.

Such reflections recall the story of an actress who, having played with
moderate success in New York, confessed her ambitions to a companion on
shipboard. She wished to repeat her triumphs on the stage in France in
French, in Italy in Italian, in Germany in German. "Now," said her unfeel-
ing companion, "you have only to learn to act in English in New York."

Academic persons, too, have their exotic hungers. The *mise-en-scène* has
become too routine; the freshmen are all identical, the sophomores are
more drearily because less freshly so; the faces and the food at the Faculty
Club have become a dull habit; the academic calendar is depressingly unvarying. The feeling grows that it is not the academic life that has become

stale, but its local setting. Even visits for a week or a term to neighbouring institutions are not enough. The small college, it is true, is not the large university; it has its different, intimate charm. The country college is not the city one, patently and often delightfully enough. There are in autumn no reddening maples on a city block. It is only a stone's throw from Columbia to Amherst or Williams or Wesleyan; it might be several thousand miles. Overnight one is among the colonnades and the Virginia gentlemen of Charlottesville, or the homespun and pastoral kindness and trans-Allegheny common-sense of Wabash College, Indiana. I had known these things were true, and I had enjoyed discovering them. And yet things never were different enough. I had always envied the half-missionary professors in China and Japan. They came back trailing clouds of Oriental glory, though their clothes and accents, and even their points of view, had not changed. I had pictured Lafcadio Hearn's delights in lecturing on English poetry to Japanese students, to the tinkling, I liked to imagine, of neighbouring temple bells. I had friends, indeed, who had taught in the Orient and who seemed and claimed to have learned as much from their students as they had taught them, to have borrowed as much from Oriental pupils and from the novel setting as they had brought to them. Sometimes, it is true, I had had that same experience on my own campus, but after ten years or more at the same institution, I felt I had become anæsthetized, at least for the time being, to all that local students could teach me, or to such atmosphere as one could breathe in on Morningside Heights. It was, therefore, with no small pleasure one day in Rome about seven years ago, that, being on leave of absence from Columbia, I received an invitation from the American University at Beirut in Syria to give three lectures there on the Philosophy of Religion. I was, somebody there had learned, on my way to Syria. I was planning to follow as well as I could the footsteps of St. Paul, about whom, in possibly a ten thousandth book on the theme, I was planning to say something new. In Syria was Damascus, and from Syria one went to Antioch. It turned out, however, that I learned most in Syria not from the Street Called Straight in Damascus, where they show you the alleged spot where Paul was lowered in a basket. I learned nothing at Antioch, for I did not reach there. Unlike Paul, I was given pause by the difficulties of transport, far less arduous, I am prepared to admit, than they were in his day. What I learned was little about Paul, and what I did learn I found out from Syrian sophomores, from whom I found out or had confirmed something about the nature of all sophomores and about American education and perhaps ultimately about education itself.

The American University at Beirut, as everyone knows (at least everyone in Beirut and in Presbyterian circles in America) was founded about sixty years ago as a mission college. It was intended, by means of a four-year

American college course, with attendant chapel services, to bring Christianity to the heathen of the Near East. Its missionary work has long since become subtler and no less difficult or rewarding; it has tried for many years now to do just what colleges in America try to do: to bring education to students. Syria is under French mandate now, of course, but A.U.B. English, as it is called locally (and it is very good English, too), is encountered in remote spots all over Syria. I found it to be the chief means of communication in the bazaars of Damascus.

The American University at Beirut is really a typical small-town American college. Its organization and its atmosphere, especially its faculty social life, are simply Connecticut or New Hampshire transplanted to the Mediterranean. Its site is certainly different, perched as it is on a headland over a ravishing Mediterranean bay with sometimes snow-capped mountains visible from the campus, and always the intensely blue sea. In setting it is a semi-Oriental Riviera. But in the President's house, and among the senior faculty members and among the staff (the young men directly out of college who come out for three years), I felt I had been here before. The older faculty members, some of whom had been teaching in Syria for thirty years and spoke Arabic fluently, had none the less succeeded in creating the atmosphere and the expectations, social and moral, of a small sectarian college town. The *Atlantic Monthly* was on the living-room table, and all that was missing was Colonial architecture.

The students were another matter. They suggested not Middletown but Tarsus, said to have been the crossroads of the ancient world. There were coal-black youths from the Sudan, Jewish as well as Arab students from Palestine, Coptic Christians and Mohammedans from all over Syria, and a Persian prince, and (I could scarcely believe my ears, but the accent was unmistakable) some Brooklyn boys studying in the excellent medical school.

It was a frightening challenge to speak about the Philosophy of Religion to a student body of that mixed provenance. But I had just heard Gene Tunney, on a world tour, address a chapel audience at Beirut. He had spoken, apparently quite intelligibly to his audience, on themes redolent of an American Boy Scout morality. And surely there was no better or more appropriate place to speak on the themes of comparative religion than here where Coptic Christians, Mohammedans, Jews, and Presbyterians were mingled in the matrix of an American college curriculum, studying English by the sea on whose shores all the religions of the ancient world had grown and flourished. Was I not engaged in studying the diverse origins of Christianity in the maelstrom of the Mediterranean cults of the first century? The maelstrom was still perpetuated here. The thought gave me courage and so too did the elaborate yet spontaneous courtesy of the students with whom I had spoken. Two of them took the odd trouble of teaching me by rote enough Arabic to make a few introductory remarks in that language. They said it would be a compliment to the audience and the audience would feel more at home with me. I followed their suggestion, apologizing for not continuing in Arabic as there might be a few present who did not understand. Either that introduction or something else seemed to put me *en rapport* with my listeners; after the first five minutes it seemed as natural to be talking about philosophy in West Hall on the Beirut campus as in Philosophy Hall at Columbia. I felt I was among friends.

That feeling was pleasantly and, as it turned out, oddly confirmed the next day. I was sitting in my room in the guest dormitory, staring out at the sea in incubative intervals—or I liked to think they were such—in my preparations for the second lecture. There was a knock on the door. I opened to see a pleasant young man, squat, black-haired, dark-skinned. I tried at once to guess his nationality. Syrian, I judged. I tried to guess his year in the college. Sophomore, somehow, I was sure.

He was elaborately apologetic about disturbing me. But he had some questions to ask. I motioned him to a chair.

"Do you ever give personal advice to students?" he asked.

"When I am asked, I cannot always refrain," I replied.

"Well, I've come for personal advice," he said. "I was at your lecture last night, and I felt you could give it to me."

"But there was nothing personal about the lecture," I said. "It was pretty remote from any personal problems whatever, as I remember it."

"Yes, but still I have a feeling that you would understand student problems, and I've got some."

"You are very flattering," I said, "but I should feel very hesitant about giving advice here. I hesitate at home, but I suspect the problems of a Syrian sophomore—you are a sophomore, aren't you?"—he nodded—"are rather different from those of a sophomore in America. I've only been at the University of Beirut three days, and in Syria less than a week, and I've never been to the Near East before."

He fumbled nervously. "Just the same," he said, "there are a few things I should like to ask you."

"Let me ask you one thing first myself," I said. "Are you Syrian?"

"No," he said, "Egyptian, Mohammedan; my father is a business man in Cairo. We don't get on awfully well any more. Especially since I've come away to college. I've grown rather irreligious, you know, and it makes trouble when I come home."

"You've possibly turned Christian," I said.

"Oh, no," he said, looking shocked, "nothing like that. I just have lost my religion altogether, and a sense of family."

"And you don't want to go into business, do you?"

He looked surprised at the guess, but went on.

"Do young men of eighteen or nineteen in the West begin to have very different ideas from those of their parents?" he asked.

I smiled. "This sounds just like home."

"You can't tell how upsetting it is, all these new ideas one gets at college," he said, "about freedom and dancing and sex and what not. I don't suppose Western students have to make so much of an adjustment; they don't come from one world to another when they come from home to college, do they? It's all one, the Western world, isn't it?"

My mind leaped back to "Tex" Goldschmidt, who had come to Columbia from a strict Lutheran family in San Antonio, Texas; to Stanley Smith, who had arrived in New York from a strict and genteel suburban family in Verona, New Jersey; to Joe Farrell, who had been brought up in a Catholic parochial school in Boston; to Arthur Calder, the son of a pious Scotch widow; to the young Puritan from a New Hampshire village who had come not only to New York but also to Gide and to Henry James. I told my young Egyptian about them and how they, too, in college had come upon a new world in which each, in his own way, had had to make some adjustment. He looked intensely surprised.

"But fathers don't expect their sons in the West to follow the same way of life that they led, do they?" he said.

"Many of them do."

"And to have the same ideas?" he said dubiously.

"Even that," I said.

"And do the ideas students in the West get at college seem to them so different from what they hear at home, as many of the ideas I've picked up in classes here and from other students appear to me?"

"Quite as much," I insisted.

"But the changes in life cannot be so rapid in the West as they have been here in the last twenty-five years."

"Oh, yes, they can, I am sure; but I rather thought," I said, "that here in the East things don't change so rapidly."

He looked at me again in the greatest surprise.

"I went to the Muslim University in Cairo," I explained, "where students seem to be listening as they did in the Middle Ages, and, I am told, to the same things, the Koran chiefly, and explanations of it."

"Oh, but that's rather a backwater; none of *my* friends go there. I'm talking about *modern* youth in the East."

"Well, what personal advice does a modern youth in the Near East want?" I said.

"I wondered what I ought to do about ideas," he replied, "and *should* I go into my father's business when I get my degree. My father expects me to be a business man, but I don't want to, and all the professions are over-crowded. It's very difficult for a young man these days, especially a college man here in the Near East. What do *you* advise me to do?"

I have in my time advised young men not to go into the teaching profession, not to become professional philosophers, especially if they were genuinely philosophers; I have with a certain glibness told them they were born lawyers or business men or journalists or writers, but I hesitated, I admit, to advise this young Egyptian as to a career. Though, as I thought about it afterwards, I reflected there was no special reason for diffidence. My Egyptian visitor was worried about a career in Cairo, Egypt, and had trouble accommodating his ideas to those of his father and his family there. But it might just as well have been Cairo, Illinois. A sophomore hailing from there would also have had a naïve faith that a professor could advise about a career and counsel about morals. I once had written about a youth named Richard Kane whom college had "unprepared for life." Here he was, slightly darker-skinned, on the shore of the Sophoclean sea. I had not in months felt so near home.

I felt at home, too, but less so, the next day when crossing the campus I ran into a group of young Syrians who hailed me and said they had some questions to ask. "We've been discussing the difference between moral standards in the East and West," one of them said.

"A profound question to raise on a Saturday in spring," I said.

"Well, we have, and there are one or two questions we should like to ask you," one of them said. He looked at his companions in some obvious embarrassment.

"Go ahead; ask him," one of the group insisted encouragingly.

"Well," the embarrassed young man said, "well, is it true that in the West young men actually go out dancing with young women without necessarily creating a scandal by doing it?"

"Oh, yes," I said, "quite the usual thing, really; it happens every day."

"But it would ruin a Mohammedan girl's reputation, and a young man's too, in some ways," he said. "We wondered whether that is really true, what we hear about the West, that young men and women associate quite freely. I doubt whether that will ever be true here in Syria."

"But you do go dancing," I said, "don't you?"

"Oh, yes," was the reply, "but not with respectable girls; that is, not with respectable *Mohammedan* girls. It's a different story with Jewish or Christian ones. The West must be a very different place."

We adjourned to a neighbouring café for some of the Arabic coffee, with its pure and clear flavour that I had come to love. We discussed the differences in collegiate morals of New York and of Syria, the differences seeming to disappear as we talked.

I had once forgathered with a similar group (who called themselves The Thinkers) in Urbana, Illinois. The only difference in temper I could feel (and it was not so much a difference in temper as a difference in form) was in the sense of form itself that these young men had. Centuries of tradition or ritual of courtesy seemed to be bred in them. American undergraduates would have been no less kindly and hospitable, but there would have been a less finished expression of their kindness and hospitality.

"The Syrians have a great gift for friendliness," I said as we finally rose to leave.

"They have that gift, sir, to those who have it," was the suave reply from one of the group. I have known only one sophomore who would have thought of that reply in America, and he was regarded as fantastically precious by his classmates—and by me.

But I was to have one other introduction to the student mind of Syria, this time to a senior, not to a sophomore. I was again sitting in my room in West Hall. The visitor this time was a tall, coal-black youth with shining teeth and eyes. He was dressed in a neat, blue pin-striped suit, a handkerchief peeping out of his breast pocket and a book (it turned out to be a novel by Virginia Woolf) under his arm. His accent was not that of the American University at Beirut, but distinctly English. Except for that I should have been inclined to guess, had I met him on a train, that he was an educated American Negro.

I wondered whether he, too, was coming for advice. He was not. He began at once by saying that he had not any very good claim on my time, that he had no special problem, that he had not even come to discuss the subjects which I had touched on in the lectures. He wished only to talk over some things he had been reading lately. What did I think of Virginia Woolf? Did I not think Aldous Huxley carried his sceptical cynicism too far? Was T. S. Eliot really such a first-rate critic as people pretended? He rather doubted it, but he was a great poet, or at least technically a very competent one. He had heard he ought to read Gide and Proust but he did not read French and it was hard to come by them in English. It was hard to come by books at all where he lived. (The last time I had listened to this flood of literary undergraduate criticism, it was in New York, though in that accent I had most recently heard it in Oxford.)

"Where *do* you live?" I asked.

"In the middle of the Sudan," he said.

"Pretty far off from literary interests, isn't it?" I said. "Are you going back there?"

"Yes," he said a little sadly. "I've been sent here on a scholarship and I expect the Sudan is the place I shall go back to. I shall be a schoolmaster in a small village. I shan't have much chance to talk about this sort of thing." His eyes brightened. "But one could become a poet out there, I think. You have no conception of the distance and the solitude—it's made for meditation; and the bright clarity of the stars—have you ever been to the desert?"

"*Just*," I replied.

"But you should live there to know what it's like. It's lonely and splendid. Only I shan't have any one to talk to, really, and a writer needs people."

"He doesn't need literary people, does he?" I asked. "You could write just the same."

"Yes, but one loses touch, and, what's more, one loses English."

"You could write in Arabic."

"There isn't a public for Arabic; those who read, read the Koran really: and I want to write in English."

I have often since thought of my lonely black schoolmaster in his village in the Sudan, though no lonelier, I think, than a poet I know in North Dakota, nor than a man of letters on the plains, almost as spacious as those of the Sudan, of Kansas. I had often suspected that there is no geography of the spirit, and a sojourn among students in Syria convinced me I had been right—or did it? I suddenly reflected that the pattern of American college life was surprisingly definite; this son of the Sudan had for four years been living, spiritually speaking, on American soil. And there are Americans, too, in the midst of their Sudans, lonely, amid distances and solitudes, and meditating, like this black youth, under the bright clarity of a starry Western sky, and far from any one who speaks their language or moves in their realm of spirit.

Let's Away With Study

FROM *Carmina Burana*

*"The scholars," wrote a twelfth-century monk, "are wont to roam around
the world and visit all its cities, till much learning makes them mad, for
in Paris they seek liberal arts, in Orleans authors, at Salerno gallipots, at
Toledo demons, and in no place decent manners."*

*But they left behind, in their pursuit of the lighter arts, such fresh
and charming songs as "Let's Away With Study." They were, of course,
sung in Latin, as befitted scholars, perhaps with one hand embracing a
tavern wench, the other a mug of wine.*

LET'S away with study,
  Folly's sweet.
Treasure all the pleasure
  Of our youth:
Time enough for age
  To think on Truth.
So short a day,
And life so quickly hasting
And in study wasting
  Youth that would be gay!

'Tis our spring that slipping,
  Winter draweth near,
  Life itself we're losing,
  And this sorry cheer
Dries the blood and chills the heart,
  Shrivels all delight.
Age and all its crowd of ills
  Terrifies our sight.

So short a day,
And life so quickly hasting,
And in study wasting
    Youth that would be gay!

Let us as the gods do,
    'Tis the wiser part:
Leisure and love's pleasure
    Seek the young in heart.
Follow the old fashion,
    Down into the street!
Down among the maidens,
    And the dancing feet!
So short a day,
And life so quickly hasting,
And in study wasting
    Youth that would be gay!

There for the seeing
    Is all loveliness,
White limbs moving
    Light in wantonness.
Gay go the dancers,
    I stand and see,
Gaze, till their glances
    Steal myself from me.
So short a day,
And life so quickly hasting,
And in study wasting
    Youth that would be gay!

                    [*Tr. Helen Waddell*]

2

Class

"NOTHING is so firmly believed as what we least know," wrote Montaigne, and he inscribed on his seal the phrase *"Que sais-je?"*—What do I know?—as lifelong reminder.

In the ideal, the university classroom has been the place for large questions and, sometimes, for great answers; not a storehouse for scattered scraps of fact, but an arena where ideas have been free to clash and where knowledge is provoked rather than distributed. The memorable teachers have been those who chalked up on their classroom blackboards this query of Montaigne's. But these are the rare teachers, no more common than the rare student who is able to read and comprehend and seek to answer the chalked question.

For of students and of teachers there are all kinds—the curious and the ones too easily answered, the hopeful and the early defeated, the swift and the laggard in the pursuit of learning. The classroom can be stimulating; it can be trying; it can also be boring. But at its best, at its most memorable and exciting, it is more than the sum of its parts. In the classroom's golden moments and golden hours it is transformed into a living entity and the fellowship of its members becomes transfigured with the collective will to strive for enlightenment and knowledge. One of this century's great teachers, the late Felix Adler, said, "The place where men meet to seek the highest is holy ground."

The selections which follow here were collected in the belief that the unique atmosphere and meaning of the college classroom in all its aspects would emerge from their reading.

GEORGE BOAS

Freshman Adviser

FROM *Harper's Magazine*

If we are to believe George Boas, the look of misery that faculty advisers wear is not natural. It is an occupational badge of recognition and can be seen in its finest flower on the faces of freshman advisers. Almost all faculty advisers have problems, of course, but freshman advisers have the fresh- man in addition, Boas explains. However, he's philosophical about it, which is not too surprising: he's taught philosophy at Johns Hopkins for the past thirty years.

WE ARE sitting pencil in hand, surrounded by college catalogues, rules and regulations, directories, handbooks, mimeographed slips with last-min- ute changes of courses on them, folders with big cards for the students' rec- ords, pads with two carbons on which to write out schedules. We are all washed and clean, fresh from a summer in which we were supposed to rest and which we spent making enough money to fill out the gap between our salaries and a living wage. We are all resigned to the winter that is before us, teaching, coal bills, committee meetings, those tonsils of Susie's, aca- demic freedom, subscription to the Symphony, student activities, what price a decent pair of shoes. . . . We smile at each other and sigh at the mass of paper. We have never learned all the rules. How can anyone learn them? Different ones for students in the college of arts and sciences, pre-meds, en- gineers. But what are rules anyway?

Here they come. . . .

His name is Rosburgh van Stiew. One can see he is one of the Van Stiews —and if one can't, he'll let one know soon enough. That suit of fuzzy tweed, that regimental cravat, that custom-made shirt. Right out of *Vanity Fair.* Already he has the Phi Pho Phum pledge button in his buttonhole.

He speaks with a drawl. It is the voice of his mother's *face-à-main.* He

101

has slightly wavy blond hair—his mother still has a crinkly white pompadour, like Queen Mary's. He has weary eyes.

No use to smile.

"Very well, Mr. Van Stiew. Have you any idea of the courses you'd like to take?"

"No . . . aren't there some things you sort of have to take?"

"Freshman English and Gym."

"Well, I may as well take them."

"History?"

"Do you have to?"

"No. You can take Philosophy, Political Science, or Economics instead."

Mr. Van Stiew tightens his cravat.

"Guess I'll take History."

"Ancient or Modern?"

"Well—when do they come?"

"Modern at 8:30, Wednesdays, Thursdays, and Saturdays; Ancient at 9:30, Mondays, Tuesdays, and Wednesdays."

"Oh, Ancient."

Mr. Van Stiew looks shocked that one should have asked.

One shouldn't have.

"Very well, Ancient History."

That leaves three more courses.

"One of the fellows said to take Art Appreciation."

"Yes, you could do that. But sooner or later you are required to take French and German and a laboratory science."

"Couldn't I put them off until next year?"

"You can until you're a senior."

"I think I'll put them off then. I don't want too heavy a schedule."

"Mathematics?"

"Do I have to?"

"It all depends. What are you going to major in?"

"Do I have to major?"

"More or less."

"When do I have to decide?"

"Next year."

So it goes with Mr. Van Stiew. He is using his right of election, his free will. His personality must not be crushed. He will have a Liberal Education, be a member of the Tennis Team, the Dramatic Club, and manager of the Glee Club. And as a prominent alumnus, he will see to it that the Football Team is never oppressed by a fastidious faculty.

Enter Mr. William Hogarth.

Hogarth is from the city Technical High School. Engineer. Red hair, freckles. Ready-made blue serge.

"Math, Physics, Philosophy, German—why can't I take Chemistry too? I'll make up my French this summer. . . . No, can't take any Saturday classes, working at the Universal Clothing Outlet Saturdays."

"English Literature?"

"Do I have to? . . . All right, Professor, put it down. Where do I get my text books? Don't they have any second-hand ones? . . . Classes begin to-morrow? All right. . . . Yes, I know about the Physical Exam. Had it already. . . . No, I guess I know everything now."

"If you need any information, Mr. Hogarth, I'm in my ——"

"Thanks, don't believe I will."

He's gone.

Woof! One lights a cigarette.

A presence is before one, grinning. Lots of yellow hair parted in the middle, rising on each side of the part and falling like too ripe wheat. Head slightly to one side. Very red face.

Timidly shoves forward receipted bill from the Treasurer's Office.

Fred Wilkinson.

Mr. Wilkinson doesn't know what he's going to major in as yet—"you see, I may not stay here four years." A glance at his high-school record makes that more than probable.

"English and Physical Training, that is, Gym."

"Can't I be excused from that?"

"Have you a physical disability?"

"I'm not sure . . ."

"Well, we'll put it down anyway and you can talk it over with the doctor."

"French? German?"

"I'm not very good on languages."

"Mathematics?"

"Heavens, no!"

"Philosophy?"

"What's that?"

"It's—it's part of the business of philosophy to find out, Mr. Wilkinson."

One stops in time.

"I don't believe you'd like Philosophy. Physics? You have to take one science."

"Isn't there one where you take a trip in the spring?"

"Geology?"

"Is that where you study rocks and things?"

"Yes." God forgive me.

"I guess I'll take that."

"History?"

Quick response. The eyes actually grow bright.

"Oh, yes, History. My brother said to take History."

"Good, that's that anyway. . . . Ancient or Modern?"

"A—what?"

"Ancient or Modern?"

Mr. Wilkinson looks as if he were going to cry. His lower lip seems to swell. His eyes blink. But he is only thinking.

"Which do you study Keats and Shelley in?"

"Which History course?"

"Yes. My brother studied Keats and Shelley. That's the course I want. Don't they come in History?"

"They are undoubtedly a part of history" (one grows pontifical) "but I don't believe they usually are discussed in the History courses."

"I'm sure my brother studied them here."

"Maybe it was the History of English Literature."

"Would that have Keats and Shelley?"

"I imagine so."

Mr. Wilkinson is dubious.

"Well, I tell you, Professor. Couldn't you put it down, and then if it isn't all right maybe I could change it afterwards. I could change it, couldn't I, you know, if I didn't like it, if they didn't teach Keats and Shelley in it? I could change it, couldn't I?"

Why not? Mr. Wilkinson will flunk out at mid-term anyway.

So we go.

The pad of the three carbons grow thinner and thinner. The atmosphere grows thicker and thicker. The advisers grow stupider and stupider. The day grows shorter and shorter. By night all schedules are made. To-morrow classes will begin. And after to-morrow Mr. Van Stiew, Mr. Hogarth, Mr. Wilkinson, and the rest will begin dropping courses, adding courses, shifting courses about until they have left of their original schedules only English Literature and Gym which are required in the Freshman year.

GEORGE MILBURN

A Student in Economics

FROM *No More Trumpets*

> George Milburn's "A Student in Economics" has the quiet, unembroi-
> dered feel of immediate personal experience. For those who tried to work
> their way through school during the depression '30s, this was the reality
> of college life.
>
> Milburn attended the University of Tulsa for a while, then drifted
> around the country searching for a job, together with millions of other
> young people. It was during this period that he collected the songs for
> an anthology he later edited, The Hobo's Hornbook.

ALL of the boys on the third floor of Mrs. Gooch's approved rooms for
men had been posted to get Charlie Wingate up that afternoon. He had
to go to see the Dean. Two or three of them forgot about it and two or
three of them had other things to do, but Eddie Barbour liked waking
people up. Eddie stuck his weasel face in at Charlie's door just as the alarm
clock was giving one last feeble tap. The clock stood on the bottom of a
tin washpan that was set upside-down on a wooden chair beside the bed.
The alarm had made a terrific din. Eddie had heard it far down the hall.
The hands showed two o'clock. Pale needles from a December sun were
piercing the limp green window shade in a hundred places.

Eddie Barbour yelled, "Aw right, Charlie! Snap out of it!" He came
into the chilly room and stood for a moment staring vaguely at the ridge
of quilts on the sagged iron bed. The only sound was the long, regular
sough of Charlie Wingate's breathing. He hadn't heard a thing. Eddie
made a sudden grab for the top of the covers, stripped them back and began
jouncing the sleeper by the shoulders. Charlie grunted every time the bed
springs creaked, but he nuzzled his pillow and went on sleeping. Eddie
went over to the study table where a large, white-enameled water pitcher

stood and he came back to the bed with the water, breathing giggles. He tipped the water pitcher a little and a few drops fell on the back of Charlie's neck without waking him. Eddie sloshed the icy water up over the pitcher's mouth. A whole cupful splashed on Charlie's head. Charlie sat up quickly, batting his arms about, and Eddie Barbour whinnied with laughter.

"Arise, my lord, for the day is here," he said, going across and ceremoniously raising the crooked window shade. Charlie sat straight up among the rumpled quilts with his head cocked on one side, staring dully. He had slept with his clothes on. He sat up in bed all dressed, in a soldier's brown uniform, all but his shoes and roll puttees.

"You got army today?" Eddie asked, putting the pitcher down.

Charlie looked at him for a moment and blinked. Then he said in a voice stuffy with sleep, "Naw. I had army yesterday. I got army make-up today." He worked his mouth, making clopping noises.

"What time you got army make-up, Charlie? When you come in from class you said get you up because you had to go see the Dean at two-thirty."

"Yeah, I do have to go see the Dean at two-thirty. But I got army make-up too. I got to make up drill cuts from three till six." All at once he flopped back down on the bed, sound asleep again.

"Hey!" Eddie cried, jumping forward. "Come out of that! Wake up there, Charlie! You can't sleep no more if you got to see the Dean at two-thirty. You just about got time to make it." He jerked him back up in bed.

"Screw the Dean," Charlie said; "two hours' sleep ain't enough."

"Is two hours all the sleep you got last night?"

"Where you get the 'last night'? I worked all night last night. I had classes till noon. Two hours' sleep was all I got today. And darn little more yesterday or the day before. When is Sunday? Sunday's the first day I'm due to get any real sleep. Two hours' sleep is not enough sleep for a man to get."

He plumped his stockinged feet onto the cold floor and got up stiffly. He went over to the washstand, where he picked up his tooth brush and tooth paste and a bar of soap and slowly took his face towel down from beside the warped looking-glass. He came back to where his shoes lay and stood looking at the toilet articles in his hands as if he had forgotten what he meant to do with them. He dumped them on the bed, took the pan with the alarm clock on it and set it on the floor. Then he sat down on the chair and picked up one of the heavy army shoes, held it and felt it and studied it carefully before he put it on. He put on the other shoe with equal deliberation and stood up without lacing either of them. He took his things up from the bed and started off for the bathroom, his loose shoes clogging. Eddie Barbour followed him down the drafty hall.

The creosote disinfectant that Mrs. Gooch used in her bathrooms gave off a strong odor. "Dag gum bathroom smells just like a hen coop," Charlie said thickly as he stood in front of the white-specked mirror twisting his face. He wouldn't need a shave for another day. He had a fairly good-looking face, tan and thin, with ringlets of black hair tumbling down over his forehead. His large ears stuck straight out. He looked at his image with dark eyes made narrow by two purplish puffs under them, and he yawned widely.

Eddie Barbour stood leaning against the jamb of the bathroom door. He said, "You ought to try and get more sleep, Charlie."

"Are you telling *me?*" Charlie said, running water in the face bowl. Eddie Barbour was a freshman too.

II

Charlie Wingate came walking along University Boulevard toward the campus, hunched up in his army overcoat. The raw December wind whipped his face and made him feel wide awake. He passed a bunch of fraternity men pitching horseshoes in the drive beside the K.A. house. Two or three, sprucely dressed, gave him impersonal glances as he passed. They did not speak, and he walked past self-consciously, seeing them without looking toward them.

When he reached the business section opposite the campus he turned in at the white-tiled front of The Wigwam. The noon rush was over and Nick was not at the cash register. A few noon "dates" were still sitting in the booths along the wall. Charlie walked straight back along the white-tile counter and sat down on the end stool. Red Hibbert was standing by the coffee urns reading the sports section. When Charlie sat down Red folded his newspaper slowly and came over to wait on him. Charlie sat with his cheeks resting on the heels of his hands.

"How's it, Chollie, old boy, old boy?" Red Hibbert said.

"Not bad. Give me a cup of javy without and a couple of them Grandma's oatmeal cookies over there, Red. Where's Nick?"

Red scooted the plate with the cookies on it down the glassy white counter top and came along with the cup of black coffee. "This is Nick's day for Kiwanis," he said. "It looks to me like you'd stay home and get some sleep once in a while. You're dyin' on your feet."

"I am going to get some sleep Sunday, don't you never worry. I have to go see the Dean this afternoon. And I got make-up drill at three o'clock. I've got to make up some drill cuts."

"What you got to go see the Dean about?"

"I don't know what about; here's all it said." Charlie reached in his overcoat pocket and pulled out a jagged window envelope and a mimeographed postal card. He pushed the envelope across the counter along with the postal card. "I got that other in the morning mail too."

Red took the printed form from the Dean of Men's office out of the envelope and glanced at it. Then he picked up the postal card. It was headed,

Fourth and Final Notice

You are hereby summoned to appear before the chairman of the Student Senate Committee on Freshman Activities, Rm 204 Student Union Bldg., not later than 4 P.M., Friday afternoon. It will be to your advantage not to ignore this summons as you have three previous ones. This is positively the last opportunity you will be given to rectify your delinquency. Should you fail to appear this time, steps will be taken to bring you.

(signed)   Aubrey H. Carson, Chrmn

Com. on Frshmn Actvts.

Red waggled the postal card. "What you going to do about this?"

"Tear it up like I did the others, I guess. I know what they want. They want to try and make me buy one of them damn' freshman caps."

"Take a tip from me, Charlie: I'd go see them. It won't hurt nothing, and it might be a lot easier on you in the long run."

"Hell, what can they do?"

"Plenty. They could sick the Black Hoods onto you."

"Ah! The Black Hoods, that bunch of amateur ku kluckers!"

"Call 'em amateurs if you want to, Charlie, but it wasn't only but last Friday night they took that little Jew-boy, Sol Lewis, out of the rooming house where I stay. It look to me like they did a pretty professional job on him. They used the buckle-end of a belt on him. They claim he was a stool pigeon for the University."

"Stool pigeon! Ah, you know that guy wasn't a stool pigeon, Red."

"We-ell, I'm not saying one way or the other. Anyhow, that's what you're up against when you take to fooling with that Student Committee on Freshman Activities, Charlie."

"Prexy claimed in his opening address at the first of school that he had put a stop to these masked frats and all this hazing."

"Yeah, he said he had; but how's he going to put a stop to the Black Hoods? He can't kick out all the biggest shots in the University, can he? All the big shots on the campus are Black Hoods. Football stars and fellas like that. You won't see the President kicking guys like that out of the University."

"Maybe not, but—why, hell, that freshman cap business is nothing but a racket. That's all it is. Damn' if I let 'em scare me into paying a dollar for a little old sleazy green cloth cap!"

"O.K., Charlie; I guess you know what you want to do."

"Anyway, how could I get around to see that committee before four o'clock this afternoon, and see the Dean at two-thirty, and go to make-up drill from three till six? I'll be late to drill and get bawled out by the captain again. The captain's already about to flunk me for cuts. That's what's getting me down—Military. It's this Military that's getting me down."

"Jees, I don't know, Charlie; seems like I get a bigger kick out of army than I do any other course I got. They sure learn you more in army than they do in anything else *in* this University."

"Yeow, you learn plenty in army, all right. But what I don't like is the compulsory part. I don't think they ought to be allowed to make it compulsory for freshmen and sophomores. That's just like they had it over in Germany before they got rid of the Kaiser."

The red-haired boy gave him a startled look. He frowned heavily. "Charlie," he exclaimed, "where are you getting all these radical ideas you been spouting around here lately?" Charlie peered at him. Red's face was set in earnestness.

"Why, that's not a radical idea," Charlie said, pushing back his empty coffee cup. "That's just a plain historical fact, that's all that is. I don't see where they got any right to make Military Training compulsory. This is supposed to be a *free* country. That compulsory stuff is what Mussle-leany and birds like that pull."

"But, Charlie, it's all for your own benefit. The University is just looking out after your own interests."

"How do you figure they're looking out for *my* interests?"

"Well, for one thing, when the next war comes we'll all be officers, us fellas that got this training in college. We'll go right into the regular army as officers. There's where we'll have the edge on guys that never did take advantage of a college education. Person'ly, when the next war comes along, I'm not hankerin' after any front-line trenches. And you know darn' well they're not going to stick their college-trained officers into front-line trenches to get shot. So there's where I figure us guys in R.O.T.C. will have a big advantage."

"Yeah, you might be right, at that, Red. But I'm not kicking about R.O.T.C. It's just the compulsory part I'm kicking against."

Red perked his head and scowled impatiently. "Charlie, they *got* to make it compulsory. If it wasn't compulsory, how many of the fellas would enroll in it? They have to make Military compulsory in order to give the fullest benefits. What good could they do if only a few of the fellas was taking it?"

"Anyway, I know some it's not compulsory for," Charlie said stubbornly. "Last night there was a Phi Gam pledge in here bragging about how he got out of Military. He told them at the first of school he didn't want to take Military. They told him he *had* to take it—required of all able-bodied freshmen. Couldn't get his degree without it. So he had to go buy his army shoes. Well, he got the shoe store to send the bill to his old man. His old man is one of these they call 'em pacifists. When his old man gets the bill for his kid's army shoes, maybe you think he don't get the President of this University on long distance and tell him where to head in it. And this kid didn't have to take Military, neither. His old man's a big shot lawyer in the City."

"Yeah, but you got to have pull to get away with that, Charlie."

"That's what I mean, Red. You can get away with plenty in this University if you got the pull."

III

Charlie Wingate loped up the steps of the Administration Building, hurried through the revolving doors, and walked past hissing steam radiators down the long hall to the Dean of Men's office. He was ten minutes late. Before he opened the frosted-glass door he took out a pair of amber-colored spectacles and put them on. Then he went in and handed his summons to the secretary.

"The Dean will see you in a moment," she said. "Please take a chair."

Charlie sat down and gave an amber-hued glance about the outer office. Three dejected freshmen, holding their green caps, were waiting with him. He recognized none of them, so he picked up a week-old copy of the *Christian Science Monitor* and started to read it. But the room was warm and he immediately went to sleep. He had his head propped back against the wall. The newspaper slipped down into his lap. His amber-colored glasses hid his eyes and no one could see that they were closed. He was awakened by the secretary shaking him. She was smiling and the freshmen were all snickering.

"Wake up and pay for your bed, fella!" one of the freshmen called, and everyone laughed heartily.

"I sort of drowsed off. It's so nice and warm in here," Charlie said, apologizing to the pretty secretary.

The Dean of Men got up as he entered and, with his eyes on the slip bearing Charlie's name, said, "Ah, this is Charles Wingate, isn't it?" He grasped Charlie's hand as if it were an honor and pressed a button under the edge of his desk with his other hand. The secretary appeared at the door. "Miss Dunn, will you bring in Wingate's folder—Charles W-i-n-g-a-t-e. How do you like college by now, Wingate? Eyes troubling you?"

"Pretty well, sir. Yes, sir, a little. I wear these glasses."

The secretary came back with the folder and the Dean looked through it briefly. "Well, Wingate, I suppose you're anxious to know why I sent for you. The unpleasant truth is, Wingate, you don't seem to be doing so well in your college work. Your freshman adviser conferred with you twice about this, and this week he turned your case over to me. My purpose, of course, is to help you. Now, to be quite frank, Wingate, you're on the verge of flunking out. Less than a third of the semester remains, and you have a failing grade in English 101, conditional grades in Psychology 51 and Military Training; three hours of F and four hours of D, almost half your total number of hours. On the other hand, you have an A average in Spanish 1 and a B in Economics 150. Wingate, how do you account for your failing English when you are an A student in Spanish?"

"To tell you the truth, sir, I got behind on my written work in English, and I've never been able to catch up. And I don't really have to study Spanish. My father is a railway section foreman in my home town, and he's always had a gang of Mexicans working for him. I've been speaking Mexican ever since I was a kid. It's not the pure, what they call Castilian, Spanish, but I probably know almost as much Spanish as my professor."

"How about this B in Economics? That's a fairly high grade."

"Yes, sir. Doctor Kenshaw—he's my Ec professor—doesn't give exams. Instead he gives everyone a B until he calls for our term papers. We don't recite in his class. We just listen to him lecture. And the grade you get on your term paper is your semester grade."

"Ah! What you students term a pipe course, eh, Wingate?"

"Not exactly, sir. We have to do a lot of outside reading for the term paper. But I'm counting on keeping that B in Ec."

"That's fine, Wingate. But it appears to me that it's high time you were getting busy on some of these other grades, too. Why can't you dig in and pull these D's up to B's, and this F up to at least a C? You've got it in you. You made an unusually high grade on your entrance exams, your record shows. Graduated from high school with honors. What's the trouble, Wingate? Tell me!"

"I don't know, sir, except I work at night and—"

"Oh, I see it here on your enrollment card now. Where do you work?"

"I work nights for Nick Pappas, down at The Wigwam."

"How many hours a night do you work?"

"Ten hours, sir. From nine till seven. The Wigwam stays open all night. I eat and go to eight o'clock class when I get off."

"Very interesting, Wingate. But don't you suppose that it would be advisable to cut down a bit on this outside work and attend a little more closely to your college work? After all, that's what you're here for, primarily —to go to college, not work in café."

"I couldn't work fewer hours and stay in school, sir. I just barely get by as it is. I get my board at The Wigwam, and I pay my room rent, and I've been paying out on a suit of clothes. That leaves only about a dollar a week for all the other things I have to have."

"Wingate, shouldn't you earn more than that, working ten hours?"

"I get the regular, first-year-man rate, sir. Twenty cents an hour. It's set by the University. Nick takes out a dollar a day for board. Pays me five dollars a week in cash."

"Can't you arrange for a little financial support from home?"

"No, sir, I'm afraid I couldn't. I have two brothers and two sisters at home younger than I am. It wouldn't be right for me to ask my father to send money out of what he makes."

"But surely you could get out and land something a little more lucrative than this all-night restaurant job, Wingate."

"No, sir. Twenty cents an hour is standard rate for working students, and I haven't found anything better. Nick says he has at least thirty men on the waiting list for this job I have."

"Well, there's this about it, Wingate. The University is here, supported by the taxpayers of this State, for the purpose of giving the young men and women of this State educational opportunities. The University is not here for the purpose of training young men to be waiters in all-night restaurants. And, so far as I can see, that's about all you are deriving from your University career. So it occurs to me that you should make a choice: either find some way to devote more attention to your college work or drop out of school altogether. We are very loathe to encourage students who are *entirely* self-supporting. And yet, I will admit that I know any number of first-rate students who are entirely self-supporting. There's Aubrey Carson, for example. Quarterback on the football team, delegate to the Olympics, president of the Student Senate, and he's a straight A student. Aubrey Carson was telling me only last week that he hasn't had any financial assistance from home since he enrolled as a freshman. Aubrey is a fine example of the working student."

"Yes, sir; but look at the job Carson has. He works for a big tobacco company, and all he has to do is hand out Treasure Trove cigarettes to other students. The tobacco company pays him a good salary for passing out samples of their cigarettes."

"Why, Wingate, you surely must be mistaken about that. I don't believe Aubrey Carson smokes. In fact, I know he doesn't smoke. He's one of the finest all-'round athletes in this country."

"No, sir; I don't say he smokes either. But that's the straight stuff about his job with the cigarette company. They figure it's a good advertisement to have a popular guy like Aubrey Carson passing out Treasure Troves. Sort of an endorsement."

"All the same, Wingate, it doesn't reflect a very good attitude on your part, criticizing the way one of your fellow students earns his college expenses."

"Oh, I didn't mean to criticize him, sir. I was only saying—"

"Yes, yes, I know; but all this is beside the point. We're here to discuss the state of your grades, Wingate. The fact is, you are on probation right now. As you must know, any student who is passing in less than half his work is automatically suspended from the University and must return to his home. Now one F more and out you'll go, Wingate. That's just being frank with you."

"I'd hate to have to go back home like that, sir."

"Well, you'd have to. If you flunk out, the University authorities are obliged to see that you return to your home immediately."

"I'd hate that, sir. I'd hate to go back home and have to live off my family, and that's probably what I'd have to do. I had a letter from mother yesterday, and she says that nearly all the boys who graduated from high school with me are still there, loafing on the streets and living off their old folks. I don't like that idea. Mother's proud of me because I'm working my way through college. You know there are not many jobs to be had nowadays, sir, and I'd hate to have to go back home and loaf."

"It *is* a problem, I'll confess, Wingate. But what's the point in your coming to the University and working all night in a café and then flunking your class work? Moreover, your freshman adviser reports that you make a practice of sleeping in class. Is that true?"

"Well, yes, sir. I suppose I do drop off sometimes."

"Pretty impossible situation, isn't it, Wingate? Well, I've given you the best advice I can. Unless you can alter your circumstances I suggest that you withdraw from the University at once. We have six thousand other students here who need our attention, and the University has to be impartial and impersonal in dealing with these problems. Unless you can find some means to avoid flunking out I suggest withdrawing beforehand."

"Withdrawal would be a disgrace to me, sir. If I withdrew and went back home now, everyone at home would say that I had been expelled. You know how small towns are."

"Ah, now, Wingate, when you begin dealing with small-town gossip, I fear you're really getting outside my province. But I should think you'd prefer honorable withdrawal to flunking out."

"I believe I'll try to stick it through, sir. I'll try to remove the conditional grades, and maybe I can luck through on my finals."

"I hope you can, Wingate. As long as you feel that way about it, good luck to you." The Dean of Men stood up. Charlie stood up too. The Dean put out his hand and showed his teeth in a jovial smile and bore down hard on Charlie's knuckles. "I'm counting on you strong, old man," he said, encircling Charlie's shoulders with his left arm. "I know you have the stuff and that you'll come through with flying colors one of these days."

"Thank you, sir," Charlie said, grinning tearfully while the Dean gave his shoulder little pats. He edged toward the door as soon as the Dean released him, but when he reached it he hesitated and pulled the postal card out of his pocket. "Oh, pardon me, sir, but there's something I forgot to ask you. I got this in the mail today. I've been a little bothered about what to do about it."

The Dean of Men took the mimeographed card and read it quickly. "Why, I should say that you ought to go see what they want, Wingate. You shouldn't ignore things of this sort, you know. It's all a part of the normal activities of college life. No reason for antagonizing your fellow-students by ignoring a request of this kind."

"All right, sir; I'll go see them."

"Why, to be sure, go see them! Always keep in mind that the University is a social as well as an educational institution, Wingate."

IV

Room 204, Student Union Building, was a newly finished, rather barren office that smelled dankly of lime in the fresh plaster. It was fitted with a metal desk painted to imitate painted walnut, a large brass spittoon, a square metal waste-paper basket, a green metal filing cabinet, a large bank calendar, a huge pasteboard shipping case, and Aubrey H. Carson, who had the freshman cap concession.

Charlie Wingate hesitantly opened the door and saw Aubrey H. Carson tilted back in a chair, his feet on the metal walnut desk, reading a copy of *Ballyhoo*.

"Co-ome in! Co-ome in!" Aubrey Carson called loudly without putting down his magazine. "All right, old timer. What's on your mind?"

Charlie held out the mimeographed card. Carson held his magazine a moment longer before accepting the card. He shoved his hat down over one eye, turning the card, looking first at the back, then at the name on the front. "Um-m-m," he grunted. He reached over to a drawer in the filing cabinet without taking his feet down and flipped through the cards. He looked at the name on the postal card again, pulled a card out of the file, and drew his thick lips up into a rosette. He looked at the file card in silence.

"Wingate," he said at last in a severe tone, "you have been dilatory. Indeed, Wingate, I might even go so far as to say you have been remiss. At the beginning of this semester you applied for and received a refund on your student ticket fee. That signifies that you have not attended a single football game this season, and that you have no intention of honoring any of the University's athletic spectacles with your presence this season. Also, the record discloses that you did not register at the Y.M.C.A. freshman mixer. Neither did you respond to polite solicitation for a trifling monetary pledge to the Memorial Stadium Fund. And, most heinous offense of all, Wingate, we find that you have yet to pay in one dollar for your freshman cap, prescribed by your seniors and purveyed to you on a non-profit basis by the Student Committee on Freshman Activities. And yet, Wingate, I find you duly enrolled and attending classes in this here now University. Wingate, what possible excuse do you have for such gross neglect of University tradition? Speak up!"

Charlie said meekly, "Well, I work nights and it's hard for me to get here in the daytime, and I can't afford to buy a cap."

"What's this!" Carson exclaimed, jerking his legs down from the desk top and banging the desk with two flat hands. "Why, boy, this is treason! You mean you can't afford *not* to buy a freshman cap."

"No, I just came to tell you that a dollar has to go a long way with me and that I need every cent I earn to stay in school. So I wish you'd please excuse me from buying a freshman cap."

Carson's lean, florid face suddenly became rigid and he stuck his jaw out with his lower teeth showing and, in spite of his marcelled taffy pompadour and his creased tailored suit, he again looked very much as he did in all the sporting section photographs. "See here, Wingate," he said, hard-lipped, "you're still a freshman at this University. You'll have to wait another year before you can start saying what you will do and won't do, see? Now we've been patient with you. You've been in school here three months without putting on a freshman cap. Do you realize that over eighty-five per cent of the freshman class came in here and bought their caps before the first week of school ended? Now who do you think *you* are, Wingate— Mr. God? You're going to get you a cap, and you're going to wear it. See? No ifs, ands, or buts about it. And if you don't leave this office with a green cap on your head then I don't mind telling you that we've got ways of getting one on you before another day passes."

"Well, if I buy one it's going to put me in a bad hole. All the money I've got is what I saved out to pay my room rent this week."

"Listen, fella, if we let horsefeathers like that go here, half the freshman class wouldn't be wearing freshman caps right now. Now I've said all I'm going to to you. Do you want your green cap now or will you wait till later? That's all I want to know. I don't aim to give you any high-pressure sales talk on something that's already been decided for you. Take it or leave it."

Carson reached over into the large pasteboard box, groped far down in it, and brought forth a small green monkey cap. He tossed it on the desk. Charlie Wingate stuck his forefinger in his watch pocket and pulled out a small pad of three carefully folded dollar bills. He unfolded them and laid one on the desk and picked up the cap. Carson put the dollar in his pocket and stood up.

Charlie stood holding his cap. He scuffed the cement floor with his shoe toe and began doggedly, "The only thing is—"

"Aw, that's O.K., Wingate, old man," Carson said suavely. "No hard feelings whatsoever." He held out a freshly opened pack of cigarettes. "Here, have a Treasure Trove on me before you go."

v

That night all the stools along the counter at The Wigwam were filled when Charlie Wingate came in, still dusty from the drill field. He got himself a set-up back of the counter and went into the kitchen. He moved about the steam-table, dishing up his dinner. He dragged a stool over to a zinc-covered kitchen table and sat down to eat. The kitchen was warm and steamy and the air was thick with the odors of sour chili grease and yellow soap melting in hot dishwater. Charlie's fork slipped through his fingers, and he began nodding over his plate.

Fat Kruger, the night dishwasher and short-order cook, yelled, "Hey, there, wake up and pay for your bed!" Charlie jerked his head up and looked at the ponderous, good-humored cook with half-lidded eyes. "Why'n't you try sleeping in bed once in a w'ile, Charlie?" Fat said in a friendly tone. "You're going to kill yourself if you don't watch out, trying to go without sleep."

"Don't worry, Fat. I can take it," Charlie said.

Almost two hours had to pass before it would be the hour for him to come on, but not time enough for him to walk back to his room and catch a nap, so he took the book on which he had to make an outside reading report in Economics 150 and went up to the last booth to study until nine o'clock. He fell asleep and he did not wake up until Red Hibbert, going off, shook him and told him that it was almost time for him to come on. He closed his book and went back to the washroom. The acrid stench of the mothballs that Nick used to deodorize the latrine cleared his head. He took down his apron and tied it on over his army breeches. Then he slipped into a white coat.

The usual black-coffee addicts came dribbling in. When the telephone rang, Charlie answered it, jotting down short orders to go. The delivery boy came in and went out and banged off on his motorcycle with paper bags full of "red hots" and nickel hamburgers and coffee in paper cylinders. The Wigwam's white tile shone under the inverted alabaster urns. There was a pale pink reflection in the plate-glass window as the Neon sign outside spelled and re-spelled "Wigwam Eats. Open All Night." A party of drunken Betas came in at ten-thirty and seated themselves noisily in the last booth. They tossed Charlie's economics book out into the aisle with a whoop, and he came and picked it up and took their orders in silence while they kidded him about his flap ears and the grease on his white coat. At eleven o'clock the last whistle at the University power house blew for the closing hour, and a couple of lingering "dates" scurried out. Finally the drunks left, after one had been sick in a corner of the booth. The delivery boy came coasting up at midnight and checked in and roared away again on his motorcycle. The long small hours began inching past.

At one o'clock Charlie finished cleaning up the drunk's mess and he had cleared off the last of the tables. The Wigwam was empty, so he opened the book he must read for Ec 150. He had read a few lines when a bunch of girls from the Theta house down the street came charging in, giggling and talking in gasps and screams, their fur coats clutched over their sleeping pajamas. It was long after the closing hour, and they told Charlie to keep an eye out for the University night watchman. They took up the two back booths and they consulted The Wigwam's printed menu card without failing to read aloud the lines "Nick (Pericles) Pappas," "We Employ Student Help Exclusively," and "Please Do Not Tip. A Smile Is Our Reward" with the customary shrieks. Nearly all ordered filet mignon and French fries, which were not on the menu, but two or three ordered pecan waffles and coffee, which were. When he had served their orders Charlie went back to his book again, but the low buzz of their talk and their sudden spurts of laughter disturbed him and he could not read. At a quarter of two they began peering around corners of their booths. They asked Charlie in stage-whispers if the coast were clear.

Charlie went to the door and looked out on the street and beckoned widely with his arm. They trooped out with their fur coats pulled tight, their fur-trimmed silken mules slapping their bare heels. Charlie went on back to clear away their dishes. They had left about thirty cents as a tip, all in cents and nickels. The coins were carefully imbedded in the cold steak grease and gluey syrup and putty-colored cigarette leavings on their plates. Charlie began stacking the plates without touching the money. He carried the dirty dishes back and set them through the opening in the kitchen wall. Fat Kruger came to the opening and Charlie went back to his book.

Fat called, "Hey, Charlie, you leavin' this tip again?"

"You're damn' right, I'm leaving it!" Charlie said. "I can get along without their tips. They leave it that way every time. I guess they think I'll grabble on their filthy plates to get a lousy thirty cents. It takes a woman to think up something like that."

"Charlie, you're too proud. I don't see where you can afford to be so proud. The way I figure it, thirty cents is thirty cents."

"Hell, I'm not proud, Fat. I just try to keep my self-respect. When those sorority sows come in and plant their tips in the dirt and grease of their plates, damn' if I'll lower myself to grub it out."

He sat down on a counter stool with the economics book before him, trying to fix his mind on it. He read a page. The print became thin blurred parallels of black on the page. His eyelids kept drooping shut and he propped the muscles with his palms at his temples, trying to keep his eyes open. His head jerked forward and he caught it and began reading again. Soon his face lowered slowly through his hands and came to rest on the open book.

Fat Kruger came through the kitchen swinging door and tiptoed up front. Fat stood grinning, watching Charlie sleep. Cramped over with his head on the counter, Charlie snored softly. Fat gave his head a gentle shove, and Charlie started up to catch his balance.

"For God sakes, guy, you're *dead!*" Fat howled. "Don't you never get no sleep except like that?"

"What time is it?" Charlie said, yawning and arching his back.

"Half-past two."

"Jees, is that all?"

"Charlie, go back there and lay down on the kitchen table. I'll watch the front for you. Nobody'll be coming in for a while."

As he was talking old Uncle Jim Hudson ambled in, a bundle of sweaters, overcoats, and grizzled dewlaps, his black timeclock slung over one shoulder by a leather lanyard. Uncle Jim laid his long, nickled flashlight carefully on the counter and eased himself onto a stool. He ordered a cup of black coffee and in a lecherous wheeze began telling dirty stories selected from his twenty years' experience as a campus night-watchman. Fat Kruger nickered loudly after each telling, and Charlie jerked his eyes open and smiled sleepily. It was three-thirty when Uncle Jim left. Charlie opened his book again.

"Charlie, I wouldn't put my eyes out over that damn' book if I was you, when you're dyin' for sleep," Fat said.

"I've got to get it read, Fat. It's my outside reading in Economics and the whole semester grade depends on it. It's the hardest book to keep your mind on you ever saw. I've been reading on it for over a month and I'm only half through, and he's going to call for these reports any day now. If I flunk Ec I flunk out of school."

"Why mess with reading it? I know a guy over at the Masonic Dorm who'll read it and write your report for two bucks. He writes all my English themes for me, and I'm making a straight A in English. He only charges

fifty cents for short themes and two bucks for term papers. You ought to
try him."

"Hell, Fat, you get five dollars a week from home. Where am I going
to get two dollars for hiring a guy to read this book?"

"Charlie, I just can't figure you out. You never do get any real sleep.
You sure must want a college education bad. It don't look to me like you
would figure it's worth it."

"Oh, it's worth it! It's a big satisfaction to my folks to have me in college. And where can a man without a college degree get nowadays? But
I'll tell you the truth, I didn't know it was going to be like this when I
came down here last Fall. I used to read *College Humor* in high school,
and when fellows came home from University for the holidays, all dressed
up in snappy clothes, talking about dates and football and dances, and using
college slang—well, I had a notion I'd be like that when I got down here.
The University publicity department sent me a little booklet showing how
it was easy to work your way through college. So here I am. I haven't had
a date or been to a dance or seen a football game since I enrolled. And
there are plenty of others just like me. I guess I'm getting a college education, all right—but the only collegiate thing I've been able to do is go to
sleep in class."

"How you get by with sleeping in class, Charlie?"

"I wear those colored spectacles and prop myself, and the profs can't
see I've got my eyes closed."

Fat waggled his heavy face mournfully. "Boy, it sure is tough when a
man don't get his sleep."

"Yeah, it is," Charlie said, looking down at his book again. "I'll get a
break pretty soon, though. I'd rather chop off a hand than to flunk out of
University before I'd even finished one semester."

VI

The tardiest of the hundred students enrolled in Dr. Sylvester C. O.
Kenshaw's Economics 150 straggled into the lecture room and made their
ways to alphabetically-assigned chairs with much scuffling and trampling
of toes and mumbled apologies. Ec 150, renowned as a pipe course, was
always crowded. Doctor Kenshaw was the celebrated author of seven textbooks on economics, five of which his students were required to buy each
semester. Doctor Kenshaw's national reputation as an economist permitted
him to be erratic about meeting his classes, but fame had never dimmed his
fondness for student flattery. The only students who ever flunked Ec 150
were those who gave affront to Doctor Kenshaw by neglecting to buy his
textbooks or by not laughing at his wit or by being outrageously inatten-
tive to his lectures.

Doctor Kenshaw was late that morning. Charlie Wingate sat in his chair on the back row in an agony of waiting. He had on his amber glasses and he could fall asleep as soon as Doctor Kenshaw opened his lecture. But he had to stay awake until then. There was a slow ache in the small of his back. The rest of his body was numb. He had not taken off his army shoes for twenty hours, and his feet were moist and swollen. Every time he shifted position his arms and legs were bathed in prickling fire. He kept his eyes open behind the amber lenses, watching the clock. Small noises of the classroom came to him as a low, far-off humming.

When the clock on the front wall showed nine after eleven the seated class began stirring as if it were mounted on some eccentric amusement-park device. Excited whispers eddied out on the warm air of the steam-heated lecture room. "He's giving us another cut!" "He's not meeting this class today!" "He's got one more minute to make it!" "Naw; six more! You have to wait fifteen minutes on department heads."

There was a seething argument on this point, but when the clock showed fourteen minutes after eleven a bold leader sprang up and said, "Come on, everybody!" All but five or six especially conscientious students rose and milled after him toward the door. Charlie Wingate followed, thoroughly awakened by the chance of getting to bed so soon. The leader yanked the door open and Doctor Kenshaw stumbled in, all out of breath, his eyeglasses steamed, his pointed gray beard quivering, a vain little man in a greenish-black overcoat.

"Go back to your seats!" Doctor Kenshaw commanded sternly as soon as he could get his breath. He marched over to his lecture table and planked down his leather brief case. He took off his overcoat and began wiping the steam from his eyeglasses while the students hurried back to their chairs. "It does seem to me," he said, his voice quavering with anger, "that it would be no more than courteous for this class to await my arrival on those rare occasions when I am delayed. Day after day you come lagging into my classes, and I have always been extremely lenient in giving credit for attendance, no matter how tardy your arrival. Certainly it is no more than my privilege to ask that you wait for me occasionally."

A few students exchanged meaning glances. They meant, "Now we're in for it. The old boy has on one of his famous mads."

"Today, I believe I shall forego delivering my prepared lecture," Doctor Kenshaw went on in a more even voice, but with elaborate sarcasm, "and let *you* do the talking. Perhaps it would be meet to hear a few outside reading reports this morning. All of you doubtless are aware that these reports were due last week, although I had not expected to call for them at once. I trust that I have impressed you sufficiently with the importance of these reports. They represent to me the final result of your semester's work in this course. The grades you receive on these reports will be your grades for the semester. Let us begin forthwith. When your name is called, you will rise and read your report to the class." He opened his roll book.

"Mr. Abbott!" he called. Mr. Abbott stammered an excuse. Doctor Kenshaw passed coldly on to Miss Adams, making no comment. All through the A's it was the same. But with the B's an ashen, spectacled Miss Ballentyne stood up and began reading in a droning voice her report on *The Economic Consequences of the Peace.* Obviously Doctor Kenshaw was not listening to her. His hard little eyes under craggy brows were moving up one row and down the other, eager for a victim. On the back row, Charlie Wingate's propped legs had given way and he had slipped far down into his seat, fast asleep. When Doctor Kenshaw's preying eyes reached Charlie they stopped moving. Someone tittered nervously and then was silent as Doctor Kenshaw jerked his head round in the direction of the noise. Miss Ballentyne droned on.

When she had finished, Doctor Kenshaw said dryly, "Very good, Miss Ballentyne, very good, indeed. Er—ah—would someone be kind enough to arouse the recumbent young gentleman in the last row?"

There was a murmur of laughter while everyone turned to look at Milton Weismann nudging Charlie Wingate. Doctor Kenshaw was running down the list of names in his small record book. Milton Weismann gave Charlie another stiff poke in the ribs, and Charlie sprang up quickly. Everyone laughed loudly at that.

"Mr.—ah—*Wingate,* isn't it? Mr. Wingate, your report."

"Pardon me, sir?"

"Mr. Wingate, what was the title of the book assigned to you for report in this class?"

"Theory of the Leisure Class by Veblen, sir."

"Ah, then, that's the explanation. So you were assiduously engaged in evolving your own theory of the leisure class. Is that right, Mr. Wingate? You have evidently concluded that Economics 150 is the leisure class."

The class rocked with laughter. Doctor Kenshaw, pleased with his pun and flattered by the response to it, found it hard to keep his face straight. Suddenly he was back in good humor. "Mr. Wingate's theory is quite apparently one to which the majority of this class subscribes. Now I try to be lenient with students in this class. Surely no one could describe me as a hard taskmaster. But I resent your implication that I have been too easygoing. Now these reading reports were assigned to you last September, and you have had ample time to prepare them. I'll not call for any more of them today, but at the next session of this class I expect every one of these papers in. As for you, Mr. Wingate, if you'll see me directly after class, I'll be glad to hear any explanation or apology that you may wish to make. I want most of all to be fair. I have always given every student the benefit of the doubt until a student deliberately flouts me with his indifference. But I am capable of being quite ruthless, I assure you."

"Thank you, sir," Charlie mumbled. He suffered a slow torture, trying to keep awake until the class bell rang. He rolled his hot, red-veined eyes up with drunken precision to see the clock. Fifteen minutes had to pass before the bell would ring.

When the bell rang the class arose quickly and began clumping out. Several co-eds and men, politickers and apple-polishers wangling for A's, crowded about the lecture table. Doctor Kenshaw always remained behind after each class to accept their homage. But today he looked up over the heads of the eager group. He silenced their inane questions and flagrant compliments by placing his right forefinger against his thin, unsmiling lips. "Sh-h-h!" he said. The apple-polishers turned their heads in the direction of his gaze and then, giggling softly, tiptoed away. When the last had gone out, Doctor Kenshaw unscrewed his fountain pen and opened his roll book. He ran his finger down the list until he came to "Wingate, C." and in the space opposite under "Smstr Grd" he marked a precise little F.

A whiffling snore escaped Charlie Wingate in the back of the room. Doctor Kenshaw looked back across the varnished chair rows with a frown of annoyance. He took his overcoat from its hanger, slipped into it, and strapped up his brief case. He jammed on his hat and strode out of the lecture room, slamming the door. The noise made a hollow echo in the empty room, but it did not disturb Charlie Wingate. He slept on behind his amber glasses.

MAX SHULMAN

How a Writer Is Made

FROM *Barefoot Boy with Cheek*

In a sense, Max Shulman never left college, despite such exurbanite excursions as Rally Round the Flag, Boys, *for since his days at Minnesota and his work on the staff of the undergraduate humor magazine there, he has celebrated campus life with warm wit in books and stories.*

Shulman's Barefoot Boy with Cheek, *from which this selection was taken, is a hilarious exposé of life at Minnesota and its immediate environs; it was made into a successful musical in the Forties.*

Où est mon chapeau?—ANATOLE FRANCE

ST. PAUL and Minneapolis extend from the Mississippi River like the legs on a pair of trousers. Where they join is the University of Minnesota.

I stood that day and gazed at the campus, my childish face looking up, holding wonder like a cup, my little feet beating time, time, time, in a sort of runic rhyme. A fraternity man's convertible ran me down, disturbing my reverie. "Just a flesh wound," I mumbled to disinterested passers-by.

With eager steps I proceeded to explore the campus. All around me was the hum of happy men at work. Here were masons aging a building so they could hang ivy on it. There were chiselers completing the statue of Cyrus Thresher, first regent of the University. It was Thresher, as you know, who said, "It takes a heap o' learnin' to make a school a school." Yonder were landscapers cleverly trimming a twelve-foot hedge to spell "Minnesota, Minnesota, rah, rah, ree. Little brown jug, how we love thee."

The architecture at Minnesota is very distinctive, and thereby hangs a tale. It goes back a good many years, back to the time when the mighty, sprawling University was just an infant. At that time Art Chaff, the son of a wealthy Minneapolis flour miller named Elihu Chaff, was expelled from

123

Harvard for playing buck euchre on the Sabbath. Old Elihu was deeply incensed by the indignity. He was determined that Art should go to college, and, moreover, to a bigger college than Harvard.

So Elihu went to work on the University of Minnesota campus. He erected twenty buildings. They all looked like grain elevators, for that is what Elihu intended to use them for after Art had been graduated. But Elihu never fulfilled his plan.

One week end Elihu went fishing, accompanied only by an Indian guide named Ralph Duckhonking. They went into a deep forest, and after two days Duckhonking came out alone. He was wearing Elihu's suit and carrying all of his valuables. He said he knew nothing about Elihu's disappearance. Duckhonking was indicted for murder, but he was never tried because it was impossible to obtain twelve English-speaking veniremen in that judicial district. Duckhonking walked about free until he died more than twenty years later of nepotism. This case later became famous as the *Crédit Mobilier* scandal.

Elihu's elevators, therefore, remained part of the University. In fact, out of respect to Elihu, all the buildings which were subsequently erected on the campus were built to resemble grain elevators.

But this was no time to be gawking about the campus. I had things to do. First I had to see Mr. Ingelbretsvold, my freshman adviser, about making out a program of studies for the year. Obtaining directions from a friendly upperclassman who sold me a freshman button, freshman cap, subscription to *Ski-U-Mah*, the campus humor magazine, a map of the campus, and a souvenir score card of last year's home-coming game, I proceeded to the office of Mr. Ingelbretsvold.

A line of freshmen stood in front of his door. I knew how they must feel, about to embark on this great adventure, and I could not help cheerily hollering "Halloa" to them. They stoned me in an amiable fashion.

At last a voice came from behind the door bidding me come in. How my heart beat as I opened the door and trod across the luxuriant burlap rug to Mr. Ingelbretsvold's desk.

"My name is Asa Hearthrug and I've come for advice," I said.

He stood up and smiled at me kindlily. "Sit down, young man," he said, "and have a glass of kvass." He pointed at the pitcher and glasses.

"Thank you," I said, making a low curtsey.

"Well, it's certainly a nice day."

"Yes," I agreed. "Almost twelve inches of rain since sunup."

"That's what I meant," he said. "It's a nice rain. It will help the potato crop."

"Yes," I agreed, "it should wash out every potato in Minnesota."

"That's what I meant," he said. "It will get rid of those damn potatoes.

People are eating altogether too many potatoes. But enough of this meteorological chitchat. Let's get down to business. First of all, I want you to know that I'm your friend."

I licked his hand gratefully.

"You are about to enter a new phase of your life. I wonder whether you realize just how important this is."

"Oh, I do, sir, I do," I exclaimed.

"Shut up when I'm talking," he said. "Now, I have a little story that I like to tell to freshmen to impress them with the importance of college. I have had a great many students who were graduated from Minnesota and went out to take their places in the world come back after many years and say to me, 'Mr. Ingelbretsvold, I can never thank you enough for that little story you told me when I first came to the University.' Yes, young man, this story has helped a great many people, and I hope it will help you."

"So tell it already," I said.

"Well, sir, when I was a boy I had a good friend named Kyrie Eleison. We went through grade school and high school together, and on the night we were graduated from high school I said to him, 'Well, Kyrie, what are you going to do now?'

" 'Oh,' he said, 'I've got a chance to get a job in a nepotism business in North Dakota.'

" 'Kyrie,' I told him, 'don't take it. Come to college with me, or else you'll always regret it.'

"But he didn't choose to take my advice. I went to college, and he took the job. Yes, he did well at his work. By the time he was thirty he had seventy-five million dollars, and he has been getting richer ever since. He built a fine big house in which he holds the most lavish social affairs in the whole Northwest.

"Well, sir, one night I was invited to a party at Kyrie's house. I rented a suit and went. The house was filled with prominent people. A hundred-and-twenty-piece orchestra was playing. When we went in for dinner the table groaned with all sorts of expensive delicacies. And at the head of the table sat Kyrie, the monarch of all he surveyed.

"But during the course of the dinner a well-dressed young woman leaned over and said to Kyrie, 'Who was the eighth avatar of Vishnu?' and Kyrie, for all his wealth and power, did not know the answer."

"How ghastly!" I cried, throwing up my hands.

"Yes," said Mr. Ingelbretsvold. "You will find that sort of thing all through life. People come up to you on the street and say, 'Does a paramecium beat its flagella?' or 'How many wheels has a fiacre?' or 'When does an oryx mate?' and if you have not been to college, you simply cannot answer them."

"But that cannot happen to me. I am going to the University," I said.

"Ah, but it can," Mr. Ingelbretsvold answered. "It happens to many who go to college."

"But how?"

"You see, my boy, a great many people go to college to learn how to *do* something. They study medicine or law or engineering, and when they are through they know how to trepan a skull or where to get a writ of estoppel or how to find the torque of a radial engine. But just come up to them and ask how many caliphs succeeded Mohammed or who wrote *Baby Duncan's Whistling Lung* and they stare at you blankly."

I shuddered. "Oh, please, Mr. Ingelbretsvold," I begged, "what must I do?"

"You must do like I tell you. You must let college make you a well-rounded-out personality. That is the chief function and purpose of this University: to make you a well-rounded-out personality. Now you get out a pencil and paper and write down the names of the courses I am going to give you. If you follow this program you will find yourself a well-rounded-out personality."

I took out a pencil and poised it over my dickey bosom.

"Ready. Here they are: Races and Cultures of Arabia, Egypt and North Africa; Ethnology of India; History of Architecture; Greek; Latin; Sixteenth-Century Literature; Seventeenth-Century Literature; Eighteenth-Century Literature; Nineteenth-Century Literature; Twentieth-Century Literature; Geography; Ancient History; Medieval History; Modern History; Ancient Philosophy; Modern Philosophy; Contemporary Philosophy; History of Religion; American Government; British Government; Chinese Government; Japanese Government; Lett Government; First Aid; Public Health; General Psychology; Psychology of Learning; Psychology of Advertising; Psychology of Literature; Psychology of Art; Psychology of Behavior; Animal Psychology; Abnormal Psychology; Norwegian; Swedish; Danish; French; German; Russian; Italian; Lett; Urban Sociology; Rural Sociology; Juvenile Sociology; Statistical Sociology; Criminology; Penology; Elocution; Speech Pathology; and Canoe Paddling.

"That will do for a start. As you go into these courses you will find others that will interest you too."

"And these will make me a well-rounded-out personality?" I asked.

He laughed gently. "Oh no, my boy. That is only a small but essential part of rounding out your personality. There is the social life too." He nudged me and winked. "A fellow can have a good time here."

"Sir," I said, and blushed.

"But you'll soon find out all about that. Now, one more thing. In addition to the work you do for these courses I have named you should do a

lot of reading that has not been assigned in your classes. Do you read anything now?"

"A mystery story now and then," I confessed.

"Oh, have you read Rex Snout's latest, *The Case of the Gelded Gnu?*"

"No, but I read the one before that, *The Case of the Missing Lynx*."

"I missed that one. What was it about?"

"Well, a horribly mutilated corpse is found on the railroad tracks near
Buffalo. This corpse is in such a state that it is impossible to identify it
or even to tell whether it is a man or a woman. The story is concerned
almost entirely with trying to establish the identity of the corpse. In the
end it is discovered that it is not a corpse at all, but a pan of waffle batter
that fell out of the window of a New York Central dining car."

"How interesting. Well, I guess that's all the time I can give you. Others
are waiting," he said, taking cognizance of the stones they were throwing
through the window.

"Just one more thing, Mr. Ingelbretsvold," I said. "I don't know quite
how to say this, but I think I would like to be a writer when I grow up.
Will the program you made out for me help me to be a writer?"

"Why, bless you, child," Mr. Ingelbretsvold said, "you follow that program and there's nothing else you can be."

A Lonely Year

FROM *Look Homeward, Angel*

Thomas Wolfe's novels are the great sprawling autobiography of a lonely man. His Eugene Gant is Wolfe himself, "a hulking, shaggy, slow-moving colossus." Wolfe entered the University of North Carolina—the Pulpit Hill of his fiction—at fifteen. In his constant, soul-searching quest, the restless Wolfe found no satisfying answers, either at the university or afterward, in his short lifetime of intense and passionate seeking. He died at thirty-two, but he lived long enough to record his searching in torrents of magnificent self-revealing prose.

Wolfe was editor of his college paper and magazine at Chapel Hill. He was graduated in 1920.

EUGENE'S first year at the university was filled for him with loneliness, pain, and failure. Within three weeks of his matriculation, he had been made the dupe of a half-dozen classic jokes, his ignorance of all campus tradition had been exploited, his gullibility was a byword. He was the greenest of all green freshmen, past and present: he had listened attentively to a sermon in chapel by a sophomore with false whiskers; he had prepared studiously for an examination on the contents of the college catalogue; and he had been guilty of the inexcusable blunder of making a speech of acceptance on his election, with fifty others, to the literary society.

And these buffooneries—a little cruel, but only with the cruelty of vacant laughter, and a part of the schedule of rough humor in an American college—salty, extravagant, and national—opened deep wounds in him, which his companions hardly suspected. He was conspicuous at once not only because of his blunders, but also because of his young wild child's face, and his great raw length of body, with the bounding scissor legs. The undergraduates passed him in grinning clusters: he saluted them obediently,

128

but with a sick heart. And the smug smiling faces of his own classmen, the wiser Freshmen, complacently guiltless of his own mistakes, touched him at moments with insane fury.

"Smile and smile and s-mile—damn you!" he cursed through his grating teeth. For the first time in his life he began to dislike whatever fits too snugly in a measure. He began to dislike and envy the inconspicuous mould of general nature—the multitudinous arms, legs, hands, feet, and figures that are comfortably shaped for ready-made garments. And the prettily regular, wherever he found it, he hated—the vacantly handsome young men, with shining hair, evenly parted in the middle, with sure strong middling limbs meant to go gracefully on dance-floors. He longed to see them commit some awkward blunder—to trip and sprawl, to be flatulent, to lose a strategic button in mixed company, to be unconscious of a hanging shirt-tail while with a pretty girl. But they made no mistakes.

As he walked across the campus, he heard his name called mockingly from a dozen of the impartial windows, he heard the hidden laughter, and he ground his teeth. And at night, he stiffened with shame in his dark bed, ripping the sheet between his fingers as, with the unbalanced vision, the swollen egotism of the introvert, the picture of a crowded student-room, filled with the grinning historians of his exploits, burned in his brain. He strangled his fierce cry with a taloned hand. He wanted to blot out the shameful moment, unweave the loom. It seemed to him that his ruin was final, that he had stamped the beginning of his university life with folly that would never be forgotten, and that the best he could do would be to seek out obscurity for the next four years. He saw himself in his clown's trappings and thought of his former vision of success and honor with a lacerating self-contempt.

There was no one to whom he could turn: he had no friends. His conception of university life was a romantic blur, evoked from his reading and tempered with memories of Stover at Yale, Young Fred Fearnot, and jolly youths with affectionate linked arms, bawling out a cheer-song. No one had given him even the rudimentary data of the somewhat rudimentary life of an American university. He had not been warned of the general taboos. Thus, he had come greenly on his new life, unprepared, as he came ever thereafter on all new life, save for his opium visions of himself a stranger in Arcadias.

He was alone. He was desperately lonely.

But the university was a charming, an unforgettable place. It was situated in the little village of Pulpit Hill, in the central midland of the big State. Students came and departed by motor from the dreary tobacco town of Exeter, twelve miles away: the countryside was raw, powerful, and ugly, a rolling land of field, wood, and hollow; but the university itself was buried in a pastoral wilderness, on a long tabling butte, which rose steeply above the country. One burst suddenly, at the hill-top, on the end of the strag- gling village street, flanked by faculty houses, and winding a mile in to the town centre and the university. The central campus sloped back and up over a broad area of rich turf, groved with magnificent ancient trees. A quadrangle of post-Revolutionary buildings of weathered brick bounded the upper end: other newer buildings, in the modern bad manner (the Peda- gogic Neo-Greeky), were scattered around beyond the central design: be- yond, there was a thickly forested wilderness. There was still a good flavor of the wilderness about the place—one felt its remoteness, its isolated charm. It seemed to Eugene like a provincial outpost of great Rome: the wilder- ness crept up to it like a beast.

Its great poverty, its century-long struggle in the forest, had given the university a sweetness and a beauty it was later to forfeit. It had the fine authority of provincialism—the provincialism of an older South. Nothing mattered but the State: the State was a mighty empire, a rich kingdom— there was, beyond, a remote and semi-barbaric world.

Few of the university's sons had been distinguished in the nation's life —there had been an obscure President of The United States, and a few Cabinet members, but few had sought such distinction: it was glory enough to be a great man in one's State. Nothing beyond mattered very much.

In this pastoral setting a young man was enabled to loaf comfortably and delightfully through four luxurious and indolent years. There was, God knows, seclusion enough for monastic scholarship, but the rare ro- mantic quality of the atmosphere, the prodigal opulence of Springtime, thick with flowers and drenched in a fragrant warmth of green shimmering light, quenched pretty thoroughly any incipient rash of bookishness. In- stead, they loafed and invited their souls or, with great energy and enthu- siasm, promoted the affairs of glee-clubs, athletic teams, class politics, fra- ternities, debating societies, and dramatic clubs. And they talked—always they talked, under the trees, against the ivied walls, assembled in their rooms, they talked—in limp sprawls—incessant, charming, empty Southern talk; they talked with a large easy fluency about God, the Devil, and philos- ophy, the girls, politics, athletics, fraternities and the girls— My God! how they talked!

"Observe," lisped Mr. Torrington, the old Rhode's Scholar (Pulpit Hill and Merton, '14), "observe how skilfully he holds suspense until the very end. Observe with what consummate art he builds up his climax, keeping his meaning hidden until the very last word." Further, in fact.

At last, thought Eugene, I am getting an education. This must be good writing, because it seems so very dull. When it hurts, the dentist says, it does you good. Democracy must be real, because it is so very earnest. It must be a certainty, because it is so elegantly embalmed in this marble mausoleum of language. Essays For College Men—Woodrow Wilson, Lord Bryce and Dean Briggs.

But there was no word here of the loud raucous voice of America, political conventions and the Big Brass Band, Tweed, Tammany, the Big Stick, lynching bees and black barbecue parties, the Boston Irish, and the damnable machinations of the Pope as exposed by the *Babylon Hollow Trumpet* (Dem.), the rape of the Belgian virgins, rum, oil, Wall Street and Mexico.

All that, Mr. Torrington would have said, was temporary and accidental. It was unsound.

Mr. Torrington smiled moistly at Eugene and urged him tenderly into a chair drawn intimately to his desk.

"Mr.—? Mr.—?—" he said, fumbling at his index cards.

"Gant," said Eugene.

"Ah, yes—Mr. Gant," he smiled his contrition. "Now—about your outside reading?" he began.

But what, thought Eugene, about my inside reading?

Did he like to read? Ah—that was good. He was so glad to hear it. The true university in these days, said Carlyle (he did hope Eugene liked rugged old Thomas), was a collection of books.

"Yes, sir," said Eugene.

That, it seemed to him, was the Oxford Plan. Oh, yes—he had been there, three years, in fact. His mild eye kindled. To loaf along the High on a warm Spring day, stopping to examine in the bookseller's windows the treasures that might be had for so little. Then to Buol's or to a friend's room for tea, or for a walk in the meadows or Magdalen gardens, or to look down into the quad, at the gay pageant of youth below. Ah—Ah! A great place? Well—he'd hardly say that. It all depended what one meant by a great place. Half the looseness in thought—unfortunately, he fancied, more prevalent among American than among English youth—came from an indefinite exuberance of ill-defined speech.

"Yes, sir," said Eugene.

A great place? Well, he'd scarcely say that. The expression was typically American. Butter-lipped, he turned on the boy a smile of soft unfriendliness:

"It kills," he observed, "a man's useless enthusiasms."

Eugene whitened a little.

"That's fine," he said.

Now—let him see. Did he like plays—the modern drama? Excellent.

They were doing some very interesting things in the modern drama. Barrie
—oh, a charming fellow! What was that? Shaw!

"Yes, sir," said Eugene. "I've read all the others. There's a new book
out."

"Oh, but really! My dear boy!" said Mr. Torrington with gentle amazement. He shrugged his shoulders and became politely indifferent. Very well,
if he liked. Of course, he thought it rather a pity to waste one's time so
when they were really doing some first-rate things. That was *just* the trouble,
however. The appeal of a man like that was mainly to the unformed taste,
the uncritical judgment. He had a flashy attraction for the immature. Oh,
yes! Undoubtedly an amusing fellow. Clever—yes, but hardly significant.
And—didn't he think—a trifle noisy? Or had he noticed that? Yes—there
was to be sure an amusing Celtic strain, not without charm, but unsound.
He was not in line with the best modern thought.

"I'll take the Barrie," said Eugene.

Yes, he rather thought that would be better.

"Well, good day. Mr.—Mr.—?—?" he smiled, fumbling again with his
cards.

"Gant."

Oh yes, to be sure,—Gant. He held out his plump limp hand. He did
hope Mr. Gant would call on him. Perhaps he'd be able to advise him on
some of the little problems that, he knew, were constantly cropping up
during the first year. Above all, he mustn't get discouraged.

"Yes, sir," said Eugene, backing feverishly to the door. When he felt
the open space behind him, he fell through it, and vanished.

Anyway, he thought grimly, I've read all the damned Barries. I'll write
the damned report for him, and damned well read what I damn well please.

God save our King and Queen!

He had courses besides in Chemistry, Mathematics, Greek, and Latin.

He worked hard and with interest at his Latin. His instructor was a
tall shaven man, with a yellow saturnine face. He parted his scant hair
cleverly in such a way as to suggest horns. His lips were always twisted in
a satanic smile, his eyes gleamed sideward with heavy malicious humor.
Eugene had great hopes of him. When the boy arrived, panting and break-
fastless, a moment after the class had settled to order, the satanic professor
would greet him with elaborate irony: "Ah there, Brother Gant! Just in
time for church again. Have you slept well?"

The class roared its appreciation of these subtleties. And later, in an
expectant pause, he would deepen his arched brows portentously, stare up
mockingly under his bushy eyebrows at his expectant audience, and say,
in a deep sardonic voice:

"And now, I am going to request Brother Gant to favor us with one of his polished and scholarly translations."

These heavy jibes were hard to bear because, of all the class, two dozen or more, Brother Gant was the only one to prepare his work without the aid of a printed translation. He worked hard on Livy and Tacitus, going over the lesson several times until he had dug out a smooth and competent reading of his own. This he was stupid enough to deliver in downright fashion, without hesitation, or a skilfully affected doubt here and here. For his pains and honesty he was handsomely rewarded by the Amateur Diabolist. The lean smile would deepen as the boy read, the man would lift his eyes significantly to the grinning class, and when it was over, he would say:

"Bravo, Brother Gant! Excellent! Splendid! You are riding a good pony —but a little too smoothly, my boy. You ride a little too well."

The class sniggered heavily.

When he could stand it no longer, he sought the man out one day after the class.

"See here, sir! See here!" he began in a voice choking with fury and exasperation. "Sir—I assure you—" he thought of all the grinning apes in the class, palming off profitably their stolen translations and he could not go on.

The Devil's Disciple was not a bad man; he was only, like most men who pride themselves on their astuteness, a foolish one.

"Nonsense, Mr. Gant," said he kindly. "You don't think you can fool me on a translation, do you? It's all right with me, you know," he continued, grinning. "If you'd rather ride a pony than do your own work, I'll give you a passing grade—so long as you do it well."

"But—" Eugene began explosively.

"But I think it's a pity, Mr. Gant," said the professor, gravely, "that you're willing to slide along this way. See here, my boy, you're capable of doing first-rate work. I can see that. Why don't you make an effort? Why don't you buckle down and really study, after this?"

Eugene stared at the man, with tears of anger in his eyes. He sputtered but could not speak. But suddenly, as he looked down into the knowing leer, the perfect and preposterous injustice of the thing—like a caricature— overcame him: he burst into an explosive laugh of rage and amusement which the teacher, no doubt, accepted as confession.

"Well, what do you say?" he asked. "Will you try?"

"All right! Yes!" the boy yelled. "I'll try it."

He bought at once a copy of the translation used by the class. Thereafter, when he read, faltering prettily here and there over a phrase, until his instructor should come to his aid, the satanic professor listened gravely and attentively, nodding his head in approval from time to time, and saying, with great satisfaction, when he had finished: "Good, Mr. Gant. Very good. That shows what a little real work will do."

And privately, he would say: "You see the difference, don't you? I knew at once when you stopped using that pony. Your translation is not so smooth, but it's your own now. You're doing good work, my boy, and you're getting something out of it. It's worth it, isn't it?"

"Yes," said Eugene gratefully, "it certainly is——"

By far the most distinguished of his teachers this first year was Mr. Edward Pettigrew ("Buck") Benson, the Greek professor. Buck Benson was a little man in the middle-forties, a bachelor, somewhat dandified, but old-fashioned, in his dress. He wore wing collars, large plump cravats, and suede-topped shoes. His hair was thick, heavily grayed, beautifully kept. His face was courteously pugnacious, fierce, with large yellow bulging eyeballs, and several bulldog pleatings around the mouth. It was an altogther handsome ugliness.

His voice was low, lazy, pleasant, with an indolent drawl, but without changing its pace or its inflection he could flay a victim with as cruel a tongue as ever wagged, and in the next moment wipe out hostility, restore affection, heal all wounds by the same agency. His charm was enormous. Among the students he was the subject for comical speculation—in their myths, they made of him a passionate and sophisticated lover, and his midget cycle-car, which bounded like an overgrown toy around the campus, the scene of many romantic seductions.

He was a good Grecian—an elegant indolent scholar. Under his instruction Eugene began to read Homer. The boy knew little grammar—he had learned little at Leonard's—but, since he had had the bad judgment to begin Greek under some one other than Buck Benson, Buck Benson thought he knew even less than he did. He studied desperately, but the bitter dyspeptic gaze of the elegant little man frightened him into halting, timorous, clumsy performances. And as he proceeded, with thumping heart and tremulous voice, Buck Benson's manner would become more and more weary, until finally, dropping his book, he would drawl:

"Mister Gant, you make me so damned mad I could throw you out the window."

But, on the examination, he gave an excellent performance, and translated from sight beautifully. He was saved. Buck Benson commended his paper publicly with lazy astonishment, and gave him a fair grade. Thereafter, they slipped quickly into an easier relation: by Spring, he was reading Euripides with some confidence.

But that which remained most vividly, later, in the drowning years which cover away so much of beauty, was the vast sea-surge of Homer which beat in his brain, his blood, his pulses, as did the sea-sound in Gant's parlor shells, when first he heard it to the slowly pacing feet and the hexametrical drawl of Buck Benson, the lost last weary son of Hellas.

Dwaney de clangay genett, argereoyo beeoyo—above the whistle's shriek, the harsh scream of the wheel, the riveter's tattoo, the vast long music endures, and ever shall. What dissonance can quench it? What jangling violence can disturb or conquer it—entombed in our flesh when we were young, remembered like "the apple tree, the singing, and the gold"?

SIMEON STRUNSKY

A Sophomore's Soul

FROM *The Patient Observer*

A writer friend said of Simeon Strunsky that he "carried on a quiet love affair with New York City and with America" in his "Topics of the Times," a column he wrote for The New York Times *for a decade and a half, until his death in 1948. His personal essays have an unobtrusive charm and engaging tolerance very much their own, evident in this glimpse we take with him into the inscrutabilities of a sophomore's psyche.*

Strunsky was Columbia 1900 and was student editor of the university's literary monthly.

A SOPHOMORE'S soul is not the simple thing that most people imagine. I am thinking now of my nephew Philip and of our last meeting. This time, he was more than usually welcome. I was lonely. The family had just left town for the summer and the house was fearfully empty. I sat there, smoking a cigarette amid the first traces of domestic uncleanliness, when I heard him on the stairs. The dear boy had not changed. Dropping his heavy suitcase anyways, he seized my hand within his own huge paw and squeezed it till the tears came to my eyes. His voice was a young roar. He threw his hat upon the table, thereby scattering a large number of papers about the room, and then sat down upon my own hat, which was lying on the arm-chair, on top of several July magazines. I had put my hat down on the chair instead of hanging it up, as I should have done, because the family was away and I was alone in the house.

Might he smoke? He was busy with his bull-dog pipe and my tobacco jar before I could say yes. He explained that he was sorry, but he found he could neither read, write nor think nowadays without his pipe. He admitted that he was the slave of a noxious habit, but it was too late, and he might as well get all the solace he could out of a pretty bad situation. But, as I look at Philip, I cannot help feeling that his fine colour and the sparkle in his blue eyes and his full count of nineteen years make the situation far

136

HE: But I say, what—
SHE: It's quite all right, sir. I'm a daughter of the Absent-minded Professor, and I'm a bit absent-minded myself.

THE HIGHER EDUCATION

Relative to Practical Economics

. . . which is replaced with a yellow slicker at the passing of the first collegiate year . . .

For example—the black slicker of the frosh . . .

Then to the male parent falls the lot of the black slicker—thus the equalization!

The Useful Mistletoe

Back in the '20s everyone of college age knew the drawings of John Held, Jr. Everyone who grew up, went to college and survived the jazz era can recall that it was impossible to pick up a copy of the now-defunct *Life*, *Judge*, or *College Humor* without seeing at least one of his wonderfully funny drawings of sheiks and shebas, fraternity dances, or decorated slickers and Tin Lizzies. His name has become synonymous with the raccoon coat he so hilariously caricatured. (All drawings from *Held's Angels*, copyright 1952 by John Held, Jr., and Frank B. Gilbreth, Jr., published by Thomas Y. Crowell; used by permission.)

The Phi Beta Kappa Student's Car

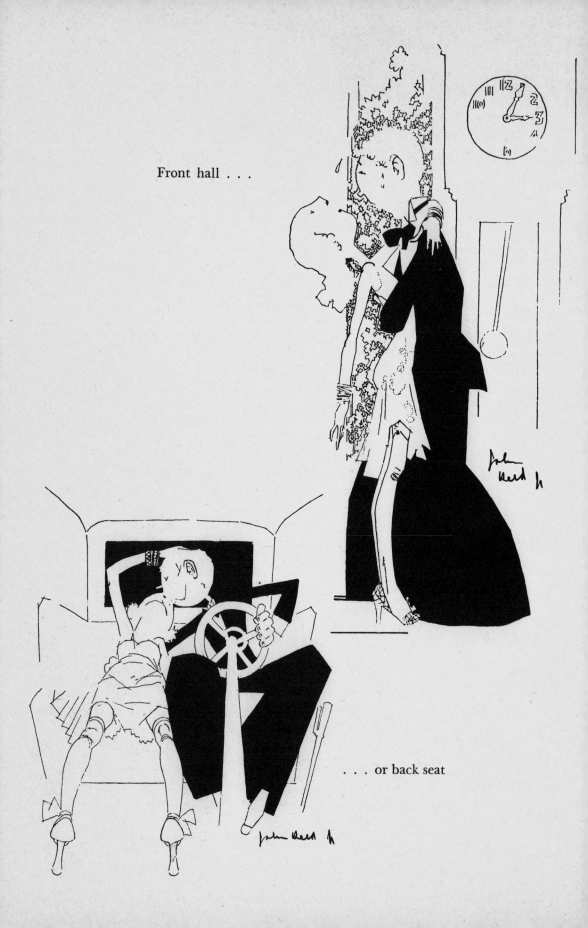

Front hall . . .

. . . or back seat

What's sauce for the gander . . .

. . . is apple sauce for the goose.

less desperate than he portrays it. Philip is not a handsome lad, but he will be a year from now. At present he is mostly hands and feet, and his face shows a marked nasal development. Before Philip has completed his junior year, the rest of his features will have reasserted themselves, and the harmony of lineament which was his when he was an infant, as his mother never tires of regretfully recalling, will be restored. Until that time Philip must be content to carry the suggestion of an attractive and eager young bird of prey.

Philip lights pipe after pipe as he dilates on his experiences since last I saw him. The moralising instinct is very weak in me. I cannot find it in my heart to censure Philip's constant mouthing of the pipe. I, too, smoke, and I am not foolish enough to risk my standing with Philip by preaching where I do not practise. Besides, I observe that the boy does not inhale, that his pipe goes out frequently, and that his consumption of matches is much greater than his consumption of tobacco. So I say nothing in reproof of his pipe.

But it is different with his language. Philip, I observe regretfully, is profane. I am not mealy-mouthed myself. There are moments of high emotional tension when silence is the worst form of blasphemy. But Philip is profane without discrimination. His supply of unobjectionable adjectives would be insufficient to meet the needs of the ordinary kindergarten conversation. He uses the same swift epithet to describe certain brands of tobacco, the weather on commencement day, the food at his eating-house, his professors of French and of mathematics, the spirit of the incoming freshman class, and the outlook for "snap" courses during the coming year.

It is not my moral but my æsthetic sense that takes offence, so I ask Philip whether it is the intensity of his feelings that makes it impossible for him to discuss his work or his play without continual reference to the process of perdition and the realm of lost souls; or whether it is habit. No sooner have I put my question than I am sorry. There is nothing the young soul is so afraid of as of satire. It can understand being petted and it can understand being whipped; but the sting behind the smile, the lash beneath the caress, throws the young soul into helpless panic. It feels itself baited and knows not whither it may flee. I have always thought that the worst type of bully is the teacher in school or in college who indulges a pretty talent for satire at the expense of his pupils. It is a cowardly and a demoralising practice. It means not only hitting some one who is powerless to retort, it means confusing the sense of truth in the adolescent mind. Here is some one quite grown up who smiles and means to hurt you, who says good and means bad, who says yes and means no. The young soul stares at you and sees the standards of the universe in chaos about itself.

And I feel all the more guilty in Philip's case because I know that the lad speaks only a mechanical lingo which goes with his bull-dog pipe and the aggressive shade of his neckwear and his socks. The very pain and alarm my question raises in him shows well enough that his soul has kept young and clear amid his world of "muckers" and "grinds" and "cads" and "rotten sneaks," and all the men and things and conditions he is in the habit of depicting in various stages of damnation. "Now, you're making fun of me," says Philip. "We fellows don't know how to pick out words that sound nice, but mean a—I beg your pardon—a good deal more than they say. Anyhow, I suppose, if I try from now on till doomsday I shall never be able to speak like you."

Bless his young sophomore's soul! With that last sentence Philip has seized me hip and thigh and hurled me into an emotional whirlpool, where chills and thrills rapidly succeed each other. Because I am fifteen years older than Philip the boy invests me with a halo and bathes me in adoration. I am fifteen years older than he, I am bald, obscure, and far from prosperous, and there is unmistakably nothing about me to dazzle the youthful imagination. Yet the facts are as I have stated them. Philip likes to be with me, copies me without apparently trying to, and has chosen my profession—so he has often told me—for his own. I am pretty sure that he has made up his mind when he is as old as I am to smoke the same brand of rather mediocre tobacco which I have adopted for practical reasons. I am sometimes tempted to think that Philip, at my age, intends to be as bald as I am.

Hence the alternate thrills and chills. I am by nature restless under worship. The sense of my own inconsequence grows positively painful in the face of Philip's outspoken veneration. There are people to whom such tribute is as incense and honey. But I am not one of them. I have tried to be and have failed. I have argued with myself that, after all, it is the outsider who is the best judge; that we are most often severest upon ourselves; that if Philip finds certain high qualities in me, perhaps there is in me something exceptional. I even go so far as to draw up a little catalogue of my acts and achievements. I can recall men who have said much sillier things than I have ever said, and published much worse stuff than I have ever written. I repeat to myself the rather striking epigram I made at Smith's house last week, and I go back to the old gentleman from Andover who two years ago told me that there was something about me that reminded him of Oliver Wendell Holmes. By dint of much trying I work myself up into something of a glow; but it is all artificial, cerebral, incubated. The exaltation is momentary, the cold chill of fact overtakes me. There is no use in deceiving one's self. Philip is mistaken. I am not worthy.

But that day Philip rallied nobly to the situation. My little remark on strong language had hurt him, but he saw also that I was sorry to have hurt him, and he was sorry for me in turn. "I don't in the least mind your telling me what you think about the way we fellows talk," he said. "That's the advantage of having a man for one's friend, he is not afraid of telling you the truth even if it hurts. And then, if you wish to, you can fight back. You can't do that with a woman."

"Have you found that out for yourself!" I asked him.

He looked at me to see if again I was resorting to irony. But this time he found me sincere.

"Women!" Philip sniffed. "I have found it doesn't pay to talk seriously to a woman. There is really only one way of getting on with them, and that's jollying them. And the thicker you lay it on, the better." He put away his pipe and proffered me a cigarette. "I like to change off now and then. I have these made for me in a little Russian shop I discovered some time ago. They draw better than any cigarette I have ever smoked. Of course, there are women who are serious and all that. There are a lot in the postgraduate department and some in the optional literature courses. But you ought to see them! And such grinds. None of us fellows stands a ghost of a chance with them. They take notes all the time and read all the references and learn them by heart. You can't jolly *them*. They wouldn't know a joke if you led them up to one and told them what it meant. I think co-education is all played out, don't you? Home is the only place for women, anyhow. Do you like your cigarette?"

The Patient Observer, it may possibly have been gathered before this, is somewhat of a sentimentalist. He liked his cigarette very well, but through the blue haze he looked at Philip and could not help thinking of the time—only two short years ago—when he, the Patient Observer, with his own eyes saw Philip borrow a dollar from his mother before setting out for an ice-cream parlour in the company of two girl cousins. The Patient Observer has changed little in the last two years; his hair may be a little thinner and his knowledge of doctors' bills a little more complete. But in Philip of to-day he found it hard to recognise the Philip of two years ago. And the marvels of the law of growth which he thus saw exemplified moved the Patient Observer to throw open the gates of pent-up eloquence. He lit his pipe and began to discourse to Philip on the world, on life, and on a few things besides.

And when it was time for both of us to go to bed, Philip stood up and said, "I wish I came every day. You don't know what a bore it is, listening to that drool the 'profs' hand you out up there." His fervent young spirit would not be silent until, with one magnificent gesture, he had swept the tobacco jar to the floor and shattered two electric lamps. Then he went to his room and left me wondering at the vast mysteries that underlie the rough surface of the sophomore's soul.

IRWIN EDMAN

Flowers for a Professor's
Garden of Verses

FROM *Innocent Merriment*

Professor Irwin Edman, whose essay "Syrian Sophomores" appears earlier in this book, here comments feelingly in verse on a teacher's sad lot.

A TEACHER should impart what's true
At least what they allow him to;
A college teacher should not vex
His pupils with his thoughts on sex;
He should keep mum if he has odd
Views on the character of God.
He should dismiss as red inventions
All but the three well-known dimensions,
Not teaching logic, which might hurt
Young minds impeccably inert,
Nor ever question any truths
Their nurses taught these darling youths.
No skepticism—that might lead them
To use their heads if they should need them.
Only such views by housewives favored—
Be, teacher, be vanilla-flavored.
Make your lectures chocolate fudge
Fit to be nibbled by a judge;
Cookies sweet enough to dish up
Before a bon-bon loving bishop,
Or shall we say, an angel layer

To set before an upright mayor.
Then will your thoughts be sure to keep
Your students sound, and sound asleep.
And keep for you, though far from clever,
Your job—and what a job!—forever!

J. S. STEVENSON

Propaganda

FROM *The Yale Record*

⌂ *Everybody complains that college catalogues can make pretty dull reading. But it's like talk about the weather—nobody does anything about it.*

    Or, at least, nobody did until J. S. Stevenson suggested some revisions, in The Yale Record. *Here they are, with the streamlined, high-pressure, tail-fin approach. If it's good for General Motors . . . the conclusion should be obvious.*

GLANCING through some magazines last week-end, I was struck with the idea that Yale today in its traditional arch-conservatism is missing out on something really big going on in the world around it. Yale, like any University, has certain aims for herself and for her students, yet she does not convey these aims with any degree of inducement, compared with modern living. It would seem extremely likely to me that Yale in the future, in order to survive, will have to do a far better job of selling its ideas. Yale will either learn that it pays to advertise, or cease to exist.

For example, Yale's first problem must always be to bring students to her halls. Fifty years hence will see the following poster in high schools and prep schools all over the country:

SENIORS!!!

FOR QUICK RELIEF FROM THE
DRUDGERY OF WORK OR ARMED SERVICE

TRY

YALE

LARGE ROOMING FACILITIES   NIGHTLY ENTERTAINMENT
SUPERB CUISINE
APPROVED BY WOMAN'S HOME COMPANION

WRITE FOR OUR FREE BOOKLET ON RIOTS

Once a man is in Yale, three of the largest questions that must be answered will be then, as now, concerning his problems in the academic, social, and athletic fields. The advertising possibilities for getting men to take certain courses are extremely fertile. The Old Campus and college bulletin boards will undoubtedly look something like the following:

IT'S NEW! ENCHANTINGLY LOVELY!

REVAMPED ECONOMICS 12

THEORIES OF ADAM SMITH,

RICARDO, KEYNES

PLUS

THE EXCITING IDEAS OF MALTHUS ON

SEX AND POPULATION INCREASE

PLUS

LATEST DISCOVERIES IN MONETARY

THEORY AND FISCAL POLICY

ENJOY THE THOROUGH GENTLE ACTION OF

THIS NEVER-BEFORE OFFERED COURSE

SEE YOUR ADVISOR   DO IT TODAY

Or:

ASTRONOMY 49

RARE ANTIQUE IMPORTED TEXTS

& INSTRUCTORS

MORE STUDENTS THAN EVER BEFORE ARE

PASSING BECAUSE OF ASTRONOMY 49

89% AVERAGE GUARANTEED

NO OTHER COURSE CAN MAKE THAT

STATEMENT!!!

Or better still:

ENGLISH 21

BECAUSE . . .

In the field of social activities, the Yale Man's companionship will be competed for with a poster like this:

SMITH GIRLS

ROUNDER, FIRMER, MORE FULLY PACKED

OUT-PERFORM ALL OTHER BRANDS

1994 MODELS JUST OUT!

LIBERAL TRADE-IN ALLOWANCE

$2.00 DOWN—ALL YOUR LIFE TO PAY

NOW SHOWING IN THIRD DIMENSION

As far as athletics are concerned, football probably has the least problem, yet the Bowl is rarely filled. This clearly indicates that the pep rally as an advertising device has got to go. It will be replaced by ads of the following type:

BOTHERED BY POST-NASAL DRIP?
COME TO THE YALE BOWL AND SEE
J. OLIVAR AND HIS ELATING ELI ELEVEN
LISTEN TO THE MUSIC OF
K. WILSON AND HIS YALE BAND
CALL RAY TOMPKINS FOR RESERVATIONS

The Rugby team, on the other hand, has a real problem, one which will easily be solved, however, by use of the common jingle:

BE HAPPY, GO RUGBY
BE HAPPY, GO RUGBY TEAM
BE HAPPY, GO RUGBY
GO RUGBY TEAM TODAY!

Yale's best, though often most poorly attended spectator sport is chess. Their problem will be solved when they learn that the following can draw thousands:

TIRED? RUNDOWN? OVERWORKED?
IS YOUR ROOM TOO NOISY TO SLEEP IN?
COME OUT AND WATCH YALE CHESS
IN ACTION!

This is Yale of the future if there is to be any Yale at all. The change it will bring will be stupendous, colossal, terrific, magnificent, unequalled— different, anyway.

ROBERT PENN WARREN

The Life and Work of
Professor Roy Millen

FROM *Circus In The Attic*

⌂ *Poet, teacher, critic and Pulitzer Prize winner (All the King's Men) Robert Penn Warren has the capacity for showing in his writings that in any single action may be discovered the refined essence of a man's lifetime. He has done so, brilliantly, in this story of a professor and a student.*

Warren taught at Louisiana State University, and is a graduate of Vanderbilt, where he was founding editor of the Southern Review. *Currently, he is a professor of playwriting at the Yale Drama School.*

PROFESSOR Roy Millen had loved his wife devotedly, and now, in the spring of the year 1937, she was dead. He had not realized before how much she had meant to him, how his own life had described its orbit, as it were, within the steady and beneficent influence of her being. If she had dominated the course of his life, it had not been by isolated, individual acts of superior will, but rather by defining, subtly but more completely year after year, the very atmosphere he breathed. His position at the university, the long tranquil evenings at the bridge table with the light glinting subduedly on the exciting and rich designs of the royal cards, the friends at the table, the respectful greeting in the corridors and on the street, the very food he put into his mouth—all of these items had been defined by her. He had never protested against this, not even fleetingly, in the privacy of his own mind. Day after day, year after year, he had accepted it as part of the inevitable furniture of his life, just as he had accepted the sound of her voice and the expression of her face. If he felt anything, it was a kind of gratitude. Any little act he could do for her—and it comforted him now to remember that he had always tried to do the little things she wanted,

153

especially after her health failed—had only been the proper manifestation of his gratitude, or at least of his candid admission that she had made him what he was.

The self which he now was—the man with the carefully brushed tufts of white hair on each side of the pink and hygienic-looking bald skull, the rimless pince-nez with the black cord, the well-pressed but somewhat worn suits, blue or medium gray according to the season, the cleanly cut nails, the thoughts that came into his head—that self, too, had been defined by her. And during the twenty-odd years of his life with her, he had remembered more and more rarely the other self which he had been before his marriage. He did not like to remember that other time, for those years had been painful and long, so painful that even in recollection something of the distress of the old reality could revive within him. He had bent over the long rows of cotton, with the sun bearing down on his shoulders and the humid air swimming around him. He had clerked in crossroads stores. He had taught in the country schools of his native section, listening all day to the sullen or droning voices of the children and then tramping down some muddy road to his rented room in a tumble-down farmhouse. Later, long after those years were past, he would occasionally wonder, when the un-sought recollections came to him, what had sustained him, what hope had given him strength enough to go on. Looking back, he could not say. He could not remember what strength had been in him, or remember what he had hoped for, or expected. Certainly, he had not hoped for what he had actually found. Anyway, he told himself humbly, this was better than what he had hoped for. For he had scarcely known that there could be such a life as this.

By the time he was twenty-nine he had managed to get a degree from a small denominational college. For two years then, he had better teaching jobs, and saved enough to see him through a winter at the state university. When he was thirty-seven, he received a Ph.D. in English literature. That June day he stood on the platform of the auditorium, stooped and sweating under the black robe and colored hood, as though to their weight were added the weight of all the privations and distresses which had brought him to that moment, and his outstretched hand shook. That fall, quite un-expectedly, he got a small job teaching freshmen at the university. One of the regular instructors was ill, and the head of the department thriftily surmised that Millen would take the job for little or nothing. During the year the instructor died.

"Millen is a good steady man," Dr. Saunders, the head of the department, remarked to his daughter one day toward the end of the year. "It looks as if we might just keep him on another year until we can make a permanent appointment."

"Yes," Mildred Saunders said dutifully, abstractedly. She was a tallish woman, a little past thirty, with a spindly figure and plain features. Her habitual expression was kindly, however, and she had a quiet nature. A few weeks after her father's remark, she saw Millen at a faculty reception, miserable and lonely in a corner, and talked to him, remembering what her father had said. In ministering to his embarrassment and shyness, she forgot something of her own habitual diffidence. The following year, early in the session, when Dr. Saunders had Millen to his house on some piece of academic business, Mildred Saunders saw him and asked him to come again. He came more and more frequently during the year, to sit in the shadowed and dingy parlor, his bony hands with the bitten nails moving uneasily on his knees. In May he received a permanent appointment to his job, and Mildred Saunders announced her engagement to him. She had married him, and he had been devoted to her, and now she was dead.

She had died quite suddenly and ironically, just at the time when, after years of ill health, she seemed to be getting well and strong again, and they were planning to go away on a year's leave. They were planning to go to England, where he could work in one of the great English libraries and finish his book. Six years before, he had had a leave, and they had planned to go to England to work on the book, but they had gone, in the end, to southern California. He had not protested, even to himself, at the change in plans; in fact he had suggested the change. The cold, damp climate of Millersburg in winter had always been bad for his wife's asthma and neuralgia, and England might be worse. And his wife's cousins in Los Angeles could be company for her while he worked on his book. And there were some very nice libraries in California. Everybody knew that.

She had seemed better at first in California, but then, despite everything, her health had taken a turn for the worse. She had been in the hospital, and the doctors had done all they could, and the cousins had been helpful and considerate. Some days they had even gone to the hospital and he had been able to stay at home and work or go to the library. But she had been very ill, and he knew what to do for her—better, he told himself, than the cousins or even the nurses. Even after she was able to leave the hospital and go back to Millersburg she was never really well. But she was very patient and rarely lost her temper with him. Sometimes, when he sat beside her bed—for during that period she was confined to her bed almost half of the time—she would reach out to touch his hand and say: "Just leave me alone, Roy, and go work on your book. You ought to work on your book, Roy. I don't mind being alone. I've gotten used to being alone." He would say that it didn't matter, or that it was moving along nicely, that he had done quite a bit lately. Or she would say: "I'm sorry we have to spend so

much money on me, Roy, when you want to go away to work on your book."
Then he would try to comfort her.

She was dead now, but there was the book left for him. I have my book
to do, at least I have that, he concluded as soon as the first shock of grief
had worn off and he had begun to search in himself for some center of
meaning for his life. Then, day after day, as he came to accept the fact of
his loss and his mind dwelt more and more on his book, a kind of modest
excitement grew within him—an excitement so pleasurable that once or
twice, remembering in the midst of it his wife's death, he was filled with a
sense of shame and remorse.

He made his plans to go abroad, to England, to work in the libraries
there, as he and his wife had planned. It was what she would have him do, he
told himself. And the book would be a kind of monument to her. He would
dedicate the book to her. As he walked slowly back from the campus to his
house in the late afternoons or early evenings of spring, he would try to
compose the dedication, saying the words aloud to himself as he looked up
at the paling, peach-colored sky beyond the newly leafed branches. He had
decided to sail in June, as soon as he could leave after commencement.

"I hear you're going away for a year, Professor Millen," Tom Howell
said, standing respectfully before Professor Millen's office desk. Then he
added, in a dutiful tone, "To work on your book."

"Yes," Professor Millen said, "to work on my book." Then, as though
recollecting himself, he made a little gesture toward the chair in front of
the desk, and said, "Won't you have a seat, Howell?"

"Are you going to finish it in a year?" Howell asked, and sat down.

"I still have a little research to do. I have to settle a few points—points
which can't be settled in libraries in this country. I have to do some work
yet in one of the great English libraries." Professor Millen paused, looking
over the green lawn outside his office window. "But I'll get it written within
the year. Practically everything is in order. Though, of course," he paused
again, looking at Tom Howell, who listened respectfully and with what
seemed to be interest, "I'll have to do a good deal of retouching—style and
so on, you know—" he waved his hand modestly in the air, "when I get
back."

"I'm hoping—" the boy hesitated, fumbling in his pocket to draw out a
folded paper, "I'm hoping to be able to go abroad next year. If I can make
it. That's what I wanted to see you about, Professor Millen."

"Anything I can do, I'll be glad to do."

"It's a scholarship. A French scholarship, and I was hoping you'd recommend me. I've had a lot of work with you, and all. The French Department will recommend me, but I've done my minor in English, you know.
What you'd say would count a lot."

"Howell," Professor Millen said, judicially putting the tips of his fingers together and inspecting the boy, "I've never had a better student than you are. Possibly never one as good. I'll say that in my recommendation. I'll write a strong one." He felt his enthusiasm mounting as he spoke, and a warmth suffused him as though at the prospect of some piece of happiness, some success, for himself.

"I certainly appreciate it," the boy said. "This is about the only thing I've got in sight for next year, and I'm graduating. Oh, I reckon I could get a little teaching job or something for a year or two to save up some money to go on. I don't think I ought to ask my family for any more—they've been swell, putting me through college and giving me that trip to France two years back—"

"Yes, yes," Professor Millen said abstractedly, "oh, yes, you did go over one summer, didn't you?"

"Oh, that was just for fun," Howell said, "but this time it would be for work. And when I get back I ought to be able to get a pretty good job so I could save enough to get my Ph.D. quick. Up East."

"A year of study in France will be a fine opportunity," Professor Millen said. That enthusiasm and warmth which had filled him like a promise of happiness was waning now, he did not know why. He wished the boy would get up and go and leave him alone.

"Oh, it'll be an opportunity," Howell agreed, "and I'm not going to waste it. The work'll be fun, and there ought to be a little fun besides. I was in Paris for two weeks—and you know how Paris is, it sort of knocks you off your feet. You've been there?"

"Yes, yes," Professor Millen said hurriedly, impersonally, almost impatiently, averting his face from the boy and looking off across the patch of lawn, wondering why he had lied, why he had told the boy he had been to Paris. He watched some students, two boys and a girl, who moved across the sunlit, open space. They moved lingeringly. It seemed that they would never be across that bright, open space of green where the sun was. Then they were gone, hidden by the screen of foliage.

Professor Millen turned and brought his gaze to rest again on the boy. The boy was leaning forward, his face smiling. Professor Millen saw, as for the first time, the blond, crisp hair combed back from the square forehead, the confident gaze of the blue eyes, the comfortable, confident way the coat hung from the good shoulders.

The boy stood up. "I've stayed too long. I know you've got a lot of work to do."

"No," Professor Millen said.

"And I certainly appreciate your recommendation. The address of the scholarship committee is on here," he said, and laid a printed sheet on the desk. "That's the circular, and all the information."

"I'll attend to it right away," Professor Millen said.

"Thank you," the boy said, and was gone.

For a few minutes Professor Millen sat here, his eyes on the bare wall opposite his desk. Then he read the circular. He laid it back on the desk and pressed a button. When the secretary came in, he handed her the printed sheet. "The address is on that," he said, and waited while she copied it. Then he said, "I'll give you the letter." He studied the bare wall for a moment, then began: "Gentlemen. I can truthfully say that I take the most sincere pleasure in recommending to you Mr. Thomas Howell. In my long career as a teacher I have never had a better student. He has an acute and penetrating intelligence, and, as is so often not the case with young men of his capacity, the patience and honesty of a true scholar. I am sure that if he is appointed to—" He hesitated, looking at the wall. "I am sure that—" he said at last, then stopped.

The secretary, her pencil poised above her pad, waited while Professor Millen seemed to withdraw, to sink within himself. Her foot made a slight reproachful scraping sound as she changed her position in the chair. She, too, began to look out the window, where Professor Millen's gaze now was fixed.

"That's all—all for the present," Professor Millen said, suddenly. "Just hold that and I'll finish later. I've just thought—" he managed to look directly at her—"of something else I've got to do. There's something else."

After the secretary had left the office, closing the door softly behind her, he did not move for some time. Then he again looked out the window. The shadows were lengthening over the smooth lawn. The faintest premonitory flush was touching the puffs of white cloud visible toward the top of his window. Before long now he would be going home. He picked up the circular. He read it again, very carefully, dwelling on it almost painfully, as though he were an illiterate trying to extort some secret from the words. He lifted his eyes from the sheet and stared at the chair where the boy had sat leaning forward, the pleasure shining on his clear, handsome face, the good coat riding easy on his shoulders, saying, "—you know how Paris is, it sorts of knocks you off your feet. You've been there?"

Professor Millen let the circular slip from his lap to the floor. Then, decisively, he reached into the drawer of his desk and took out a sheet of paper. He wrote rapidly in his large, firm script:

GENTLEMEN:

I have been asked to recommend Mr. Thomas Howell to you for a scholarship for study in France. As you will observe from a transcript of his academic record, with which no doubt you have been provided, he has made the grade of *A* in all of his work in the English department of this institution, and I understand that his grades in French (his major subject) have been very high. This achievement, of course, deserves consideration, but candor compels me to say that a superficial facility and cleverness seem to characterize his mind. I do not wish to prejudice the committee against his case, and I may be wrong in my estimate; certainly, I hope that the committee will consider him very carefully. But I do feel that he lacks solidity of character, the spirit of patient inquiry, and what might be termed the philosophical bent.

Very respectfully yours,

ROY MILLEN,

Professor of English.

Without looking up, he addressed an envelope hurriedly, the pen making a dry, scratching sound. Then he blotted and stamped the envelope, inserted the sheet, put the letter into his pocket, picked up his hat, and left the office. He would, he remembered, pass a postbox on his way home.

G. I.

FROM *The New Yorker*

The author of The Man in the Grey Flannel Suit *here turns his attention to those old-young men of Cassino, North Africa, Okinawa, who went back to school. They were, for the most part, disoriented, too quickly and too destructively come of age, the possessors of skills in the arts of war, men who had looked on a living nightmare before fully growing out of the dreams of childhood. Returned as students to the academic world, their adjustment was—in a sense—backwards, to adolescence. Sloane Wilson, who served in the Navy during World War II and now teaches at the University of Buffalo, tells us in this story about these men and about those years immediately after the war when they returned to our campuses.*

WHEN I first got out of the service, I went home to look over the businesses which were waiting for me to come and show them how to do things. There didn't seem to be many. The four years I'd been in the service had been largely spent in command of various kinds of very small ships, and upon my discharge I found myself suited only for the job of yacht captain. Since neither my wife nor I felt that yachting offered a very promising career, it was obvious that I would have to start at the bottom of something and work up. I didn't mind the idea too much, and for a few weeks I was content to sit around celebrating the fact that I was home. However, after almost four years of being an officer, I'd become used to automatic advancement, and while I waited for a job to materialize, it made me uncomfortable to realize that each day was not necessarily bringing nearer a raise in pay and position. Finally I got so nervous that my wife suggested I go back to college to finish the courses I had painlessly if patriotically left early in 1942. The idea appealed to me, for in the life of a student, as well as in the life of a naval officer, time is almost automatically progress. Harvard agreed to take me back, and very shortly we moved into an apartment in a building adjoining the Yard in Cambridge. I filled out all the Army application forms for educational benefits under the GI Bill of Rights, which demanded not only a marriage certificate but a witnessed and notarized statement that my wife and I were living together. My wife got a job and I got three pairs of gray flannel trousers, a tweed sport coat, and a green baize book bag.

On registration day I set off across the cloistered Yard. My feelings were a mixture of the misty-eyed nostalgia of the returned alumnus and the practical jauntiness of the undergraduate, topped by a slight sense of the ridiculous. The paths were crowded with laughing boys, and I found myself exaggerating their youth. By the time I reached the steps of University Hall, I had talked myself into thinking I was a patriarch. Just before I opened the door to go in, I was overjoyed to meet a contemporary, Tom Spencer, a guy I had known in the Philippines. He'd been wounded six months before the fighting ended and had been sent home with a bad leg. During the long nights of the war, he had arrived at the conclusion that true wisdom is impossible without a thorough knowledge of physics. I knew about this because I had spent many hours in officers' clubs talking to him about it, but I had thought his plans were as vague and evanescent as those we all had had out in the Pacific. Besides, he wasn't a Harvard man, so it was a big surprise to meet him there on the steps of University Hall. He was walking with a cane. We greeted each other warmly. He told me that he was living with his wife and two children in an apartment not far from mine. His wife also was working. As soon as we got through expressing our joy at seeing each other, he asked me what courses I had decided to take. I told him I was going to complete the number of courses I still needed for a degree by studying history. All my scholastic life I'd avoided history because of its reputation as a time-consuming subject that demanded unusual feats of memory, and now I thought I might as well fill in this gap in my education. Tom immediately launched a drive to convince me that I should start all over again and abandon liberal arts for a physics diploma, but I stepped on that idea right away. He accepted defeat gracefully, and we started through the enrollment program together.

Registration was quite a job. The forms and blanks never quite seemed to apply to Tom and me, and we kept having to ask one of the clerks how to fill them out. First of all, we had to explain that we did not want to live in the college dormitories. We were told that the only students who did not have to live in dormitories were local boys who lived with their families. We said we *were* living with our families, and the clerk said that was all right, then. The next problem was filling out the form that called for the name of "parent or guardian." At this point I was about to write down a long explanation, but Tom said a friend of his who'd been in his outfit in the Philippines and had entered Harvard under the GI Bill of Rights a term earlier had told him it would be much easier merely to list our wives as our guardians. Then the bills, official notices, and so on would automatically come to our homes, and everything would be all right. I reluctantly wrote down my wife's name. I could picture the dean having grave talks with her if I got into trouble.

After we'd filled out all the forms, Tom and I stopped at a table where a man asked us what athletics we planned to go out for. I said none. I figured my wife would consider it a little too much if I told her I couldn't help her with the shopping because I had to go down and try out for the class baseball team. Next we were asked to subscribe to a dance designed to introduce undergraduates to Radcliffe students. I balked at this, too. By the time I was all enrolled, I felt rather shaken.

I took Tom back to the apartment to have lunch with my wife and me. My wife's lunch period is only three-quarters of an hour, and we had to hurry so she could get back to her job. Tom said he usually got lunch and did the dishes for his wife, but my wife said Tom and I must have a lot to talk about and she insisted on doing the cooking herself. Tom and I sat at the table while she waited on us, and when we were through, she put on her coat and I walked down to the car with her. I helped her in, watched her drive off, and walked back to the apartment. I didn't have any classes till ten the next morning.

My first class the next day was Russian history. The professor began with the early days, before the first czar, and it was pretty interesting. Behind me sat a sallow youth with glasses who kept trying to tell a short boy in the seat next to mine about a date he had had the night before with a girl named Betty. He said he had kissed her. The professor talked on about how the various Russian states had been incorporated. The short boy beside me said he didn't know that Betty could be kissed. I took notes.

After the class was over, I met Tom outside the Physics Building. Neither of us had a class for another hour, and we walked over to the Square. We started to go into a drugstore full of hatless boys drinking cokes.

"The hell with it," Tom said. "Let's go get a beer."

We found a nice, gloomy little bar next to a garage. Over the shelves of whisky bottles were hung enlarged photographs of all the football teams from 1902 on. The bartender was a nice, old-fashioned-looking man with his hair combed over his forehead.

"Two cold ones," Tom said.

We climbed on stools and put our books down on the bar. The bartender set the dripping beers before us, and we moved our books to the floor. We drank our beers and ordered two more. We drank them slowly.

The bartender wiped some glasses. When he had finished, he leaned on the bar and seemed to want to join our conversation.

"What did you think of the last Yale game?" he asked finally.

"I don't know," Tom said. "I didn't see it." That seemed to discourage the bartender, who began polishing the beer spigots.

When we'd emptied our glasses, Tom asked me, "How much does your wife make?"

"Thirty dollars a week," I said.

"Mine makes thirty-five," Tom said. "The beers are on me."

By Faculty Action

FROM *The New Yorker*

ⵣ *James Reid Parker has specialized in deceptively gentle-seeming stories of faculty lives and mores, about which he learned at first hand during his years of teaching college English. In this story of a faculty committee checking off a list of freshmen students who have not made the grade, Parker's understated comment (that the student must be tailored to the curriculum, not the curriculum to the student) perhaps goes further to explain our current concern with collegiate training than do many louder-voiced pronouncements.*

WHY tradition ordained that faculty meetings should take place in the Jedediah Gryce Science Library nobody seemed to know. Even in that very building, the architectural sore spot of the college, there were more comfortable retreats than the particular room, panelled in dingy walnut and badly lighted, which was reserved for faculty meetings. These grim assemblies had been held in the library for a century, and it would have required a complex rigmarole of committees and subcommittees—for such is the academic custom—to draft a measure proposing a change, a measure which could be submitted to the faculty for consideration, argument, and perhaps eventual adoption. As yet no one had cared to turn the wheels of this frightening machinery.

When young Dr. Sargent came to this room one day in February, he did so in response to a summons which had said, "There will be a meeting on Friday afternoon in the Jedediah Gryce Science Library at four o'clock to determine by faculty action whether the deficient students whose names appear on the enclosed list are to be warned, suspended, or expelled by the Administration. Your presence is urgently requested."

Sargent, who was in his first year of teaching, had already noticed that all messages to the faculty were sonorous, and for some reason suggestive of impending doom. He reflected that this one sounded like an invitation to the *Parlement de Paris* for the purpose of clearing up some little matters relating to the guillotine.

Ever since he had received the summons, he had been puzzled. Two of the proscribed students were enrolled in courses that he was giving. Neither man was brilliant, certainly, and one was extremely stupid. The other was intelligent, although his approach to the art of study had been more emotional than judicious. Sargent knew Peterson and Logan fairly well. Peterson, who had been baffled from the first by work he was not equipped to do, had not been a problem. Sargent was merely sorry that Peterson had elected a curriculum which could never be anything better than miasma to him. It was hard to generalize about Logan, except to say that he studied enthusiastically everything that he liked, ignoring the work that didn't interest him. With Sargent alone he had struck a middle course, refraining from wholehearted enthusiasm or wholehearted ennui. Knowing that Logan had bolted to extremes elsewhere, Sargent was anxious to learn how this particular case history was going to be thrashed out. In reviewing Logan's scholastic status, the other instructors and professors would certainly contribute helpful material, and Sargent felt that if something useful could be done, during this gathering of the faculty clan, to establish Logan's general intellectual equipment and his special needs the depressing atmosphere of the Jedediah Gryce Science Library might be forgiven to a certain extent.

Peterson was checked off early in the session. Glad to see him weeded out by general consent, Sargent voted "yes" to the expulsion without remorse. As the meeting went along, however, Sargent was a little troubled to find that the consent was almost as general in all other cases. Failure in one course meant "liability to warning;" failure in two, "liability to suspension;" failure in three, "liability to expulsion." The Dean, reading the names, announced the liability in question, and the faculty, after a few minutes of rather malapropos discussion, voted. Sargent grew very tired of such phrases as "not good college material," "something of a dreamer, and my department isn't interested in dreamers, ha-ha-ha," "inclined to loaf," "ability to edit a college newspaper does not condone an inability to grasp the fundamentals of 'Fluids and Heat,'" and so on.

In each case, Sargent was consumed by a desire to know more than he heard. *Why* inclined to loaf? *Why* unable to grasp "Fluids and Heat"? It seemed so idiotic not to feel around for reasons. Obviously it was logical to check off someone who was not only incompetent in "Fluids and Heat" but in everything else. Just as obviously, it was illogical to take similar action with someone who was incompetent only in certain fields. After about an hour, it dawned upon him that the problem of adjustment and correction was regarded as far less pressing than the problem of getting through the list.

He heard the tumbrils coming to take away Charles Gardiner Logan, Jr., and the certainty of the verdict oppressed him.

"Logan," said the Dean. "C. G. Logan, Jr., liable to expulsion."

Logan, it developed, had failed three subjects, had done moderately well under Sargent, and had earned an excellent record in biology and chemistry.

Sargent, feeling a little conspicuous in the bright cloak of the Scarlet Pimpernel, went into battle on the side of Logan, biology, and chemistry. "A very interesting case. Very," he said.

"Logan has failed in three of his courses during the first semester," the President pointed out. He was not officiating at the meeting, which came under the jurisdiction of the Dean.

"He impresses me as being a remarkable student," said Sargent, conscious that he resembled a small boy who has just said something particularly defiant in front of the whole family. "May I call the attention of the faculty to his eminently satisfactory status in chemistry and biology?" (Sargent felt that he might win his point if he spoke the patois.)

The departments of chemistry and biology, who had been prepared to give Logan up as a lost cause, sat up now and confirmed Sargent vigorously. The Dean had not expected Logan, C. G., to provoke controversy, and was mildly surprised. "Dr. Sargent seems to feel that Logan is a not unpromising student," he announced, thinking it his duty to say something juicy and to the point.

"It would be interesting to know *why* Logan is deficient in certain subjects and not in others," Sargent persisted. "This marks only the first half of his freshman year, and I don't think it's too late for us to study his curriculum, and alter it. Possibly a change of course altogether would be the best thing, in Logan's case. I'm not sure. However, I should like to place myself on record as opposing the expulsion of a student of Logan's calibre when he has been with us for the comparatively brief period of one semester."

Exhausted by the strain of assuming the rôle of saviour, and by the business of presenting his defence with academic stateliness, Sargent sat back in his tall, uncomfortable chair and took a deep breath.

"The first semester of the freshman year is in the nature of a proving ground," interposed the President. "We must expect a certain number of students, of whom Logan seems to be representative, to suffer from our method of discarding."

Sargent murmured to himself. An august member of the faculty, old Dr. Mabbott, gracefully brandished his sword in support of tradition. "Mr.

Logan has revealed to me none of the recognized symptoms of an ability to—er—comprehend the intricacies of history, or to perform any similar operation which requires the human brain to—um—function. I fear that this lends credence to our president's appraisal of Mr. Logan's talents."

Confident that this utterance would bring the whole unpleasantness to an end—which, indeed, it did—Dr. Mabbott began to chat in an undertone with the professor next to him. They pursued a more interesting topic.

The Dean requested those who favored the expulsion of Charles Gardiner Logan, Jr., to say "yes." Biology and chemistry obeyed the command of precedent, and the guillotine fell. "Those opposed, 'no,' " he added for Sargent's benefit.

"No," said Sargent wearily.

RANDOLPH BOURNE

The President of
Pluribus University

FROM The History of a Literary Radical

From the vantage point—or is it such a vantage?—of some four decades, it is difficult to recall the ardent radicalism which imbued a segment of college youth in the days immediately preceding the First World War. It is hard, too, to comprehend the degree to which their universities were the testing grounds for their feckless idealism, to grasp the extent to which their rebellion was against cynicism—rather than a cynical pose of seeing through what they deemed to be false. Whether or not they were misguided, they were certainly more vocal than the so-called silent generation, and frequently exercised their academic freedom to attack those who were their immediate power figures, father symbols if you will, the very faculty which taught them. Seen in this perspective, even the late Nicholas Murray Butler, probably the prototype of the protagonist in the following savagely satiric selection, might have accorded it an indulgent nod.

Butler was chief executive of Columbia University from 1902 to 1945. Randolph Bourne received his bachelor's and master's degrees there during Butler's tenure. He was the spokesman for the young anti-war radicals during the early days of the First World War and the influence of his writing on his own generation was deep. He died young, at thirty-two (in 1918), and with him died a strong and rather lonely protesting voice, one of the most powerful of his time, that spoke out for the courage "to go down unfamiliar ways in search of truth."

WHEN Dr. Alexander Mackintosh Butcher was elected to the presidency of Pluribus University ten years ago, there was general agreement that in selecting a man who was not only a distinguished educator but an executive of marked business ability the trustees had done honor to them-

168

selves and their university as well as to the new president. For Dr. Butcher had that peculiar genius which would have made him as successful in Wall Street or in a governor's chair as in the classroom. Every alumnus of Pluribus knows the story told of the young Alexander Mackintosh Butcher, standing at the age of twenty-two at the threshold of a career. Eager, energetic, with a brilliant scholastic record behind him, it was difficult to decide into what profession he should throw his powerful talents. To his beloved and aged president the young man went for counsel. "My boy," said the good old man, "remember that no profession offers nobler opportunities for service to humanity than that of education." And what should he teach? "Philosophy is the noblest study of man." And a professor of philosophy the young Butcher speedily became.

Those who were so fortunate as to study philosophy under him at Pluribus will never forget how uncompromisingly he preached absolute idealism, the Good, the True and the Beautiful, or how witheringly he excoriated the mushroom philosophies which were springing up to challenge the eternal verities. I have heard his old students remark the secret anguish which must have been his when later, as president of the university, he was compelled to entertain the famous Swiss philosopher, Monsfilius, whose alluring empiricism was taking the philosophic world by storm.

Dr. Butcher's philosophic acuteness is only equaled by his political rectitude. Indeed, it is as philosopher-politician that he holds the unique place he does in our American life, injecting into the petty issues of the political arena the immutable principles of Truth. Early conscious of his duty as a man and a citizen, he joined the historic party which had earned the eternal allegiance of the nation by rescuing it from slavery. By faithful service to the chiefs of his state organization, first under the powerful Flatt, and later under the well-known Harnes, himself college-bred and a political philosopher of no mean merit, the young Dr. Butcher worked his way up through ward captain to the position of district leader. The practical example of Dr. Butcher, the scholar and educator, leaving the peace of his academic shades to carry the banner in the service of his party ideals of Prosperity and Protection has been an inspiration to thousands of educated men in these days of civic cowardice. When, three years ago, his long and faithful services were rewarded by the honor of second place on the Presidential ticket which swept the great states of Mormonia and Green Mountain, there were none of his friends and admirers who felt that the distinction was undeserved.

President Butcher is frequently called into the councils of the party whenever there are resolutions to be drawn up or statements of philosophic principle to be issued. He is in great demand also as chairman of state conventions, which his rare academic distinction lifts far above the usual level of such affairs. It was at one of these conventions that he made the memorable speech in which he drew the analogy between the immutability of Anglo-Saxon political institutions and the multiplication table. To the applause of the keen and hard-headed business men and lawyers who sat as delegates under him, he scored with matchless satire the idea of progress in politics, and demonstrated to their complete satisfaction that it was as absurd to tinker with the fundamentals of our political system as it would be to construct a new arithmetic. In such characteristic wisdom we have the intellectual caliber of the man.

This brilliant and profound address came only as the fruit of a lifetime of thought on political philosophy. President Butcher's treatise on "Why We Should Never Change Any Form of Government" has been worth more to thoughtful men than thousands of sermons on civic righteousness. No one who has ever heard President Butcher's rotund voice discuss in a public address "those ideas and practices which have been tried and tested by a thousand years of experience" will ever allow his mind to dwell again on the progressive and disintegrating tendencies of the day, nor will we have the heart again to challenge on any subject the "decent respect for the common opinions of mankind."

President Butcher's social philosophy is as sound as his political. The flexibility of his mind is shown in the fact that, although an immutabilist in politics, he is a staunch Darwinian in sociology. Himself triumphantly fit, he never wearies of expressing his robust contempt for the unfit who encumber the earth. His essay on "The Insurrection of the Maladjusted" is already a classic in American literature. The trenchant attack on modern social movements as the impudent revolt of the unfit against those who, by their personal merits and industry, have, like himself, achieved success, has been a grateful bulwark to thousands who might otherwise have been swept sentimentally from their moorings by those false guides who erect their own weakness and failure into a criticism of society.

Dr. Butcher's literary eminence has not only won him a chair in the American Academy of All the Arts, Sciences, and Philosophies, but has made him almost as well known abroad as at home. He has lectured before the learned societies of Lisbon on "The American at Home," and he has a wide circle of acquaintances in every capital in Europe. Most of the foreign universities have awarded him honorary degrees. In spite of his stout Americanism, Dr. Butcher has one of the most cosmopolitan of minds. His essay on "The Cosmopolitan Intellect" has been translated into every civilized language. With his admired friend, Owen Griffith, he has collaborated in the latter's endeavor to beat the swords of industrial exploitation into the ploughshares of universal peace. He has served in numerous capacities on Griffith's many peace boards and foundations, and has advised him widely and well how to distribute his millions so as to prevent the recurrence of war in future centuries.

Let it not be thought that, in recounting President Butcher's public life and services, I am minimizing his distinction as a university administrator. As executive of one of the largest universities in America, he has raised the position of college president to a dignity surpassed by scarcely any office except President of the United States. The splendid $125,000 mansion which President Butcher had the trustees of Pluribus build for him on the heights overlooking the city, where he entertains distinguished foreign guests with all the pomp worthy of his high office, is the precise measure both of the majesty with which he has endowed the hitherto relatively humble position, and the appreciation of a grateful university. The relations between President Butcher and the trustees of Pluribus have always been of the most beautiful nature. The warm and profound intellectual sympathy which he feels for the methods and practices of the financial and corporate world, and the extensive personal affiliations he has formed with its leaders, have made it possible to leave in his hands a large measure of absolute authority. Huge endowments have made Pluribus under President Butcher's rule one of the wealthiest of our higher institutions of learning. With a rare intuitive response to the spirit of the time, the President has labored to make it the biggest and most comprehensive of its kind. Already its schools are numbered by the dozens, its buildings by the scores, its instructors by the hundreds, its students by the thousands, its income by the millions, and its possessions by the tens of millions.

None who have seen President Butcher in the commencement exercises of Pluribus can ever forget the impressiveness of the spectacle. His resemblance to Henry VIII is more marked now that he has donned the crimson gown and flat hat of the famous English university which gave him the degree of LL.D. Seated in a high-backed chair—the historic chair of the first colonial president of Pluribus—surrounded by tier upon tier of his retinue of the thousand professors of the university, President Alexander Mackintosh Butcher presents the degrees, and in his emphatic voice warns the five thousand graduates before him against everything new, everything untried, everything untested.

Only one office could tempt President Butcher from his high estate. Yet even those enthusiastic alumni and those devoted professors who long to see him President of the United States have little hope of tempting him from his duties to his alma mater. Having set his hand to the plough, he must see Pluribus through her harvest season, and may God prosper the work! So, beloved of all, alumni and instructors alike, the idol of the undergraduates, a national oracle of Prosperity and Peace, President Butcher passes to a green old age, a truly Olympian figure of the time.

OGDEN NASH

Between Classes

FROM *College Humor*

Rambling, stumbling couplets with outrageous rhyme are the hallmark of Ogden Nash, one of America's top-ranking humorists, whose whimsical and sophisticated verse has never been successfully imitated. A perspicacious critic once said, of the man and his nefarious work, "Ogden Nash is secure in his possession of all the best and worst rhymes outside of the rhyming dictionary." Twentieth Century Authors restricts its comments on his education to "studied at Harvard, 1921"—as though disclaiming responsibility for any consequences. Nash, himself, fills out the record with this auto-biographical poem.

OH, LISTEN to the creed of one who never even sniffed the aroma
Of a diploma;
Oh, hark, to the philosophy of a mentally undeveloped person (me)
Who didn't get within several probations of a degree;
Who departed early from the campus
Thereby breaking the hearts of his ma, his pa, his two grandmas and his two grandpus;
Who learned practically nothing during his sojourn at one of the country's prominent cultural joints
Save the following points:
First,
    That debtors are swell forgebtors.
    While the friend who to you money has lent
    Will remember it world without ent.
Second,
    That every fresh semester
    Brings with it its own fresh disester.

Third,
> That both sports clothes and décolleté
> Look quite odd when worn by ladies of the fécolleté.

Fourth,
> That trying to make a quarter do the work of a dollar
> Is like trying to get a sixteen neck into a fifteen collar.

Fifth,
> That—name of a name of a name of a name of a name!
> One should never bet real money on even the most sewed-up game.

Sixth,
> That débutantes are simply overjoyed
> To be thought hard-boiled when as a matter of fact they are only
>   Freud.

Seventh,
> That most inhabitants of dormitories
> Are splendid candidates for reformitories.

Eighth,
> That while any attempt by an undergraduate to tell the truth
>   about undergraduates is regarded as calumny
> By furious alumny
> Still, though the W. C. T. U. and the Board of Prohibition,
>   Temperance and Public Morals to hear it will be amazed,
> There is a lot more hell talked about than raised.

Ninth,
> That one's fellows rightly consider one an ass
> Should one let oneself in for a nine o'clock class—also that,

Tenth,
> The most important of one's objects
> Is to select one's courses from among the less difficult sobjects.

Eleventh,
> That alcohol is an intoxicant
> And therefore gin can often do what Moxie can't.

Twelfth,
> That Apaches and Cherokees and Choctaws
> Are nothing but amiable old S. P. C. A. agents when compared to
>   deans and proctaws.

Thirteenth and last,
> That anybody who spends even a week at any university and can't
>   learn more than this
> Deserves to be locked in a miniature golf course with one crooning
>   Eskimo, one epileptic Bantu, and one backgammon-minded
>   Swiss.

First Year Med

FROM *Arrowsmith*

There is a dichotomous aspect to the works of Sinclair Lewis: his earlier novels were biting critiques of all that he found vulgar, tawdry and unworthy in American life—which was just about everything; his later books, generally deemed less important, in many cases glorified the very attitudes and activities his earlier work scorned.

Arrowsmith, from which this selection is taken, was published in 1925 and is still considered one of the outstanding explorations in fiction of medical education and practice. Lewis was offered a Pulitzer Prize for the book in 1926, but refused it. In 1930, he became the first American to win the Nobel Prize. Here we see young Martin Arrowsmith in his first year at medical school.

IN COLLEGE Martin had been a "barb"—he had not belonged to a Greek Letter secret society. He had been "rushed," but he had resented the condescension of the aristocracy of men from the larger cities. Now that most of his Arts classmates had departed to insurance offices, law schools, and banks, he was lonely, and tempted by an invitation from Digamma Pi, the chief medical fraternity.

Digamma Pi was a lively boarding-house with a billiard table and low prices. Rough and amiable noises came from it at night, and a good deal of singing about When I Die Don't Bury Me at All; yet for three years Digams had won the valedictory and the Hugh Loizeau Medal in Experimental Surgery. This autumn the Digams elected Ira Hinkley, because they had been gaining a reputation for dissipation—girls were said to have been smuggled in late at night—and no company which included the Reverend Mr. Hinkley could possibly be taken by the Dean as immoral, which was an advantage if they were to continue comfortably immoral.

Martin had prized the independence of his solitary room. In a fraternity,

174

all tennis rackets, trousers, and opinions are held in common. When Ira found that Martin was hesitating, he insisted, "Oh, come on in! Digam needs you. You do study hard—I'll say that for you—and think what a chance you'll have to influence The Fellows for good."

(On all occasions, Ira referred to his classmates as The Fellows, and frequently he used the term in prayers at the Y. M. C. A.)

"I don't want to influence anybody. I want to learn the doctor trade and make six thousand dollars a year."

"My boy, if you only knew how foolish you sound when you try to be cynical! When you're as old as I am, you'll understand that the glory of being a doctor is that you can teach folks high ideals while you soothe their tortured bodies."

"Suppose they don't want my particular brand of high ideals?"

"Mart, have I got to stop and pray with you?"

"No! Quit! Honestly, Hinkley, of all the Christians I ever met you take the rottenest advantages. You can lick anybody in the class, and when I think of how you're going to bully the poor heathen when you get to be a missionary, and make the kids put on breeches, and marry off all the happy lovers to the wrong people, I could bawl!"

The prospect of leaving his sheltered den for the patronage of the Reverend Mr. Hinkley was intolerable. It was not till Angus Duer accepted election to Digamma Pi that Martin himself came in.

Duer was one of the few among Martin's classmates in the academic course who had gone with him to the Winnemac medical school. Duer had been the valedictorian. He was a silent, sharp-faced, curly-headed, rather handsome young man, and he never squandered an hour or a good impulse. So brilliant was his work in biology and chemistry that a Chicago surgeon had promised him a place in his clinic. Martin compared Angus Duer to a razor blade on a January morning; he hated him, was uncomfortable with him, and envied him. He knew that in biology Duer had been too busy passing examinations to ponder, to get any concept of biology as a whole. He knew that Duer was a tricky chemist, who neatly and swiftly completed the experiments demanded by the course and never ventured on original experiments which, leading him into a confused land of wondering, might bring him to glory or disaster. He was sure that Duer cultivated his manner of chill efficiency to impress instructors. Yet the man stood out so bleakly from a mass of students who could neither complete their experiments nor ponder nor do anything save smoke pipes and watch football-practice that Martin loved him while he hated him, and almost meekly he followed him into Digamma Pi.

Martin, Ira Hinkley, Angus Duer, Clif Clawson, the meaty class jester, and one "Fatty" Pfaff were initiated into Digamma Pi together. It was a noisy and rather painful performance, which included smelling asafetida. Martin was bored, but Fatty Pfaff was in squeaking, billowing, gasping terror.

Fatty was of all the new Freshmen candidates the most useful to Digamma Pi. He was planned by nature to be a butt. He looked like a distended hot-water bottle; he was magnificently imbecile; he believed everything, he knew nothing, he could memorize nothing; and anxiously he forgave the men who got through the vacant hours by playing jokes upon him. They persuaded him that mustard plasters were excellent for colds—solicitously they gathered about him, affixed an enormous plaster to his back, and afterward fondly removed it. They concealed the ear of a cadaver in his nice, clean, new pocket handkerchief when he went to Sunday supper at the house of a girl cousin in Zenith. . . . At supper he produced the handkerchief with a flourish.

Every night when Fatty retired he had to remove from his bed a collection of objects which thoughtful house-mates had stuffed between the sheets—soap, alarm clocks, fish. He was the perfect person to whom to sell useless things. Clif Clawson, who combined a brisk huckstering with his jokes, sold to Fatty for four dollars a History of Medicine which he had bought, second-hand, for two, and while Fatty never read it, never conceivably could read it, the possession of the fat red book made him feel learned. But Fatty's greatest beneficence to Digamma was his belief in spiritualism. He went about in terror of spooks. He was always seeing them emerging at night from the dissecting-room windows. His classmates took care that he should behold a great many of them flitting about the halls of the fraternity.

*   *   *

Digamma Pi was housed in a residence built in the expansive days of 1885. The living-room suggested a recent cyclone. Knife-gashed tables, broken Morris chairs, and torn rugs were flung about the room, and covered with backless books, hockey shoes, caps, and cigarette stubs. Above, there were four men to a bedroom, and the beds were iron double-deckers, like a steerage.

For ash-trays the Digams used sawed skulls, and on the bedroom walls were anatomical charts, to be studied while dressing. In Martin's room was a complete skeleton. He and his roommates had trustingly bought it from a salesman who came out from a Zenith surgical supply house. He was such a genial and sympathetic salesman; he gave them cigars and told G. U. stories and explained what prosperous doctors they were all going to be. They bought the skeleton gratefully, on the instalment plan. . . . Later the salesman was less genial. . . .

*   *   *

John A. Robertshaw, John Aldington Robertshaw, professor of physiology in the medical school, was rather deaf, and he was the only teacher in
the University of Winnemac who still wore mutton-chop whiskers. He came
from Back Bay; he was proud of it and let you know about it. With three
other Brahmins he formed in Mohalis a Boston colony which stood for
sturdy sweetness and decorously shaded light. On all occasions he remarked,
"When I was studying with Ludwig in Germany—" He was too absorbed
in his own correctness to heed individual students, and Clif Clawson and
the other young men technically known as "hell-raisers" looked forward to
his lectures on physiology.

They were held in an amphitheater whose seats curved so far around
that the lecturer could not see both ends at once, and while Dr. Robertshaw,
continuing to drone about blood circulation, was peering to the right to find
out who was making that outrageous sound like a motor horn, far over on
the left Clif Clawson would rise and imitate him, with sawing arm and
stroking of imaginary whiskers. Once Clif produced the masterpiece of
throwing a brick into the sink beside the platform, just when Dr. Robertshaw was working up to his annual climax about the effect of brass bands
on the intensity of the knee-jerk.

Martin had been reading Max Gottlieb's scientific papers—as much of
them as he could read, with their morass of mathematical symbols—and
from them he had a conviction that experiments should be something dealing with the foundations of life and death, with the nature of bacterial
infection, with the chemistry of bodily reactions. When Robertshaw chirped
about fussy little experiments, standard experiments, maiden-aunt experiments, Martin was restless. In college he had felt that prosody and Latin
Composition were futile, and he had looked forward to the study of medicine as illumination. Now, in melancholy worry about his own unreason-
ableness, he found that he was developing the same contempt for Robertshaw's rules of the thumb—and for most of the work in anatomy.

The professor of anatomy, Dr. Oliver O. Stout, was himself an anatomy,
a dissection-chart, a thinly covered knot of nerves and blood vessels and
bones. Stout had precise and enormous knowledge; in his dry voice he could
repeat more facts about the left little toe than you would have thought anybody would care to learn regarding the left little toe.

No discussion at the Digamma Pi supper table was more violent than
the incessant debate over the value to a doctor, a decent normal doctor who
made a good living and did not worry about reading papers at medical associations, of remembering anatomical terms. But no matter what they
thought, they all ground at learning the lists of names which enable a man
to crawl through examinations and become an Educated Person, with a
market value of five dollars an hour. Unknown sages had invented rimes

which enabled them to memorize. At supper—the thirty piratical Digams sitting at a long and spotty table, devouring clam chowder and beans and codfish balls and banana layer-cake—the Freshmen earnestly repeated after a senior:

> On old Olympus' topmost top
> A fat-eared German viewed a hop.

Thus by association with the initial letters they mastered the twelve cranial nerves: olfactory, optic, oculomotor, trochlear, and the rest. To the Digams it was the world's noblest poem, and they remembered it for years after they had become practising physicians and altogether forgotten the names of the nerves themselves. . . .

*   *   *

At examination-time, Digamma Pi fraternity showed its value to urgent seekers after wisdom. Generations of Digams had collected test-papers and preserved them in the sacred Quiz Book; geniuses for detail had labored through the volume and marked with red pencil the problems most often set in the course of years. The Freshmen crouched in a ring about Ira Hinkley in the Digam living-room, while he read out the questions they were most likely to get. They writhed, clawed their hair, scratched their chins, bit their fingers, and beat their temples in the endeavor to give the right answer before Angus Duer should read it to them out of the textbook.

In the midst of their sufferings they had to labor with Fatty Pfaff.

Fatty had failed in the mid-year anatomical, and he had to pass a special quiz before he could take the finals. There was a certain fondness for him in Digamma Pi; Fatty was soft, Fatty was superstitious, Fatty was an imbecile, yet they had for him the annoyed affection they might have had for a second-hand motor or a muddy dog. All of them worked on him; they tried to lift him and thrust him through the examinations as through a trap-door. They panted and grunted and moaned at the labor, and Fatty panted and moaned with them.

The night before his special examination they kept him at it till two, with wet towels, black coffee, prayer, and profanity. They repeated lists—lists—lists to him; they shook their fists in his mournful red round face and howled, "Damn you, *will* you remember that the bicuspid valve is the SAME as the mitral valve and NOT another one?" They ran about the room, holding up their hands and wailing, "Won't he never remember nothing about nothing?" and charged back to purr with fictive calm, "Now no use getting fussed, Fatty. Take it easy. Just listen to this, quietly, will yuh, and try," coaxingly, "do try to remember *one* thing, anyway!"

They led him carefully to bed. He was so filled with facts that the slightest jostling would have spilled them.

When he awoke at seven, with red eyes and trembling lips, he had forgotten everything he had learned.

"There's nothing for it," said the president of Digamma Pi. "He's got to have a crib, and take his chance on getting caught with it. I thought so. I made one out for him yesterday. It's a lulu. It'll cover enough of the questions so he'll get through."

Even the Reverend Ira Hinkley, since he had witnessed the horrors of the midnight before, went his ways ignoring the crime. It was Fatty himself who protested: "Gee, I don't like to cheat. I don't think a fellow that can't get through an examination had hardly ought to be allowed to practise medicine. That's what my Dad said."

They poured more coffee into him and (on the advice of Clif Clawson, who wasn't exactly sure what the effect might be but who was willing to learn) they fed him a potassium bromide tablet. The president of Digamma, seizing Fatty with some firmness, growled, "I'm going to stick this crib in your pocket—look, here in your breast pocket, behind your handkerchief."

"I won't use it. I don't care if I fail," whimpered Fatty.

"That's all right, but you keep it there. Maybe you can absorb a little information from it through your lungs, for God knows—" The president clenched his hair. His voice rose, and it was all the tragedy of night watches and black draughts and hopeless retreats. "—God knows you can't take it in through your head!"

They dusted Fatty, they stood him right side up, and pushed him through the door, on his way to Anatomy Building. They watched him go: a balloon on legs, a sausage in corduroy trousers.

"Is it possible he's going to be honest?" marveled Clif Clawson.

"Well, if he is, we better go up and begin packing his trunk. And this ole frat'll never have another goat like Fatty," grieved the president.

They saw Fatty stop, remove his handkerchief, mournfully blow his nose —and discover a long thin slip of paper. They saw him frown at it, tap it on his knuckles, begin to read it, stuff it back into his pocket, and go on with a more resolute step.

They danced hand in hand about the living-room of the fraternity, piously assuring one another, "He'll use it—it's all right—he'll get through or get hanged!"

He got through.

SYLVAN KARCHMER

Hail Brother and Farewell

FROM *Epoch*

For many a G.I. back at college after the war, it was as though his life had been cloven into three parts. There was the time before the war, when the world was made up of a jalopy, a date, football games and classes; there were the years of basic and fatigue, of 120 mm. mortar fire and the smell of death; and then there was the return.

In this moving story, Sylvan Karchmer shows us the confused gropings of those men who found there was no real returning.

THE May afternoon Andy and Reid came up to Forster's office, he had just finished his last class for the day, and was covetously eyeing the comfortable leather couch which occupied a corner of his cheerful office, while he deliberated whether to take a nap or to wait until he had gone through last Thursday's themes. It was his sole complaint against the department; he had no grader, and freshmen themes were never a pleasant prospect, least of all when the couch loomed up so invitingly.

He had decided upon the nap—he always did—when he heard Andy's knock.

"Hello," called Andy familiarly. "We need some expert advice. Can you get your nose out of that book long enough to have a cup of coffee with us?"

Last year Forster had come back to the university after a four years' absence. Three of those years had been spent in the army, and upon his return he was surprised to find many of his former army buddies enrolled here as students.

He considered himself rather fortunate, therefore, that he taught none of them. Somehow he could not picture himself talking solemnly about Andrea del Sarto or injured Hermione to the ex-lieutenants with whom he had drunk inferior cognac and swapped tall tales in pyramidal tents during the dark long nights of the Italian campaign.

The boys, for their own part, once they discovered he was back, were always dropping in. They were never too busy to reminisce . . . their first night at sea—the countercharge at Oggioli—the green champagne at Sculpari's—and how skinny Forster was when he first got into the division. They were never tired telling each other that he weighed less than a hundred and thirty pounds, though you wouldn't think so now to look at his large, comfortable frame . . .

Andy, in particular, was a frequent caller at the office. He had a good-natured face, dotted here and there with freckles. In uniform he had seemed a man; now in sport shirt and sleeves rolled to his elbows he was no more than a boy.

With Reid, the other caller, Forster had only a speaking acquaintance. He was dark, rather serious-faced, and Forster remembered he had always kept very much to himself.

Once the two were in the office it was Reid who spoke up. "It's me," he said with a little apologetic laugh. "I thought it'd be easier to explain myself over a cup of coffee."

"I'll tell you," said Forster, lapsing into army lingo, "I'm pretty busy." Only last Friday Andy had spent two hours up here, shooting the breeze, as they said in the army . . . and the nap had suffered.

"Oh," exclaimed Reid. The corners of his mouth drooped. "Guess we shouldn't have barged in like this." He made an uncertain gesture in the direction of the door.

"Wait," said Forster, remembering this was Reid's first visit up here. "If there's anything I can do . . ."

Reid made a face. "I'm stuck on a paper. But I'll come back." Again he made a gesture towards the door.

"That's silly," said Andy. He leaned over to light his cigarette from Forster's. "You're already here—go ahead and shoot." He turned back to Forster. "I'm the one suggested you, Doc. I said Doc Forster just gobbles up that literary stuff. Why, I remember one night you spouted Hamlet to us in dago talk."

Forster felt himself wincing, but he laughed. In a way Andy and his gang served a purpose. They brought back war days—the dull nights—the bad food—and the anxious moments of the campaign. It was different now—this quiet corner, this tranquil, peaceful spot . . . where you put on weight and napped in the afternoon. He sighed, full of contentment, and raised his eyes to Reid.

"It's the writing course I'm taking," said Reid. "Doc, I'll tell you the whole story. During the war I was in a line company—eight months. Assault platoon. Then near the end somebody got the bright idea of sending me back to divisional headquarters to write military citations. I did write one—

before they discovered I had enough points to go home. You remember how the points system worked in those days."

He had moved to the doorway; now he came back and sat on the edge of a chair by the desk. "You didn't know Longsmith, did you, Doc?"

Forster shook his head.

Reid took a mimeographed sheet out of his pocket. "This is it," he said. "The only citation I got to write. Lt. Longsmith's . . ." Without another word he unfolded the paper and started to read:

"By direction of the President and under the provisions of Army Regulations 600–45, as amended, the Silver Star is awarded posthumously to the following officer: George Henry Longsmith (0–111111), 1st Lt., Infantry, Company C . . . For gallantry in action near Battini, Italy, on 2 May 1945."

Looking up he took a deep breath. "It's only a General Order, Doc. I just followed the form. But here's what I had in mind for my paper—I want to use the same material, just work it over in better literary form."

He had been carrying a notebook. He opened it, and some loose sheets of paper fell out. Picking one up, he read again:

"One morning while leading his rifle platoon in an early morning daylight attack Lt. Longsmith and his men were suddenly engaged by tremendous enemy machine gun rifle and 120 mm. mortar fire . . ."

Forster tried to listen, but his eye strayed to the couch. Vaguely the words created some kind of response in his mind . . . smoke funnelling from a plain, where there had been fighting . . . All behind him now. His eyelids felt heavy. He shook himself.

"Still want to listen?" Reid's eyes were upon him.

"During the course of his movements numerous shells fell within close range of Lt. Longsmith's party, and he had to urge his men to seek greater protection . . . By his own accurate fire he was able to knock out a machine gun in a house and to kill a German . . ."

Reid stopped abruptly, as if he had run out of wind. In the strong light of the room Forster noticed how bright and troubled his eyes were. "See, what I mean, Doc—just a mass of undigested words. There's no imagery in it."

Impatiently he flung down the paper. "What I'm trying to tell you is that it doesn't mean anything."

Andy was moving around the office examining the books on the shelves. "You need some pin-up girls here," he said, peering at and dismissing a Degas reproduction on the wall. "By the way," he said, "what happened to that book you were writing when you were overseas?"

There had been a book—or notes. Forster used to scribble in the moments he had to himself. That was when he first went overseas. He hadn't thought about the book in some time. He ignored Andy's interruption. "Sounds O.K. to me," he said in a cheerful voice to Reid.

"But it's the language of the general order; I'm not trying to quibble or anything, but look—." He twisted his head as if he felt a sudden pain. "The occasion calls for something—well, poetic if you like . . . Something . . . like . . ." He paused, searching his memory and his eyes sought the window. "—this—

> 'The crown o'earth doth melt. My Lord!
> O! wither'd is the garland of the war,
> The soldier's pole is fall'n; young boys and girls
> Are level now with men.'

Say," he cried. "I remembered it after all." And pleased with himself, he laughed, as his cheeks flushed, but to Forster this boyish frankness seemed only an occasional respite from some inner, deeper constraint.

"You had quite a bit of English?" he asked.

"Oh, I was an architect major before the war—just got off a lot of required English."

"And now?" asked Forster, stifling a yawn, and wishing he had not indulged in that second piece of pie at lunch.

"And now," replied Reid, "now I don't know."

"Me," said Andy, "I'm getting lined up with the Universal Oil Company, if they ever let me out of this place. They start their geologists off at two hundred fifty."

He picked up one of the china trays, which Forster used only for exhibition, and smashed his cigarette into it. "You know, Doc, we were chumps to leave Italy. I often think of the swell times I had there. Why, once I went to Stresa on leave. I had a bottle of Old Taylor and two pints of cognac. Man, I drank cognac till it was running out of my ears. Good old Italy . . ."

The pattern of his life, at least, was clear—in or out of school. Forster knew the type as he knew the rules of the grammar he taught.

"Speaking of Italy," said Reid, "Doc, did you ever get to Desanzano? On Lake Garda. You had to pass through the town when you went up to Fifth Army Headquarters."

"Oh yes, I remember—beautiful scenery."

"Do you remember seeing any olive trees up there?" asked Reid.

"I saw plenty of grapes over there," said Andy. "But what beats me is for all the grapes they had I never could figure out why the vino was so poor."

"Olive trees," said Forster, looking at Reid and remembering all at once how slim he used to be himself—not too long ago. "No, can't say I did."

"Well, look, you know 'Frater Ave Atque Vale'?—the poem, I mean. Let's see if I still know the lines . . .

> *'Row us out from Desanzano to your Sirmione, row!*
> *So they row'd and there we landed—"O Venusta Sirmio!"*
> *There to me thro' all the groves of olives in the summer glow . . .'*

See, he mentions them, but I'll be dern if I saw any."

"Tennyson, isn't it?" asked Forster, curious, despite himself, at Reid's words.

"You know it too, Doc? Let's see if I can get it straight—'groves of olives in the summer glow' . . . and then this came after:

> *'There beneath the Roman ruin where the purple flowers grow*
> *Came that "Ave atque vale" of the poet's hopeless woe,*
> *Tenderest of Romans nineteen hundred years ago.*
>
> *' "Frater ave atque vale"—as we wander'd to and fro*
> *Gazing at the Lydian laughter of the Garda Lake below*
> *Sweet Catullus' all-but-island, olive-silvery Sirmio.' "*

Forster knew it was not poetry the way Reid formed the lines—it moved too abruptly. "But Tennyson pulled a fast one on you—no olive trees, eh?" he smiled.

Reid gave him a sly glance. "You're pulling my leg, Doc."

"Well," said Forster, "you've quoted the great bard and Tennyson. Let's hear the rest of your essay. You've probably got a minor literary gem there."

Reid's face flushed again, and he stuck a cigarette into his mouth. "Pulling my leg some more," he said, but he went on:

"With this charge of twenty-five yards Lt. Longsmith swept his platoon to the house. There he drove out twenty Germans. When an enemy tank opened direct fire on the building, Longsmith, undaunted, braved the intense fire of every variety to move his men to better protection. An enemy bullet knocked off his helmet."

He stopped abruptly. "Oh, hell," he cried. "It's a damned mess. You think I'm too serious, Doc, but honestly, I can't just dash it off like I would a freshman theme. Thirty seconds after they knock off his helmet, Lt. Longsmith's going to be a dead duck—."

He got to his feet and went to the window, and though the air didn't seem too close in the office, he raised the sill a little. A fragrance of honeysuckle and roses came up from the yard.

"Look, Doc," he said, "Lt. Longsmith's a platoon leader in this—he couldn't have been over twenty-two. They don't come much older. Probably fresh out of school. Chances are he never had a job—except that one—killing krauts."

"Well, I'll be dern," cried Andy from the leather couch. "You morbid little cuss. Personally there are too many pleasant things to remember. I used to go out with a little signorina up at Stresa. Talk about your American gals . . ."

"It's not that," explained Reid. "It's just that I can't use the king's English."

"For Pete's sake," said Andy. "He's worked on the thing so much it's got him batty. Tell him it's a C paper. That's good enough for anybody." He stopped. "Still working on your book, Doc?" he asked.

Forster frowned. There was something deceptively innocent in Andy's question. Forster was puzzled by it. Then, watching Andy swinging his legs from the desk and flipping his cigarette ashes into the little china tray, he decided Andy hadn't meant a thing . . .

"Honest, it's not the grade," said Reid, talking to Forster. "It's just—just—so damned hard to say."

"We're going in circles," observed Andy.

"That's right." Reid gathered his papers. Forster watched him, and for a moment he was inclined to share Andy's opinion. What was all the fuss about. He leaned over, emptied the contents of the china tray into the waste basket, and when he talked to Reid, he sounded as he did when he was having a conference with his freshmen.

"A wise selection of facts always helps the writer. Now suppose you briefly analyze your material—what do you want to say?"

Reid pushed back his chair. "I want to open with this daylight attack. That's my start—those simple words—daylight attack. Do you know when it happened—in May, Doc—just after a shower." He paused for a minute. "May . . ." he continued. "Time for school to be out—for weekend fishing trips. On Saturdays I used to go riding in the park. Maybe Lt. Longsmith in his spare moments liked to putter around in his fatigues."

He made an impatient movement with his shoulder. "Fatigues—who thought of fatigues in those days! Maybe he liked to fix his Ford or just pull the weeds out of the violet beds . . . the point is, Doc, can you see him in that early morning attack at Battini? The enemy is using everything—remember, machine gun, rifle, 120 mm. . . ."

The words were slack now. He reached down and picked up a sheet of paper. The notes had no particular reference to what he was saying, because he didn't even glance at them as he went on: "Nine or ten shells fell within thirty yards of him—why, that's not as far as from here to the elevator door."

He made a sign with a long finger. "And here—well, along here some-place I remember while he was making a personal reconnaissance in front of his platoon, some jerry with a machine gun put three slugs through the sleeve of his jacket."

"I knew a guy in Baker Company," said Andy. "He went out on a patrol —had a sergeant with him and two other fellows. They hit a nest of krauts."

Reid went on, as if he had not heard Andy's interruption. "Those attacks, Doc, that jump off at dawn . . . You spring up from your sack—you don't know if you're dreaming or not. You sniff the morning air—you think, what a swell day it's gonna be, to fish or go riding—then you remember the attack, and you say this is a helluva way to start off the day. I don't know what Longsmith was thinking—or if he thought at all about it. Maybe he was so groggy with sleep he just rushed out without thinking."

His shoulders moved again . . . "You see, sometimes those things don't strike you till later. Here's the angle—the Lieutenant might not have paid any attention to the morning air or to the trees. He might've been so en-grossed in that patrol detail he didn't notice—not even when the slugs started to rip off his sleeve. The sands were running down on him. He'd never see another spring morning; and I betcha anything—with those shells falling around him like snow drops—he knew it too. It was *finito* for him— everything—the green fresh foliage—the wonderful smell of a spring morn-ing . . . He was out there killing for dear life, holding on to some kind of crazy hope that he'd shoot his way through and come back."

Reid picked up his cigarette case. He didn't seem to be talking to any-one in particular now. Forster waited. "I don't know," Reid said quizzically, "I've got the feeling even if he had come back after those 120s and all . . ." He touched the disorderly sheets of his essay ". . . he'd always smell the gunpowder in the morning air. It's got a dry, suffocating smell."

He stopped again, his eyes going to the window; then he said in an al-most insensible voice: "That's what death smells like."

Forster waited again. Outside he heard some birds. This was May, too, he remembered. He felt he should say something, and when he spoke he picked his words carefully. "Find your theme—state it simply—but first you have to see it," he said.

But it didn't do any good. He was a comfortable, cheerful man—he de-tested intensity in any form. "Forget it," he said finally. Yes, this was the only sensible advice. "Go out and drink some beer with the boys. Don't worry about it." Yes, that was it—mustn't worry about it. Not that important. He stood up. "Drop in again, fellows," he smiled. "Always like to chew the fat with you guys."

Andy grinned. "About time for another beer bust," he said.

But Reid said nothing; only when they went out the door he went first, looking neither to the right nor left of him . . . walking like a man telling a story or listening attentively to one being told.

After they had gone Forster sat down at his desk. At last, he decided, stretching himself leisurely. Then he remembered the themes—should be grading them. But he made no attempt to get them, nor did he feel like doing anything else. He wondered for a minute what was the matter with him.

ROBERT BENCHLEY

What College Did to Me

FROM *The Early Worm*

A friend once said of Robert Benchley that he led "one of the most insanely complicated private lives of our day, and did it, on the whole, with extraordinary composure." He was a columnist, playwright, actor, critic, radio and movie star and a few other things. Stephen Leacock, no mean jester himself, called Benchley "perhaps the most finished master of the technique of literary fun in America."

Benchley was Harvard 1912 himself, but "What College Did to Me" might be deemed a not too lunatic facsimile of life at any old alma mater.

M Y COLLEGE education was no haphazard affair. My courses were all selected with a very definite aim in view, with a serious purpose in mind— no classes before eleven in the morning or after two-thirty in the afternoon, and nothing on Saturday at all. That was my slogan. On that rock was my education built.

As what is known as the Classical Course involved practically no afternoon laboratory work, whereas in the Scientific Course a man's time was never his own until four p. m. anyway, I went in for the classic. But only such classics as allowed for a good sleep in the morning. A man has his health to think of. There is such a thing as being a studying fool.

In my days (I was a classmate of the founder of the college) a student could elect to take any courses in the catalogue, provided no two of his choices came at the same hour. The only things he was not supposed to mix were Scotch and gin. This was known as the Elective System. Now I understand that the boys have to have, during the four years, at least three courses beginning with the same letter. This probably makes it very awkward for those who like to get away of a Friday afternoon for the week-end.

Under the Elective System my schedule was somewhat as follows:

Mondays, Wednesdays and Fridays at 11:00:

    Botany 2a (The History of Flowers and Their Meaning)

Tuesdays and Thursdays at 11:00:

    English 26 (The Social Life of the Minor Sixteenth-Century Poets)

Mondays, Wednesdays and Fridays at 12:00:

    Music 9 (History and Appreciation of the Clavichord)

Tuesdays and Thursdays at 12:00:

    German 12b (Early Minnesingers—Walter von Vogelweider, Ulric
    Glannsdorf and Freimann von Stremhofen. Their Songs and Times)

Mondays, Wednesdays and Fridays at 1:30:

    Fine Arts 6 (Doric Columns: Their Uses, History and Various Heights)

Tuesdays and Thursdays at 1:30:

    French 1c (Exceptions to the verb *être*)

This was, of course, just one year's work. The next year I followed these courses up with supplementary courses in the history of lace-making, Russian taxation systems before Catharine the Great, North American glacial deposits and Early Renaissance etchers.

This gave me a general idea of the progress of civilization and a certain practical knowledge which has stood me in good stead in thousands of ways since my graduation.

My system of studying was no less strict. In lecture courses I had my notebooks so arranged that one-half of the page could be devoted to drawings of five-pointed stars (exquisitely shaded), girls' heads, and tick-tack-toe. Some of the drawings in my economics notebook in the course on Early English Trade Winds were the finest things I have ever done. One of them was a whole tree (an oak) with every leaf in perfect detail. Several instructors commented on my work in this field.

These notes I would take home after the lecture, together with whatever supplementary reading the course called for. Notes and textbooks would then be placed on a table under a strong lamplight. Next came the sharpening of pencils, which would take perhaps fifteen minutes. I had some of the best sharpened pencils in college. These I placed on the table beside the notes and books.

At this point it was necessary to light a pipe, which involved going to the table where the tobacco was. As it so happened, on the same table was a poker hand, all dealt, lying in front of a vacant chair. Four other chairs were oddly enough occupied by students, also preparing to study. It therefore resolved itself into something of a seminar, or group conference, on the courses under discussion. For example, the first student would say:

    "I can't open."

The second student would perhaps say the same thing.

The third student would say: "I'll open for fifty cents."

And the seminar would be on.

At the end of the seminar, I would go back to my desk, pile the notes and books on top of each other, put the light out, and go to bed, tired but happy in the realization that I had not only spent the evening busily but had helped put four of my friends through college.

An inventory of stock acquired at college discloses the following bits of culture and erudition which have nestled in my mind after all these years.

Things I Learned Freshman Year

1. Charlemagne either died or was born or did something with the Holy Roman Empire in 800.

2. By placing one paper bag inside another paper bag you can carry home a milk shake in it.

3. There is a double l in the middle of "parallel."

4. Powder rubbed on the chin will take the place of a shave if the room isn't very light.

5. French nouns ending in "aison" are feminine.

6. Almost everything you need to know about a subject is in the encyclopedia.

7. A tasty sandwich can be made by spreading peanut butter on raisin bread.

8. A floating body displaces its own weight in the liquid in which it floats.

9. A sock with a hole in the toe can be worn inside out with comparative comfort.

10. The chances are against filling an inside straight.

11. There is a law in economics called *The Law of Diminishing Returns,* which means that after a certain margin is reached returns begin to diminish. This may not be correctly stated, but there *is* a law by that name.

12. You begin tuning a mandolin with A and tune the other strings from that.

Sophomore Year

1. A good imitation of measles rash can be effected by stabbing the forearm with a stiff whiskbroom.

2. Queen Elizabeth was not above suspicion.

3. In Spanish you pronounce z like th.

4. Nine-tenths of the girls in a girls' college are not pretty.

5. You can sleep undetected in a lecture course by resting the head on the hand as if shading the eyes.

6. Weakness in drawing technique can be hidden by using a wash instead of black and white line.

7. Quite a respectable bun can be acquired by smoking three or four pipefuls of strong tobacco when you have no food in your stomach.

8. The ancient Phœnicians were really Jews, and got as far north as England where they operated tin mines.

9. You can get dressed much quicker in the morning if the night before when you are going to bed you take off your trousers and underdrawers at once, leaving the latter inside the former.

Junior Year

1. Emerson left his pastorate because he had some argument about communion.

2. All women are untrustworthy.

3. Pushing your arms back as far as they will go fifty times each day increases your chest measurement.

4. Marcus Aurelius had a son who turned out to be a bad boy.

5. Eight hours of sleep are not necessary.

6. Heraclitus believed that fire was the basis of all life.

7. A good way to keep your trousers pressed is to hang them from the bureau drawer.

8. The chances are that you will never fill an inside straight.

9. The Republicans believe in a centralized government, the Democrats in a de-centralized one.

10. It is not necessarily effeminate to drink tea.

Senior Year

1. A dinner coat looks better than full dress.

2. There is as yet no law determining what constitutes trespass in an airplane.

3. Six hours of sleep are not necessary.

4. Bicarbonate of soda taken before retiring makes you feel better the next day.

5. You needn't be fully dressed if you wear a cap and gown to a nine-o'clock recitation.

6. Theater tickets may be charged.

7. Flowers may be charged.

8. May is the shortest month in the year.

The foregoing outline of my education is true enough in its way, and is what people like to think about a college course. It has become quite the cynical thing to admit laughingly that college did one no good. It is part of the American Credo that all that the college student learns is to catch punts and dance. I had to write something like that to satisfy the editors. As a matter of fact, I learned a great deal in college and have those four years to thank for whatever I know today.

(The above note was written to satisfy those of my instructors and financial backers who may read this. As a matter of fact, the original outline is true, and I had to look up the date about Charlemagne at that.)

Campus

3

CAMPUS is more than ivy-covered buildings on spreading lawns. It is a sentiment, a state of mind, fashioned out of a multitude of impressions and encounters: out of a song fest and a beer party, out of a November football game and a blind date, out of fraternity house and class day. It is poetry read aloud and philosophy argued and bad jokes traded and impassioned debate about life and love and the state of the universe. It is, perhaps, the one tangible aspect of the university which lives most vividly in the graduate's recall. For it is here that he came to the threshold of his adult life, he and hundreds like him, to walk—literally and figuratively—in the paths of learning. The campus is the student's village green; a casual and treasured meeting ground for those whose age and aims join them for the nonce in a community whose closeness they may never again experience.

The campus is the student's bivouac and the sanctuary where he moves about in safe contentment ever aware of widening, beckoning horizons—before leaving for the outside world to assume the responsibilities and grasp the opportunities of enlightened adult-hood.

Here, then, is the campus, pictured in these selections in a variety of moods and tempers.

Blind Date

FROM *The Hickory Stick*

This unusually sensitive love story of two students at Fairview, a small midwestern college, is from Virgil Scott's book, The Hickory Stick.

Scott's novel of teachers and teaching appeared some ten years ago, was characterized by one critic as "a hard-hitting book, built out of anger and discouragement and hope." It is still notable for its clear, sharp portrayal of the seamier side of American educational practice.

HE KNEW what it was going to be like because there had been the others, especially Lois. She was in his freshman English class. She sat up in front and smiled brightly at the instructor often enough to pull down steady B's, and she wrote smooth, pretty, mechanically flawless themes on the value of literary societies and on the importance of social life to a college student. Once a month the instructor would read one of these aloud, and every time he looked up to effervesce over a phrase, she would be there in the front row, smiling brightly and nodding her head at him. She was superficially pretty and not quite feeble-minded and she had been a prize package for the Pans that year because two weeks after school had started, she had snagged a pin from the varsity fullback. It hadn't lasted long, for the pin found its way back onto a male sweater in November and from thence to the ripe breast of an Hellenic in December, but her moment of glory was still glowing a little as late as March, when Doug had invited her to go with him to see the fourth production of the Fairview Wig and Masque. It surprised him when her tinkling "Yes" came back over the dorm wire so readily. Later, after it was all over and done with, it didn't surprise him. Later it got back to him that she thought Douglas Harris was the tall, blond, tweedy Easterner who sat behind her in French.

She was waiting at the foot of the stairs in the U Building when he got there that night, just as Nancy Whatshername would be waiting when he got there this night. She was wearing a blue cloth coat with a dyed muskrat collar, and underneath this a skin-tight black dress, and when he came across the court and stopped beside her, she looked up and said, "So *you're* Doug Harris," and there was a faint "My God" underneath the words.

"Yes," he said, "I'm Doug Harris. Did you expect somebody else?" But he needed no answer to this one, for he had the answer already. He had the answer because he knew that this was the girl you always see wherever you go on college campuses. She was the one you saw whispering over a picture in her biology book, or giggling over an afternoon coke in a booth at Schmidt's Drug Store, or coming out of a Saturday night movie on the arm of a substitute halfback, or on Wednesday night waiting in the corridor of the U Building for the sorority meeting to begin. When she was with her sorority sisters, you got her mixed up with the others, because she had the same shoulder-length, end-curled hair of the anonymous color you can't call anything but brown, and the same flat-red lip line, the bow sharp-drawn against the powder-white face, and the same suggestion of bony squareness to the jaw and of broadness to the forehead, and the same voluptuous body, a body which would be awkward during her two pregnancies and heavy and soft after her menopause, and the same breasts, their heavy fullness only casually outlined by loose sweaters and by the sorority pin which was always two inches below the white line where the brassiere showed through the loosely knit wool, and the same shell-rimmed glasses, worn ostentatiously as though she would wear disfiguring spectacles flamboyantly so long as she had to wear them at all.

This was Lois, and it was also Mary Elsie Greta Ruth Sally Something-orother, and she was the daughter of the Methodist minister in Circleville, and the pride of the superintendent of the Coca Cola plant in Mechanics-burg, and the darling of the pharmacist in Wooster, and the little girl of the school principal in Elyria, and the joy of the contractor in Oberlin. She was nineteen years old, and when she was a little older the men of a nation would build her some department stores, and would trap beavers for her, and would write love stories which they would publish in the *Woman's Home Companion* for her to read; and every twenty-five years they would steal for her some trade routes from other nations, and would die screaming on the barbed wire, and would walk in parades when it was all over so that she could throw roses at them from the sidewalks; and then these men would go back to building some more department stores for her and to writing some more stories and to thickening the upholstery on Buick automobiles. And when she was forty, presidents would have to say to her, "Your sons will never die on foreign soil;" and before she was sixty, her children would be waiting impatiently for her to die; and after she was dead, Eddie Guest would write a poem about her which would make her contemporaries weep.

This was Lois, and at nineteen she was just learning from the professors how to be a liberated woman, and at eight of a March evening she was going to a college play with a seventeen-year-old boy who was dressed in a twelve-dollar suit and had nothing to say to her which she could understand. So they were silent, walking up the three flights of hollowed-out, gritty stairs to the chapel. He kept his eyes fixed on the stair treads, and he could feel the rich, dark warmth of her when his right shoulder brushed against hers on the stair turns, and he could sense the cool flick of her eyes over his face and cheap suit, and the loneliness and the hunger were like a vacuum inside him. He tried to talk to her, he wanted to talk to her easily and wittily and without self-consciousness, but it wouldn't come off because he had nothing to say to her, and this was the way it had always been.

They were quite a few minutes early that March evening, just as he was going to be early this April evening. The chapel was only a third full when they entered. He let his big paw linger a minute on her elbow and then slide stiffly down and away from her forearm when he steered her into an aisle seat. When he helped her off with the cloth coat, the warmth of her soft shoulders against his knuckles and the back of his hands was as alive as heat from a fireplace, and when she stiffened her arms and threw back her shoulders and wriggled out of her coat, he saw the curve of her breasts under the form-fitting black dress. And this was the way it always was, too, the stiff silence and the heavy emptiness and the slow, sullen desire.

"So *you're* Douglas Harris," she said again. She slitted her eyes at him when she said it, and then she turned her head and wriggled down comfortably in her seat.

"Yes," he said. "Did you expect somebody else?" He was not conscious of having repeated himself.

"I didn't know who to expect. Now I remember seeing you around."

"That's right," he said. "You're in my English class."

"Oh. Oh, yeah. Teddy's class." She giggled softly. She was very delicate about it.

"Don't you like him?"

"Who? Teddy? Sure. I like him all right. He's cute. What made you think I didn't like him?"

"Never mind." His eyes went to her breasts again, and she saw them, so he said, "I see you're a Pan."

"That's right. You're a Spartan, aren't you?"

"No."

"Oh. I thought you were. Almost *everybody* pledged Spartan this year. So *you* went Athenian."

"No," he said. "I didn't go anything."

She had a little wrinkle which now and then came out right above the plucked line of her eyebrow, and it came out now. "You didn't?"

"No," he said, "I didn't pledge."

"Why not?"

It was a subject to talk about, but he suddenly wanted to chop it off, clean and neat, the way you chop weeds with a sharp hoe.

"Maybe because I wasn't invited," he lied, and then he was sorry, for it gave her the lead she had been waiting for, it put him right in position for the kill, with his jaw sticking out soggily and his arms hanging paralyzed at his sides.

"Oh, but you *have* to be invited, it's a rule, *absolutely everybody* is guaranteed a bid to a society," she said, and then she explained it to him. He had had it explained before, but she went over it all again, slowly and patiently, in fine, organized detail. She told him how in November, after all the bids were in, the dean checked them against the enrollment, and if a name was missing, the presidents of the societies were called in and asked why this man had been overlooked, and if no one wanted him, then the society presidents drew lots to see who would have to take him, and if there were a lot of names, the dean put them in a hat and the presidents took turns drawing them out again. This was part of what they meant at Fairview when they called it a democratic institution and a Christian one, Lois explained, "so why don't you go to the dean, he'll *make* somebody take you." She was flushed and triumphant after this, and she punctuated the final sentence with a little curve at the corner of her lip. He looked down at it and at the shallow, pretty, cruel face around it and said, "Thanks. Thanks a lot. So they even shoot crap here in the name of Christianity, do they?"

"You don't understand," she said. "You must take an intelligent attitude toward this, you must—"

"Let's skip it. Let's talk about something else."

"All right. What shall we talk about?"

"How about you?" This was a lie too, he wasn't the least bit interested any more, but he had to keep talking, he had to let words blank up his mind.

"What about me?"

"Oh, where you from?"

"Morton."

"Morton? I never—"

"No one ever has. It's sixty miles straight south."

"Oh. Near the University. How come you didn't go to the University?"

"I don't know. I never gave it a thought. My father went here, that's why, I guess."

"He must be a minister."

"How'd you know?"

"Never mind," he said. "I just knew it. I just knew somehow that he was a minister at Morton."

"Yes," she said, "at Morton." And the conversation was bleeding to death, and he wanted to get her home, and when the play started, he couldn't follow it for the thick feeling in his throat. And afterwards, when he was walking her back to the dorm and she said, "Now don't forget, go in and see the dean tomorrow, he'll see that you get a bid," he felt it again. But he made himself say, "I'll do that for sure, I hope the Spartans have to take me," and she said, "Yes, you'll be lucky if they do, they're the best there is," and then they were at the dorm and he was saying, "Good night," very abruptly, and he turned before she could answer and set off at a dead run back down College Street. He had come in that night with his face hospital white. He had come in feeling sick. He had thrown himself on the bed in his room and spit his thoughts into his pillow, and the weight was there, and with it a picture of a curled lip line and peasant breasts under a tight black dress, and the ache in him was like a stone and all mixed up with mind pictures until he dropped off to sleep.

That had been March and this was April, but what was the difference, for if it wasn't Lois it was Jean Mary Alice Carmen Nancy Anita when you turned off College Street and wound up the walk into the U Building. He almost turned around and went back, he almost stood this next one up, but then he was inside, and the heavy door was falling closed behind him, and he was committed. He stopped inside the building and looked up. As always when he stopped like this and looked up at the beamed ceiling three stories above the court, he got the feeling that the roof was going to tear loose and come crashing down on him. The feeling came to him now and mingled with the vacuum ache inside him, and then he brought his eyes down and looked across the court to the stairway and the feeling was gone.

Afterwards he tried sometimes to recapture the feeling he had just then, but it would never quite come back, it always evaded him. She was leaning against the stair rail, this girl was. She was slim and boyish, and she was wearing a boy's stained leather jacket, unzipped in front, and a skirt and sweater. He could never remember the color of the skirt afterwards, though he remembered that the sweater had been very dark, blue or black. She had shoulder-length hair, as black and glossy as new carbon paper; it seemed to be straight the first time you glanced at it, but if you got closer and looked again, you saw that it had a very vague natural curl to it, like hair that has been out in a mist. The hair was brushed back behind her ears, off a cheek which from a distance looked very white against the hair, only when you came closer and looked harder, you saw the vague olive tint in it where the cool, sure line curved in under her cheekbone and then out again before it

came to her chin. This is the picture he got afterwards when he tried to remember the first time he met her, this and the saddle oxfords and the blue
anklets she was wearing, and the clean, hard, natural, unself-conscious curve
of her hip as she leaned against the stair railing and studied intently the
faces about her, as if she were memorizing them for an examination. He
remembered the picture all right, it was clear of line in his mind four years
later, it was as if he carried a photograph around in his mind; but he could
never get much further than this, he could never get back the feeling he
had when the roof of the U Building was no longer tearing loose and the
emptiness spilled out of him and he knew that this was Nancy and he also
knew that this was the girl he was going to fall in love with.

He knew this the first time he saw her, knew it while he was crossing the
court toward her. The knowledge was warm in him when he stopped in
front of her and said, "Hello, Nancy." Maybe it was something like that
inside her, too, because she looked up quickly, and there was a queer little
smile on her face, almost a serious one, and he saw the gold flecks in her
eyes, which were a razor's depth under the surface and which spilled out
past the black irises into the whites, and all she said was, "Hello, Doug.
Ready?"

That was all there was to it. No wrinkles over plucked eyebrows, no
faint "My God" underneath a polite voice, just "Hello, Doug. Ready?"
as if she had known him forever. "Yes," he said, "been waiting long?" and she
said "No, only a minute or two," and then they were climbing the stairs
together, his arm brushing hers on the landings and turning him warm
clear into his lungs, and they were walking down the corridor toward the
chapel, and her walk was a clean, swinging, rhythmic stride, none of your
choppy, stiff-legged, three-inch-heel-on-a-too-small-shoe walk. They stopped
just inside the chapel while he swept his eyes over the stage and the seats.
"Where do you like to sit?" he asked. "On the side," she said. "I like it best
on the side, where there aren't so many people." So he found them seats on
the side, halfway down, and stepped aside to let her in. He helped her
wriggle out of the leather jacket, hooking his eyes as he did so on firm, tilted
breasts. Then he looked up into her face and blushed, because her eyes and
lips were laughing into his face.

"I see you're a Pan," he said. It was the only line he could remember
when they caught him staring at their breasts.

"Yes," she said, only the laugh was still there, still on her lips and in
her eyes, letting you know you weren't kidding anybody. "Yes," she said.
"But how did you know? Are we built that much alike?"

"The pin," he said, and dropped his eyes again, and this time she
laughed out loud.

"You mean the one I forgot to wear tonight?"

"Yes," he said. "That one." And he grinned, and the blood was like a song in him.

"I don't usually wear sweaters and skirts to plays, either," she said. "But the Pans had a basketball game at six, and I had just time for a shower afterwards, so I didn't have a chance to dress up."

"I like you this way," he said. "I like you best just the way you are."

"How do you know? You never saw me any other way."

"I know," he said. "I know just the same. You look wonderful."

"Thanks," she said. "Only I am absolutely unsusceptible to flattery."

"It's not flattery, it's—" He was suddenly embarrassed, for she was putting kinks in his tongue and he was embarrassed and this night mustn't be like always. And then she laid a hand on his forearm and said, "All right, it's not flattery, and I am susceptible to it. I love it," and then it was all right again.

"Tell me about yourself," he said. "Tell me everything about you."

"In fifteen minutes?"

"In installments, then. A chapter a day."

"It's a short story, not a novel," she said. "I'm a small-town girl in a hick college. I graduate in June, major English, minors French and Latin. Next year I'll probably go to another small town and teach in a high school —if I can find a job. My father is a lawyer in Midvale, which you never heard of. I swim, skate, ski, shoot, bowl, and golf, all with equal proficiency —that is, very badly. Doc Dean has threatened to kick me out of dear old Fairview three times because I sneak smokes in the dorm, only he thinks maybe my father will pay up my back tuition sometime, so he holds off. I like to read mystery stories and I detest the Romantic poets, except Byron, and I've read all the books on sex, and I'm looking for a good husband. Anything else?"

"Any luck yet? About the husband, I mean."

"I'm not sure," she said. "You never can tell. Anyway, you're cheating."

"What do you mean?"

"It's your turn," she said. "The first principle of snagging a man is to encourage him to talk about himself. At least that's what all the books say. Women should be seen and not heard. And it's eight thirty and there go the lights and all I know about you is that your name is Douglas Harris and that you room at Ma Shipton's."

"Later," he said. "Later, I'll tell you all. In installments."

He did not watch the skit, and he did not hear the beefy laughter which splashed around them from out of the semi-dark. Her hand rested lightly on his forearm, and he could feel her shoulder pressing against him, and it was like when you wake up at three in the morning and the window is open and the wind is singing around the corners of the house and torturing a loose shingle on the siding, and there is snow drifting in through the window and onto the bed, and you think it is time to get up, only you hate to because it's so cold, and then the clock downstairs chimes and you count the strokes, geung-geunggg, geung-geunggg, geung-geunggg, three o'clock you think, only three o'clock, fourfivesixseven, four hours yet, and you turn over and bury your head in the thick covers and smell the warmth of your own body and then drop back off, and at that moment four hours is a warm and wonderfully peaceful thought because at three in the morning four hours is forever. It was like this with him, only he knew that a two-hour play couldn't last forever and that spoiled it a little.

Then at ten they were walking out of the U Building, out onto the shadowed walk which rambled through the trees and behind prexy's house to the dorm. Fifty feet down the walk she said, "Got a cigarette, Doug?" and he shook one out for her and another for himself, and cupped a match, sailor-style, and lighted hers and then his own. She took a deep drag and blew out into the dark with slow steadiness, and then she said, "Now tell me about you."

"No," he said. "Not tonight. Some other time, but not tonight. Let's not talk at all tonight."

"All right," she said. "Let's not talk at all." She rested her hand on the crook of his arm, and on the April air he could smell the leather of her jacket and the shampoo in her hair, and outside the dorm they stood quietly for a minute, not saying anything, just feeling each other's presence in the dark. It was as if there was absolutely no need for words between them, as if forever and ever there would be no need, and then he said, "What shall we do tomorrow night?" and she said, "I don't care, you tell me," and this is what he could remember afterwards about that first night.

EDMUND PEARSON

Murder at Harvard Med

FROM *Murder at Smutty Nose*

The notorious Webster-Parkman case of 1849, says Edmund Pearson, editor, bibliophile and authority on the art of murder, centered on what is probably America's most celebrated collegiate crime. Professor Webster, of Harvard, was tried and hanged for the killing and dismemberment of Professor Parkman, a colleague. One of the character witnesses at the trial was Jared Sparks, President of Harvard, and Oliver Wendell Holmes, then professor of anatomy at Harvard, testified for the state.

DOCTOR PARKMAN was walking—rapidly, as usual—through the streets of Boston, on his way to keep an appointment. He wore a black frock coat and trousers, a purple silk vest, black stock, and high hat, and his lean figure would have made him noticeable, even if his peculiar countenance had not attracted attention by itself. Boys pointed him out to other boys:

"There goes Doctor Parkman!"

Women who passed him on the street went home and told their families that they had seen "Chin." The Doctor had a protruding lower jaw, and his mouth was fitted with some conspicuous false teeth. That chin was not meaningless; he was a determined man, on his way to put an end to a long-drawn-out and vexatious business affair. Plainly there was going to be trouble for someone.

Doctor Parkman was always in a hurry, and today he was in more of a hurry than ever. He was so impatient a man, says one account, that when riding he would sometimes leave his horse in the street, and hurry ahead on foot. This morning he had been at the Merchants' Bank on State Street, and at various other places. He bought a lettuce for his invalid daughter, and left it in a bag at Holland's grocery at the corner of Blossom and Vine Streets, where he said he would soon return. Then he pushed on to his appointment, at half-past one, at the Medical College. He must get this business over, and return promptly to his dinner at half-past two—for this was the year 1849, when gentlemen dined early in the afternoon. He hoped that to-day Professor Webster would really do something to settle this infernal debt and cease putting him off with evasions, excuses, and subterfuges.

Professor Webster! The name was enough to make Doctor Parkman snarl. This was a man who held a lectureship in a medical college built on land which he—Doctor Parkman—had provided. The Parkman Chair of Anatomy in the College—occupied by Oliver Wendell Holmes—was named in Doctor Parkman's honour, as acknowledgment of the gift. And here was Webster, twice a professor, since he was also Erving Professor of Chemistry and Mineralogy at Harvard, and yet he was nothing but a defaulting, dishonourable debtor! Doctor Parkman had told him as much to his face, and to make sure that Professor Webster should be in no doubt about it, had sent him a message to the same effect within a week.

Doctor Parkman had cause to be indignant. Professor Webster, who had quickly run through the fortune inherited from his father, liked to live well and to entertain his friends. Even in Cambridge, and at that date, it was not easy to do this—and incidentally to support a wife and three daughters—on the $1,200 a year which the University paid him, with a slender addition from the sale of tickets for his lectures at the Medical College. Seven years earlier, Parkman had lent Webster $400, taking a note secured by the mortgage of some personal property. In 1847, when the loan was not fully repaid, Doctor Parkman had been one of a group of men to lend the Professor a larger sum, taking this time a note for $2,432, secured by a mortgage of all Webster's personal property, including his household furniture and his cabinet of minerals. The next year, Professor Webster, still embarrassed for lack of money, went to Doctor Parkman's brother-in-law, Robert Gould Shaw, told a pathetic tale of sheriffs and attachments, and prevailed upon that gentleman to buy the cabinet of minerals for $1,200—omitting all mention of the fact that this collection was already in pawn to Doctor Parkman. The transaction happened to come out in conversation between the brothers-in-law, and Doctor Parkman was furious.

"Those minerals are not his to sell," he exclaimed; "I have a mortgage on them, and I can show it to you!"

The Doctor was prompt and punctilious, and he expected others to be like him. He began to pursue the Professor for the debt. I do not know whether the story is true that he used to come to Webster's lectures, sit in the front row, glare at the unhappy man, and confuse him by the sight of that prognathous jaw and those shining teeth. Webster, in the months to come, did all he could to represent Parkman as an overbearing and violent persecutor of a struggling scholar, and it may be that this was merely his corroborative detail. He furnished a great amount of corroborative detail, once started, and some of it was like Pooh Bah's description of the execution of Nanki Poo, everything added for the sake of artistic verisimilitude. But Doctor Parkman certainly moved upon another source of Webster's income —the sale of lecture tickets—and after he had been fobbed off once more, threatened legal processes to get at this source of cash. On Monday night of this week he had called at the Massachusetts Medical College. Here is the scene and here is the interview, as they were described by Littlefield, the janitor.

It was in Doctor Webster's back private room. It was somewhat dark in that room. . . . I was helping Doctor Webster, who had three or four candles burning. The Doctor stood at a table, looking at a chemical book, and appeared to be reading—his back toward the door. I stood by the stove, stirring some water, in which a solution was to be made. I never heard a footstep; but the first I saw, Doctor Parkman came into the back room. . . . Doctor Webster looked around, and appeared surprised to see him enter so suddenly. The first words he said were:

"Doctor Webster, are you ready for me tonight?"

Doctor Parkman spoke quick and loud. Doctor Webster made answer:

"No, I am not ready, tonight, Doctor."

Doctor Parkman said something else. . . . He either accused Doctor Webster of selling something that had been mortgaged before . . . or something like that. He took some papers out of his pocket. Doctor Parkman said:

"It is so, and you know it."

Doctor Webster told him:

"I will see you tomorrow, Doctor."

Doctor Parkman stood near the door; he put his hand up, and said:

"Doctor, something must be accomplished tomorrow."

He then went out and it was the last time I saw him in the building.

Nothing, however, was accomplished on the morrow toward settling the trouble between the two doctors, and now it is four days later, Friday, November 23d, in the week before Thanksgiving. An unlucky Friday for both men. Professor Webster has paid a sudden and rather mysterious call at Doctor Parkman's house before nine o'clock this morning, and made an appointment to see his creditor at the College at half-past one. Could a settlement be made at the College near an anatomical theatre, and amid the "pieces of sour mortality"—as Dickens afterward described some of the furniture of the place—which could not be done at Doctor Parkman's home? Evidently both men thought so, for here is Doctor Parkman hastening to the appointment. It is quarter before two; he is seen near the building and going toward it. He enters—or so it is supposed—and then, nobody sees him again.

Such a man as Doctor Parkman could not casually disappear from the streets of Boston, in broad daylight, without causing excitement. He was too prominent and too highly connected. He does not seem to have practised as a physician (although he was M.D. of the University of Aberdeen), but, instead, he devoted himself, too energetically, to business and finance. He was willing to accommodate an acquaintance with an advance of money, and he was not above bedevilling the debtor who seemed to be evading payment. His brother was the Reverend Doctor Parkman; but his nephew, then a young man, recently from college, was to become more distinguished than any of them, as Francis Parkman, the historian. He also had the family characteristic of determination, and it was most nobly exercised. Doctor Parkman lived in a substantial and rather gloomy-looking house, still standing at Number 8 Walnut Street. When he did not come home to dinner that Friday afternoon his family were alarmed, and by the next day were in great agitation and distress. Advertisements offering rewards were put in the newspapers, the river was dredged, empty buildings and cellars were searched.

On Sunday afternoon, Professor Webster paid a sudden and surprising visit at the Reverend Doctor Parkman's house and aroused astonishment by his abrupt manner. The Professor acknowledged having had an interview with the missing man on Friday afternoon. According to this account, they had parted at the end of the interview. To other persons about the College the Professor said that he had met the Doctor by appointment, had paid him $483, and that the Doctor had rushed out with this money in his hand. The inference served to bolster up the popular theory that Doctor Parkman had been waylaid somewhere, robbed, and murdered.

Professor Webster's actions were strange, both before and after the disappearance of Doctor Parkman, and at last he completely astounded the janitor, on Tuesday, by giving him an order for a Thanksgiving turkey. It was the first gift he had ever made to Littlefield in an acquaintance of seven years. Finally, Littlefield became tired of hearing on the street that Doctor Parkman would be found in the College, and he resolved to investigate a vault below Professor Webster's own apartments. Only superficial examination of the College had been made so far, in the searches which were going on all over Boston and Cambridge. But the janitor, with crowbars and chisels, and with his wife on guard to warn him of the approach of Webster, put in parts of two or three days trying to break through a brick wall, and inspect the contents of the vault. Thanksgiving was a gloomy day with him, in spite of Profesor Webster's turkey, for he spent the morning cleaning up his own cellar, and the afternoon pounding and prying at the tough courses of brick in the vault. He had some relief at night, however, when he went to a ball given by the Sons of Temperance, where he stayed until four o'clock in the morning, and danced eighteen out of the twenty dances. Ah, there were janitors in those days!

On Friday, one week after Doctor Parkman's disappearance, Littlefield broke through the wall and looked into the vault.

"I held my light forward," he said, "and the first thing which I saw was the pelvis of a man and two parts of a leg. The water was running down on these remains from the sink. I knew it was no place for these things."

College officers and the city marshal were notified; three policemen were sent to Cambridge to bring Professor Webster to Boston, and put him under arrest.

The policemen told the Professor, when they reached his house, that a further search was to be made at the College, and that his presence was desired. He came willingly enough, and talked pleasantly with them, until he found that the carriage had been driven, not to the College, but to the jail. Then he asked:

"What does this mean?"

The officer replied:

"We have done looking for Doctor Parkman, and you are in custody for the murder of Doctor Parkman."

He became greatly agitated, requested water to drink, and then asked a torrent of questions:

"Have they found Doctor Parkman? Where did they find him? Did they find the whole of the body? How came they to suspect me? Oh! my children, what will they do? Oh! what will they think of me?"

The officer in charge told him that he must not ask questions which it would be improper for him to answer, and then asked Professor Webster if anybody had access to his private apartments in the College.

"Nobody," he replied, "except the porter who makes the fire."

He paused for a minute and then added:

"That villain! I am a ruined man!"

After a few moments spent in pacing the floor, he sat down, took something from his waistcoat pocket, and put it to his mouth. This was followed by a spasm, and he was soon helpless. The officers helped him to rise and assisted him to a cell, where he lay down. He had a serious of violent spasms, but was able, about an hour afterward, to go to the College, in charge of the officers, while a further inspection was made. At a later date, Professor Webster said that before he left the carriage, he took a dose of strychnine, which he had already prepared. He supposed that his nervous condition prevented it from acting fatally, as he thought it was a large dose.

The excitement in Boston was intense when it became known that Professor Webster had been arrested. It is said that two companies of militia were ordered out, but for what purpose, I do not know.

The list of the academic distinctions of John White Webster is rather long. His college class was that of 1811. He was Master of Arts and Doctor of Medicine of Harvard; a member of the American Academy of Arts and Sciences; of the London Geological Society, and of other learned bodies. He had written and edited some books on chemistry, and another describing one of the Azores, where his married daughter dwelt. Senator Hoar, who attended his lectures, said that he seemed "a kind-hearted, fussy person," but that his lectures were the most tedious compositions to which he ever listened. Owing to the fact that he had insisted on having fireworks at the inauguration of President Everett, the students called him "Skyrocket Jack."

At one of his chemistry lectures, there had been a violent explosion of a copper vessel, part of which flew into the back of the classroom, and except for the fact that a student was absent and there was a vacancy in the row where the metal fragment struck, one of his auditors might have been killed. The Professor had commented drily:

"The President sent for me and told me I must be more careful. He said I should feel very badly indeed if I had killed one of the students. And I should."

Professor Andrew Peabody, writing many years after the trial, said:

> Of Professor Webster I have not an unkind word to say. I never supposed him to be a great man; and he certainly was not interesting as a teacher, nor was he often successful in his chemical experiments. But he was good-natured in the classroom; and during my tutorship I was often invited to his too hospitable house, and became acquainted with his charming family.

When he was brought to trial in March, many persons still believed him innocent. Others thought that the case against him would fail, for lack of proof that the remains were those of Doctor Parkman. Some of his friends tried to induce Rufus Choate to undertake the defence, but that great attorney, after hearing the evidence, refused to enter the case unless the Professor would admit the killing, and permit him to try to convince the jury that it was manslaughter, not murder. This, the Websters refused to consider. Those who, like Charles Sumner, still believed in the Professor's innocence, probably did not understand the strength of the evidence which was to be brought forward

The trial, before Chief Justice Shaw, is one of the landmarks in the history of criminal law in Massachusetts. Everyone was impressed by the gravity of the occasion, and the proceedings were extremely dignified. The jury could not have been excelled for seriousness of purpose and religious demeanour if they had been chosen from the House of Bishops. To accommodate the great numbers of folk who wished to see something of the trial, the floor of the Court was closed to all but privileged spectators, while the general public were admitted to the gallery, where, it is astonishing to learn, a change of audience was effected by the police every ten minutes! "Except for two tumultuous movements," order and quiet were preserved, and *from 55,000 to 60,000 persons had a glimpse of the proceedings.* The trial lasted for eleven days, and the New York *Herald,* a paper of four pages, was one of many which adopted the extraordinary policy of reporting the events daily, in three or four closely printed columns, and on the front page.

The testimony of Littlefield was of great importance; he was examined for hours. He described the interview between the two doctors, and then said that on that same day Professor Webster had inquired of him about the condition of the vault where were placed the remains from the dissecting room. On Thursday, the day before Doctor Parkman disappeared, Professor Webster sent the witness to the Massachusetts General Hospital on an unsuccessful errand to get a jar of blood. Littlefield saw Doctor Parkman coming toward the College on the Friday, but did not see him enter. During the next few days, the Professor was locked in his apartment at hours which were not customary; unusual fires were burning in the furnace; a stream of water could be heard running in the sink. After the search for Doctor Parkman had begun, Webster told Littlefield that he had paid $483 and some cents to Doctor Parkman, who had hurried out with it.

The State produced evidence that the prisoner had performed a number of feats of juggling with checks and notes, which the defence could not explain. Professor Webster told Doctor Parkman's agent that he had "settled" with Doctor Parkman; as, indeed, he had, but not in the manner in which the agent was intended to understand the phrase. Fragments of false teeth were found in the furnace, and in addition to what had been discovered in the vault, other larger parts of a human body in a tea chest filled with tanbark. And Webster had had a quantity of tanbark brought in from Cambridge, during the week, by Sawin the expressman—a name familiar to generations of Harvard students.

Prisoners, at that period, were not allowed to testify, but Professor Webster's counsel entered for him a complete denial. They raised doubts whether the pieces of a human frame were those of Doctor Parkman, and suggested that, even if this were true, the fragments had been placed there by some person, unknown to Professor Webster, and perhaps in order to incriminate him. The tendency of the defence was to suggest the possible guilt of Littlefield. They tried to show, by witnesses, that Doctor Parkman had been seen later on that Friday, and in other parts of the city. Two or three witnesses appeared; some of them were mistaken as to the date, and others mistook a man of similar appearance for the Doctor.

Despite the strong net of circumstantial evidence closing around Professor Webster, the whole case for the State hinged on the proof of the identity of the remains, and in the final analysis this rested upon the evidence about the false teeth. When Doctor Nathan Keep, a friend of both men, who had made the teeth for Doctor Parkman, gave his positive evidence, and proved its correctness by fitting the mould, still in his possession, to the fragments found in the furnace, he burst into tears, as he realized that his testimony would hang the prisoner.

A large number of Professor Webster's neighbours, friends, and colleagues appeared in his behalf, and testified as to his good character. He was nearly sixty years of age, and since he was generally respected, even if not very well liked, it was difficult for the jury to believe him guilty of the offence. One of his character witnesses was Jared Sparks, president of Harvard. Oliver Wendell Holmes had testified for the State; he had been lecturing on anatomy in the room above Doctor Webster's at the time of the meeting with Doctor Parkman. Professor Webster was allowed to make a statement to the jury, and was so unwise as to accept the opportunity. He spoke for about fifteen minutes, criticizing his own counsel, and referring to details of the case brought against him. Chief Justice Shaw's charge to the jury is a celebrated address; parts of it, especially those relating to the nature and value of circumstantial evidence, are quoted in courts to-day. The case against Professor Webster was purely one of circumstantial evidence; nobody had seen the two men together at the time of the murder.

On the evening of the eleventh day of the trial, the jury went out for three hours and came in about midnight with a verdict of "guilty."

Professor Webster was sentenced to death, but the usual appeals were made in his behalf. When the application for a writ of error was dismissed, the Professor addressed the Governor and Council, and in the most solemn language protested his innocence. He used such remarkable phrases as these:

"To Him who seeth in secret, and before Whom I may ere long be called to appear, would I appeal for the truth of what I now declare . . ." and "Repeating in the most solemn and positive manner, and under the fullest sense of my responsibility as a man and as a Christian, that I am

wholly innocent of this charge, to the truth of which the Searcher of all
hearts is a witness. . . ."

Some weeks later, this address was withdrawn, and the wretched man
made a long confession, maintaining that the murder was not premeditated.
Professor Webster described his call on the doctor on the Friday morning,
and their appointment to meet that afternoon, at the College. He then
wrote:

He came, accordingly, between half-past one and two. He came in
at the lecture-room door. I was engaged in removing some glasses from
my lecture-room table into the room in the rear, called the upper
laboratory. He came rapidly down the steps and followed me into the
laboratory. He immediately addressed me with great energy.

"Are you ready for me, sir? Have you got the money?"

I replied:

"No, Doctor Parkman," and was then beginning to state my condition and make my appeal to him. He would not listen to me, but interrupted me with much vehemence. He called me "scoundrel" and "liar,"
and went on heaping upon me the most bitter taunts and opprobrious
epithets. While he was talking, he drew a handful of papers from his
pocket, and took from among them my two notes, and also an old letter
from Doctor Hosack, written many years ago, and congratulating him
(Doctor P.) on his success in getting me appointed professor of chemistry.

"You see," he said, "I got you into your office, and now I will get you
out of it."

He put back into his pockets all the papers, except the letter and
the notes. I cannot tell how long the torrent of threats and invectives
continued, and I can now recall to memory but a small portion of what
he said.

At first I kept interposing, trying to pacify him, so that I might
obtain the object for which I had sought the interview. But I could not
stop him, and soon my own temper was up. I forgot everything. I felt
nothing but the sting of his words. I was excited to the highest degree of
passion; and while he was speaking and gesticulating in the most violent
and menacing manner, thrusting the letter and his fist into my face, in
my fury I seized whatever thing was handiest—it was a stick of wood—
and dealt him an instantaneous blow with all the force that passion
could give it. I did not know, nor think, nor care where I should hit
him, nor how hard, nor what the effect would be. It was on the side of
his head, and there was nothing to break the force of the blow. He fell
instantly upon the pavement. There was no second blow. He did not
move. I stooped down over him, and he seemed to be lifeless. Blood

flowed from his mouth, and I got a sponge and wiped it away. I got some ammonia and applied it to his nose; but without effect.

Perhaps I spent ten minutes in attempts to resuscitate him; but I found that he was absolutely dead. In my horror and consternation I ran instinctively to the doors and bolted them—the doors of the lecture room and of the laboratory below. And then, what was I to do?

It never occurred to me to go out and declare what had been done and obtain assistance. I saw nothing but the alternative of a successful removal and concealment of the body, on the one hand, and of infamy and destruction on the other. The first thing I did, as soon as I could do anything, was to drag the body into the private room adjoining. There I took off the clothes, and began putting them into the fire which was burning in the upper laboratory. They were all consumed there that afternoon—with papers, pocketbook, or whatever else they may have contained. I did not examine the pockets, nor remove anything except the watch. I saw that, or the chain of it, hanging out; and I took it and threw it over the bridge as I went to Cambridge.

My next move was to get the body into the sink which stands in the small private room. By setting the body partially erect against the corner, and getting up into the sink myself, I succeeded in drawing it up. There it was entirely dismembered. It was quickly done, as a work of terrible and desperate necessity. The only instrument used was the knife found by the officers in the tea chest, and which I kept for cutting corks. I made no use of the Turkish knife, as it was called at the trial. . . .

While dismembering the body, a stream of (water) was running through the sink, carrying off the blood in a pipe that passed down through the lower laboratory. There must have been a leak in the pipe, for the ceiling below was stained immediately round it.

Professor Webster made a long and plausible appeal for commutation of sentence, basing his claim, not only on the assertion—quite possibly correct —that the blow had been struck in a momentary fit of anger,[1] but upon his argument that every act of his own showed there had been no premeditation. His call in the morning to make an appointment, so he declared, would have been an insane act if he had planned to kill Doctor Parkman.

The Governor, however, could not admit that the prisoner's word was entitled to credit, nor did his pastor, or some of his friends, venture to suggest that he could be believed. Professor Webster was hanged on the last Friday in August, 1850. He was calm and apparently resigned. He had

---

[1] Professor Peabody, in the book already quoted, expresses his firm belief that this was true. Many persons have always held the same opinion.

apologized humbly to Littlefield for the attempts to throw suspicion upon him, and he wrote a letter, in a spirit of deep contrition, to the Reverend Doctor Parkman, to make what peace he could with the family he had wronged.

Was it a coldly premeditated murder, or can it be considered man-slaughter, done in a sudden passion and under provocation? The question about the vault, the attempt to get the blood, and, perhaps, the appointment with Parkman at the College point to a plan. On the other hand, he gave more or less plausible explanations of all these things, and the absurdity of any hope to make away with such a man as Doctor Parkman, and conceal the crime, is so great as to cast doubts upon the theory of premeditation. The question seems to me impossible to answer.

The murder shows these things clearly: that a hitherto highly respectable person may commit a crime of this nature; that he may solemnly lie in the name of God, to escape punishment; and that a just conviction may be had upon circumstantial evidence. Even after the trial there were many who were unconvinced of the Professor's guilt, and A. Oakey Hall, afterward Mayor of New York, was one of those who wrote pamphlets to protest against the conviction. Mr. Hall was very severe upon what he denounced as the results of "Puritan bigotry" and "Bostonian snobbishness," but what course he took after the prisoner had confessed does not appear at this date.

The Webster-Parkman case has hardly been displaced as America's most celebrated murder, and the one which lives longest in the books of reminiscences. It will be recalled that Artemus Ward's show had "wax figgers" of "Doctor Webster in the act of killin' Doctor Parkman." Few writers of the time failed to mention the murder. Of the anecdotes which are told about it, the story related by Longfellow is perhaps the most remarkable. This was told at a dinner given to Charles Dickens, during his visit in 1869. Dickens, during the day, had visited the scene of the murder, with Doctor Holmes. A year or two before the murder, Longfellow had been one of the guests at a men's dinner at Professor Webster's, to meet a foreign visitor, interested in science. Toward the end of the evening, the Professor had the lights in the room lowered and a servant bring in a bowl of burning chemicals, which shed a ghastly glow upon the faces of the men about the table. Professor Webster rose, and producing a rope, cast it around his own neck like a noose. He then leaned over the hell fires which came from the bowl, lolled his head upon one side, and protruded his tongue in the manner of a man who had been hanged!

After the execution, it is said that the Webster family removed to Fayal, where a married daughter lived. Some years later, at a dinner party, there was a glib guest who had not caught the names of some of the Websters who were present, but merely knew that they had come from Boston. In order to make himself agreeable, he suddenly remarked:

"Oh, by the way, what ever became of that Professor Webster who killed Doctor Parkman? Did they hang him?"

Another similarly gentle yarn is of a later date. Benjamin Butler was cross-examining a witness in Court, and treating him, so the Judge thought, with unnecessary brusqueness. He reminded the lawyer that the witness was a Harvard professor.

"Yes, I know, your Honour. We hanged one of them the other day!"

But Ben Butler always had a sinful dislike of Harvard. They had refused to give him an LL.D.

The Four Horsemen

FROM *The New York Tribune*

This description of the 1924 Army-Notre Dame game scores on two counts. It is one of the very memorable pieces of sports writing, and the game it reviewed has yet to be matched for sheer thrills.

The four players who made up the South Bend backfield will live in football history and memory for a long time as "The Four Horsemen," the name Rice created for them on that big day.

There are probably no more than a handful of Phi Beta Kappas who took to sports writing. Grantland Rice, dean of the profession, became one of the learned brothers at Vanderbilt in 1901.

OUTLINED against a blue-gray sky, the Four Horsemen rode again. In dramatic lore they are known as Famine, Pestilence, Destruction, and Death. These are only aliases. Their real names are Stuhldreher, Miller, Crowley, and Layden. They formed the crest of the South Bend cyclone before which another fighting Army football team was swept over the precipice at the Polo Grounds yesterday afternoon as 55,000 spectators peered down on a bewildering panorama spread on the green plain below.

A cyclone can't be snared. It may be surrounded, but somewhere it breaks through to keep on going. When the cyclone starts from South Bend, where the candlelights still gleam through the Indiana sycamores, those in the way must take to storm cellars at top speed. Yesterday the cyclone struck again as Notre Dame beat the Army, 13–7, with a set of backfield stars that ripped and crashed through a strong Army defense with more speed and power than the warring cadets could meet.

Notre Dame won its ninth game in twelve Army starts through the driving power of one of the greatest backfields that ever churned up the turf of any gridiron in any football age. Brilliant backfields may come and go, but with Stuhldreher, Miller, Crowley, and Layden, covered by a fast and charging line, Notre Dame can take its place in front of the field.

Coach McEwan sent one of his finest teams into action, an aggressive organization that fought to the last play around the first rim of darkness, but when Rockne rushed his Four Horsemen to the track they rode down everything in sight. It was in vain that 1400 gray-clad cadets pleaded for the Army line to hold. The Army line was giving all it had, but when a tank tears in with the speed of a motorcycle, what chance has flesh and blood to hold? The Army had its share of stars in action, such stars as Garbisch, Farwick, Wilson, Wood, Ellinger, and many others, but they were up against four whirlwind backs who picked up top speed from the first step as they swept through scant openings to slip on by the secondary defense. The Army had great backs in Wilson and Wood, but the Army had no such quartet who seemed to carry the mixed blood of the tiger and the antelope.

Rockne's light and tottering line was just about as tottering as the Rock of Gibraltar. It was something more than a match for the Army's great set of forwards, who had earned their fame before. Yet it was not until the second period that the first big thrill of the afternoon set the great crowd into a cheering whirl and brought about the wild flutter of flags that are thrown to the wind in exciting moments. At the game's start Rockne sent in almost entirely a second-string cast. The Army got the jump and began to play most of the football. It was the Army attack that made three first downs before Notre Dame had caught its stride. The South Bend cyclone opened like a zephyr.

And then in the wake of a sudden cheer, out rushed Stuhldreher, Miller, Crowley, and Layden, the four star backs who helped to beat the Army a year ago. Things were to be a trifle different now. After a short opening flurry in the Army second period, Wood of Army kicked out of bounds on the Notre Dame twenty-yard line. The cloud in the West at this point was no longer than a football. There was no sign of a tornado starting, but it happened to be at just this spot that Stuhldreher decided to put on their attack and begin the long dusty hike.

On the first play the fleet Crowley peeled off fifteen yards and the cloud from the West was now beginning to show signs of lightning and thunder. The fleet, powerful Layden got six yards more and then Don Miller added ten. A forward pass from Stuhldreher to Crowley added twelve yards and a moment later Don Miller ran twenty yards around the Army's right wing. He was on his way to glory when Wilson, hurtling across the right of way, nailed him on the fifteen-yard line and threw him out of bounds. Crowley, Miller, and Layden—Miller, Layden, and Crowley—one or another ripping and crashing through, as the Army defense threw everything it had in the way to stop this wild charge that had now come seventy yards. Crowley and

Layden added five yards more and then, on a split play, Layden went ten yards across the line as if he had just been fired from the black mouth of a howitzer.

In that second period Notre Dame made eight first downs to the Army's none, which shows the unwavering power of the Western attack that hammered relentlessly and remorselessly without easing up for a second's breath. The Western line was going its full share, led by the crippled Walsh with a broken hand.

But always there was Miller or Crowley or Layden, directed through the right spot by the cool and crafty judgment of Stuhldreher, who picked his plays with the finest possible generalship. The South Bend cyclone had now roared eighty-five yards to a touchdown through one of the strongest defensive teams in the game. The cyclone had struck with too much speed and power to be stopped. It was the preponderance of Western speed that swept the Army back.

The next period was much like the second. The trouble began when the alert Layden intercepted an Army pass on the forty-eight-yard line. Stuhldreher was ready for another march.

Once again the cheering cadets began to call for a rallying stand. They are never overwhelmed by any shadows of defeat as long as there is a minute of fighting left. But silence fell over the cadet sector for just a second as Crowley ran around the Army's right wing for fifteen yards, where Wilson hauled him down on the thirty-five-yard line. Walsh, the Western captain, was hurt in the play, but soon resumed. Miller got seven and Layden got eight and then, with the ball on the Army's twenty-yard line, the cadet defense rallied and threw Miller in his tracks. But the halt was only for the moment. On the next play Crowley swung around the Army's left wing, cut in, and then crashed over the line for Notre Dame's second touchdown.

On two other occasions the Notre Dame attack almost scored—Yeomans saving one touchdown by intercepting a pass on his five-yard line as he ran thirty-five yards before he was nailed by two tacklers. It was a great play in the nick of time. On the next drive Miller and Layden in two hurricane dashes took the ball forty-two yards to the Army's fourteen-yard line, where the still game Army defense stopped four plunges on the nine-yard line and took the ball.

Up to this point the Army had been outplayed by a crushing margin. Notre Dame had put under way four long marches, and two of these had yielded touchdowns. Even the stout and experienced Army line was meeting more than it could hold. Notre Dame's brilliant backs had been provided with the finest possible interference, usually led by Stuhldreher, who cut down tackler after tackler by diving headlong at some rival's flying knees. Against this each Army attack had been smothered almost before it got under way. Even the great Wilson, the star from Penn State, one of the great backfield runners of his day and time, rarely had a chance to make any headway through a massed wall of tacklers who were blocking every open route.

The sudden change came late in the third quarter, when Wilson, raging like a wild man, suddenly shot through a tackle opening to run thirty-four yards on to midfield before he was finally collared and thrown with a jolt. A few moments later Wood, one of the best of all the punters, kicked out of bounds on Notre Dame's five-yard line. Here was the chance. Layden was forced to kick from behind his own goal. The punt soared up the field as Yeomans called for a free kick on the thirty-five-yard line. As he caught the ball he was nailed and spilled by a Western tackler, and the penalty gave the Army fifteen yards, with the ball on Notre Dame's twenty-yard line.

At this moment Harding was rushed to quarter in place of Yeomans, who had been one of the leading Army stars. On the first three plays the Army reached the twelve-yard line, but it was now fourth down, with two yards left to go. Harding's next play was the feature of the game.

As the ball was passed he faked a play to Wood, diving through the line, held the oval for just a half breath, and then, tucking the same under his arm, swung out around Notre Dame's right end. The brilliant fake worked to perfection. The entire Notre Dame defense had charged forward in a surging mass to check the line attack and Harding, with open territory, sailed on for a touchdown. He traveled those last twelve yards after the manner of food shot from guns. He was over the line before the Westerners knew what had taken place. It was a fine bit of strategy brilliantly carried out by every member of the cast.

The cadet sector had its chance to rip open the chilly atmosphere at last, and most of the 55,000 present joined in the tribute to football art. But this was the Army's last chance to score. From that point on it was seesaw, up and down, back and forth, with the rivals fighting bitterly for every inch of ground. It was harder now to make a foot than it had been to make ten yards. Even the all-star South Bend cast could no longer continue a romp for any set distances, as Army tacklers, inspired by the touchdown, charged harder and faster than they had charged before.

The Army brought a fine football team into action, but it was beaten by a faster and smoother team. Rockne's supposedly light green line was about as big as the Army's and every whit as aggressive. What is even more important, it was faster on its feet, faster in getting around.

It was Western speed and perfect interference that once more brought about Army doom. The Army line couldn't get through fast enough to break up the attacking plays, and once started the bewildering speed and power of the Western backs slashed along for eight, ten, and fifteen yards on play after play. And always in front of these offensive drives could be found the whirling form of Stuhldreher, taking the first man out of the play as cleanly as if he had used a hand grenade at close range. This Notre Dame interference was a marvelous thing to look upon.

It formed quickly and came along in unbroken order, always at terrific speed, carried by backs who were as hard to drag down as African buffaloes. On receiving the kickoff, Notre Dame's interference formed something after the manner of the ancient flying wedge and they drove back the field with the runner covered for twenty-five and thirty yards at almost every chance. It was speed that beat the Army, speed plus interference. And when a back such as Harry Wilson finds few chances to get started you can figure upon the defensive strength that is barricading the road. Wilson is one of the hardest backs in the game to suppress, but he found few chances yesterday to show his broken field ability. You can't run through a broken field until you get there.

One strong feature of the Army play was its headlong battle against heavy odds. Even when Notre Dame had scored two touchdowns and was well on its way to a third, the Army fought on with fine spirit until the touchdown chance came at last. And when this chance came Coach McEwan had the play ready for the final march across the line. The Army has a better team than it had last year. So has Notre Dame. We doubt that any team in the country could have beaten Rockne's array yesterday afternoon. East or West. It was a great football team brilliantly directed, a team of speed, power, and team play. The Army has no cause for gloom over its showing. It played first-class football against more speed than it could match.

Those who have tackled a cyclone can understand.

According to the
Encyclopedia

FROM *Encyclopædia Britannica*

Anyone who has seen, heard, or participated in collegiate cheering is aware of the infectious excitement it arouses. The rhythm, the repetitions, the nonsense words and the untrammeled unison shouting of the compelling, blood-stirring chants lend them the quality of tribal ritual.

Be that as it may (like they say), scholars will be scholars: we offer as proof this edifying, deadpan definition of "Cheering"—its linguistic origin, national variants and function, together with some familiar examples— from the authoritative and scholarly Encyclopedia Britannica.

CHEERING, the uttering or making of sounds encouraging, stimulating or exciting to action, indicating approval or acclaiming or welcoming persons, announcements of events and the like. The word "cheer" meant originally face, countenance, expression (Low Lat. *cara*), and was at first qualified with epithets, both of joy and sorrow; compare "She thanked Dyomede for alle . . . his gode chere" (Chaucer, *Troylus*) with "If they sing . . . 'tis with so dull a cheere" (Shakespeare, *Sonnets*, xcvii.). An early transference in meaning was to hospitality or entertainment, and hence to food and drink, "good cheer." The sense of a shout of encouragement or applause is a late use.

Of the different words or sounds that are used in cheering, "hurrah," though now generally looked on as the typical British form of cheer, is found in various forms in German, Scandinavian, Russian (*urá*), French (*houra*); it is probably onomatopoeic in origin. The German *hoch*, the French *vive*, Italian and Spanish *viva*, *evviva*, are cries rather of acclamation than encouragement. The Japanese shout, *banzai*, became familiar during the Russo-Japanese War. In reports of parliamentary debates "cheers" indicates that approval was shown by emphatic utterances of "hear hear." Cheering may be tumultuous or it may be conducted rhythmically by prearrangement, as in the case of the "Hip-hip-hip" by way of introduction to a simultaneous "hurrah."

Rhythmical cheering has been developed to its greatest extent in America in the college yells, which may be regarded as a development of the primitive war-cry. The original yells of Harvard and Yale are identical in form, being composed of *rah* (abbreviation of *hurrah*) nine times repeated, shouted in unison with the name of the university at the end. The Yale cheer is given faster than that of Harvard. Many institutions have several different yells; the best known of these variants is the Yale cheer, partly taken from the *Frogs* of Aristophanes:

> Brekekekéx, ko-áx, ko-áx,
> Brekekekéx, ko-áx, ko-áx,
> O-óp, O-óp, parabaloú,
> Yale, Yale, Yale,
> Rah, rah, rah, rah, rah, rah,
>   rah, rah, rah,
> Yale! Yale! Yale!

The "triple cheer" of Princeton is:

> H'ray, h'ray, h'ray,
> Tiger, tiger, tiger,
> Siss, siss, siss,
> Boom, boom, boom,
> Ah, ah, ah,
> Princetón, Princetón, Princetón!

The "railroad cheer" is like the foregoing, but begun very slowly and broadly, and gradually accelerated to the end, which is enunciated as fast as possible. Many cheers are formed like that of Toronto university:

> Varsitý, varsitý,
> V-a-r-s-i-t-y (spelled)
> VARSIT-Y (spelled *staccato*)
> Vár-si-tý,
> Rah, rah, rah!

The cheer of the United States Naval academy is an imitation of a nautical siren. The Amherst cheer is:

Amherst! Amherst! Amherst! Rah! Rah!
Amherst! Rah! Rah!
Rah! Rah! Rah! Rah! Rah! Rah! Amherst!

Besides the cheers of individual institutions there are some common to to all, generally used to compliment some successful athlete or popular professor. One of the oldest examples of these personal cheers is:

Who was George Washington?
First in war,
First in peace,
First in the heárts of his countrymén,

followed by a stamping on the floor in the same rhythm.

College yells are used particularly at athletic contests. In any large college there are several leaders, chosen by the students, who stand in front and call for the different songs and cheers, directing with their arms in the fashion of an orchestral conductor. Cheering and singing form one of the distinctive features of intercollegiate and scholastic athletic contests in America.

Drop in on Me Sometime

FROM *A Pause in the Desert*

With uncommon insight, Oliver La Farge, in this short story, portrays the student who stands on the outside looking in.

Most of La Farge's perceptive novels and stories center about American Indian life, that of the Navajos in particular. He writes of them with perhaps greater understanding than any other American writer.

La Farge studied anthropology at Harvard, was an editor of Lampoon, class poet, and won his B.A. in 1924. In Twentieth Century Authors, Stanley Kunitz points out: "To this day there are anthropologists who hope devoutly that he will fail as an author and come back to their field."

THE ROOM was furnished with what the college issued: a desk, placed dead centre under the overhead light, a table, three wooden chairs, a bed, a bureau, and an empty fireplace, the brick floor of which was free of ashes and cigarette butts. One shelf of the bookcase was almost filled with textbooks, a one-volume edition of Shakespeare, and a Bible. On the table were two notebooks and a dictionary, a cup and saucer, a plate, and a small electric stove with a saucepan on it. A calendar and two pine cones had been arranged on the mantelpiece in an effort at decoration. There was a framed photograph of a middle-aged woman on the bureau, and two neckties hung from a corner of the mirror. The room looked as if its occupant had moved in that afternoon and would leave tomorrow.

The boy paced slowly, methodically, between the fireplace and the bookcase. Passing the window, he caught the smell of the night—the new, disturbing mildness of spring—and he could hear voices below on the campus. He was tall, thin, fair-haired, with too much Adam's apple and too long a nose. He was not thinking, he was stringing out the time before he should decide to take a walk.

In a few moments he would put on necktie and coat and go downstairs. As he stepped outside, he would feel a faint anticipation, a nameless, automatic stirring of hope, which he would quickly discount by a defensive reflex, a moment of pain never admitted. Then he would stroll. If he met fellows who sat in his classes, he would walk a little faster until he passed them, but sometimes even so they would remember him and nod, or say "Hello" or even "Hello, Matterson." He would say "Hello" and go on by, letting them continue their appointed ways. His own pace, too, would be a declaration that he was going somewhere.

By one route or another he would come to the Women's School. Here his walk would be a swinging, unhesitating stride. He would not turn his head, he would just go on through, but his eyes would take in a wide range, the groups of girls and the pairs of girls and fellows. Last week, the first night of the warm weather, a man who sat next him in Biochemistry passed him with a girl. He said, "Hi, Matterson. Sparking?" He'd answered, "Hello, Newman. Just scouting," and Newman and the girl had laughed.

They were all just kids, really—as old as he, but nothing had taught them seriousness. His brain could run rings around them. He wasn't interested in their eternal play.

Beyond the School he would come out into the town, buy a paper, and then return to his room, the room he was walking up and down now, not thinking anything much except that it was time, perhaps, to go out and get a paper.

A firm knock on his door brought him up sharp. He moved to open it, then stood back and called, "Come in!"

The visitor, who entered rather self-consciously, was a well-dressed boy of medium height, neither fair nor dark, with a scrubbed, healthy face.

"Matterson?" he said. "I'm Bill Farraday. May I come in?"

"Hello. Sit down." His anger at himself for being so tense added to his stiffness.

"I live in this entry, 2 B."

Matterson knew well enough, as he knew that Farraday had his letter in hockey and was a candidate for class marshal. He nodded, watchful.

Farraday arranged himself with an effect of relaxation for which the chair was not well adapted. He looked around the room, said "Nice," then broke off. The thin boy understood; it wasn't a nice joint. Seeing that his visitor was ill at ease, he felt a shade more comfortable.

"Looks like spring had really come, doesn't it?" Farraday said. He became more assured at the sound of his own voice. "Here the winter's over, and this is the first time I've been up here." Matterson listened, guarded, protecting himself. "This college is so damn big you can't hope to know everyone, but I'd promised myself to meet all the men in this entry.

You know how it is. You get tied up in so many things and the first thing you know the ice has melted and the ball team's coming out of the cage."

Matterson said, "Yeah."

"Where do you come from? You're not from around here, are you?"

"Vermont."

"Well! Why did you pick to come here?"

"I'm going into analytical chemistry and I wanted to be under Mac-Pherson."

"Oh. Oh yeah, sure." Farraday paused again, then took off as if from a cue. "You had a scholarship?"

"Not to start with; the first two years I worked my way. Then I got the Bernstein." He was proud of that; it was the best there was in science for undergraduates. "Now I'm hoping for the Marlin Fellowship if I can get my *magna cum* all right."

Farraday looked vaguely uncomfortable. The look passed. "Good for you. I admire a guy like you and I'm glad I came up." Again his flow of talk became smooth. His voice had a flattering frankness. "Yeah, when I get out of here I'll go to Wall Street, and I guess that twenty years from now I'll be just another bond salesman living the old country-club life, and I'll be bragging about how I used to know you. I've had it easy and you've had it tough."

The Vermonter felt an unfamiliar warmth run through him. "It's been tough sometimes," he said. He hesitated, then added with an effort, "I saw you shoot that long goal against Colmouth."

"Oh, that was just luck." Farraday was visibly pleased. He pulled out a pack of cigarettes. "Smoke?"

"No thanks."

"Oh. Do you mind—"

"Go ahead."

"Come down to my rooms sometime, won't you? Sling the bull, you know. I generally have a little beer on hand—or ginger ale."

"I like beer." Matterson considered explaining that he didn't smoke on account of the expense, then decided not to.

Farraday brightened. "That's fine. I mean it. Drop in."

"Thanks." He wanted to say more, but didn't know how.

"Say, a man like you, working your way along, and then getting fellowships and things—I'd like your slant on this endowment business."

Matterson had read the ballyhoo with a mounting sense of discomfort. The University was driving for extra endowment and the Senior Class Committee had voted a graduation gift of fifteen thousand dollars, which would mean a little over twenty dollars a member. The gift was getting a big play from the Endowment Fund's publicity bureau in going after the graduates.

"Well," he said, "I guess it's a good idea."

"Yeah, I think so, too. Our tuition fees don't cover the cost of our education. When you average it up—the men on scholarships and things—the University gives us each nearly a thousand dollars." Farraday caught himself up. "Of course," he said hastily, "that's what you expect the old place to do—help men like you who really have brains. It's part of a university's proper function." He looked around. "Got an ashtray?"

"Chuck it in the fireplace."

Farraday threw the butt, then pulled out the pack again. "I guess I'm smoking a lot right now. What with the finals coming on and all the boning to do and one thing and another, I get kind of nervous." He lit up. "This endowment business on top of the rest has me about daffy. You see, I'm in charge of this entry and we're short on our quota. I dunno how it is, some of the fellows don't seem to appreciate what the old school does for them. I guess I'm a rotten collector; it kind of burns me up to get after a man if he isn't willing." He gave a short, unreal laugh. "Yeah, I hate doing it. I've upped my share to fifty bucks, though God knows, I guess it means the sheriff will be after me, what with the old unpaid bills and all." He made the last statement with a smile, as one man speaking to another of a common problem.

Matterson just watched him, saying nothing.

"I've got you down for five bucks," Farraday said. "Of course, it's up to you. You know what you can afford, spreading it over the next two months."

Matterson continued staring at him. Out of a swirl inside himself he said quietly, without a shade of defiance in his tone, "You can put me down for ten."

"Why say, that's great. Say, that's the real spirit, Matterson. Wait till I tell some of the other men that, the ones who've been holding out." He pulled at his cigarette, held it a moment, threw it in the fireplace. "Yeah, that's great. Well, look, I've got to get after some of the others now." He rose. "Don't forget to drop in on me sometime."

Matterson said, "Sure. Thanks."

Farraday answered heartily, "Thanks to you. Well, so long. Be seeing you."

"So long."

Matterson sat and stared at the long-awaited, casual disorder of the two cigarette stubs in the fireplace. Then he stood with his hands in his pockets. Ten dollars was catastrophic. Double what the rich boy thought him good for—pride stiffened in him, covering the pain of a warm moment betrayed. More slowly than usual, he tied his necktie, put on his coat, and went out.

ELLIS PARKER BUTLER

The Famous
Oklahoma-Stanford Tug-of-War

FROM *College Humor*

Paul Bunyan, who built a smokestack so tall it had to be hinged to let the clouds sail by, hadn't a thing on Bull Hyde, who pulled so hard in that famous tug-of-war that all the country between Oklahoma and California buckled up to form the Rocky Mountains—and the Rockies are there to this day to prove it, says Ellis Parker Butler.

Butler was the noted American humorist who set the whole country laughing back in the '20s with his classic, Pigs Is Pigs.

AMONG the tales they tell of Bull Hyde and Little Peewee is the one about Bull Hyde's dog Mamie. Bull and Little Peewee were juniors at the University of Oklahoma when Bull got the pup, which was only the size of a kitten then, but Bull fed it on raw beef and in a couple of weeks Mamie was as big as an ox.

She was a wonderful dog, bright green in color, and a sort of international dog—all sorts of breeds were in her. For years Little Peewee kept discovering new kinds of dog in Mamie, and as fast as he discovered a new strain in her he jotted it down in the black book.

He began on page 103, on the top line of the page, with Newfoundland, and presently he had filled all of pages 103 and 104 and was halfway down page 105, and he hadn't discovered all the kinds of dog Mamie was even then. It must have been this mixture of breeds that made Mamie grow so big. Little Peewee figured that Mamie grew one full dog size for every breed of dog in her makeup, and as he had discovered two hundred and sixty kinds of dog in Mamie by the time he had reached the middle of page 105, she was two hundred and sixty times as big as any ordinary dog. She was considerably bigger than an elephant then, and still growing.

There was a lot of complaint about Mamie to the college authorities. She had a long bushy tail, and when she was happy and wagged it the tail set up such a draft in the air that it caused cyclones which swept across Oklahoma, Kansas and Iowa, and destroyed towns and villages. Another lot of complaints came from the ranchers, because now and then Mamie would break her leash and run out on the ranches and kill three or four hundred steers playfully. But the last straw was when Mamie wagged her tail against the chapel and knocked the side wall in. Then the President issued a rule that no dogs were to be allowed on the university grounds.

The rule was so evidently aimed at Mamie that Bull Hyde became very angry. He packed up his belongings and put them in a wheelbarrow and he and Little Peewee walked across the plains to Stanford University, out in California, and took up their studies there. There were no rules against dogs at Stanford.

Bull Hyde never said a word about Oklahoma, but the President's dictum still rankled in his bosom, so to speak, and when Oklahoma challenged Stanford to a tug-of-war Bull Hyde was mighty pleased. There were some exceedingly strong men at Oklahoma then and Stanford was a little reluctant to accept the challenge, but Bull Hyde had Little Pewee go around and urge that the challenge be accepted. So it was accepted, and Bull got himself chosen on the tug-of-war team.

As soon as Oklahoma heard that Bull Hyde was to be on the team it wanted to cancel the game, because it knew Bull was still sore about the Mamie dog affair and knew what an athlete he was. For a month or two there was a lot of backing and filling—first Oklahoma would and then Oklahoma wouldn't—but finally Oklahoma agreed to let its challenge stand, provided it could make the rules.

When Stanford received the rules everybody laughed. The rules were to the effect that the tug-of-war was to be pulled, but that the Oklahoma team should remain at Oklahoma and the Stanford team remain at Stanford. When the Stanford men looked at the map they were amazed; the two universities were almost 1,500 miles apart, but Bull Hyde said it didn't matter to him—he said he would pull against Oklahoma if Oklahoma was in China.

The outcome was that a stout steel cable was obtained and stretched from Stanford to Oklahoma, and somewhere near Ouray in Colorado a knot was tied in the cable and a mark made.

On the day of the tug everyone on both sides was in fine condition and Bull Hyde never felt finer.

The Stanford team got down and braced their feet and grasped the cable and waited for the word to pull, but just then the Dean rushed out and cried that all the tug-of-war contestants but Bull Hyde had flunked in math and could not pull.

"Never mind!" Bull Hyde said, "I'll pull alone then!"

He braced his feet and set his teeth and gripped the cable hard, and just then the word came by telegraph from Ouray, "Pull!" Bull Hyde pulled. The muscles on his arms and back knotted like ropes and his face turned almost purple with exertion, and Mamie jumped around him barking and cavorting. Little Peewee stood there with the black book in his hand shouting, "Pull, Bull! Atta boy, Bull!" But the cable did not give an inch. So Bull Hyde took a deep breath and pulled harder than ever.

For full five minutes Bull Hyde pulled, not gaining an inch and not losing an inch, one man against the whole Oklahoma team. Then the Stanford Glee Club came out and sang the Stanford battle songs, but still the cable did not swerve an inch toward Bull. They could see his face grow redder and redder, and his muscles throbbed like a sore tooth, but the cable never budged. Possibly Bull Hyde might have given up if another telegram had not arrived. It was from a graduate of Stanford who happened to be at Norman, Oklahoma, and he wired: "Foul play! Oklahoma's end of the cable is tied to a concrete steel-reinforced pillar, ninety feet square, set one half mile deep into Oklahoma soil."

When Bull Hyde heard this telegram he set his jaws and a glitter came into his eyes.

"Now, just for that I will pull my darn'dest!" he said, and he reached forward and got a new grip on the cable and pulled as no man had ever pulled before.

Then, inch by inch and foot by foot, the cable began to yield and pile up behind Bull Hyde, while Little Peewee jumped and yelled with joy. Bull Hyde pulled until he had eight or ten miles of cable piled up behind him, and then he grinned triumphantly and quit pulling.

"No use," came another telegram from the Stanford man at Norman, Oklahoma, a few minutes later, "concrete pillar holds fast. Strain on cable wonderful but nothing yielding here."

It wasn't until two weeks later that folks discovered what had happened. A San Francisco man who had business at Ouray came back and reported. Bull Hyde had pulled so hard that the entire plain around Ouray had buckled up as Bull pulled Oklahoma toward California, forming what are now known as the Rocky Mountains.

There was quite a little complaining from one person and another because the plains had been squeezed up into mountains that way, and Bull Hyde promised to go over and smooth the mountains down again, but I guess he never got around to it. They were still there the last time I went to California.

S. J. PERELMAN

The Love Decoy

FROM *Crazy Like a Fox*

In the area of what Robert Benchley termed the dementia praecox field
of humor, S. J. Perelman stands unmatched. Another critic called his screwball wit the most erudite surrealism in the language. Perelman himself, in
a critical preface to a volume of his own work, signed Sidney Namlerep,
has this to say: "In his pages proliferate all the weird grammatical flora
tabulated by H. W. Fowler in his Modern English Usage—the Elegant
Variation, the Facetious Zeugma, the Cast-Iron Idiom, the Battered Ornament, the Bower's-Bird Phrase, the Sturdy Indefensible, the Side-Slip and
the Unequal Yoke-Fellow."

With this warning, then, we leave you to Perelman and his "Story of
Youth in College Today—Awake, Fearless, Unashamed."

PROFESSOR GOMPERS is ill!" The whisper spread like wildfire
through the packed classroom. A feeling of emulsion swept over me. Kindly
old Professor Gompers, whose grizzled chin and chiselled grin had made his
name a byword at Tunafish College for Women! Ivy Nüdnick, sauciest co-ed
in the class, she of the unruly locks and the candied gray eyes, leaned over
to impart the latest gossip.

"That new instructor, Russell Gipf, is subbing for him!" The color
drained slowly from my face, entered the auricle, shot up the escalator, and
issued from the ladies' and misses' section into the housewares department. I remembered Russell Gipf as a lean brown giant in tweeds whose
resemblance to Warren William had caused his suspension the year before.
It had been an ugly scandal but luckily his nose was broken in an accident soon after and the faculty had restored him. Dreamily I recalled an
autumn afternoon when I had visited him in his office in ivy-colored
Schneider to discuss a theme I had written. Through the half-open windows
drifted the mingled smell of wood smoke and freshmen. He confided that

230

he was doing research in dirty limericks for his doctor's thesis and asked if I knew any "Good Ones." In the twinkling of an eye we were in the gutter. At no time, however, did he allow himself the usual indecent proposal, and I returned to my dormitory room raging, determined never to see him again.

An impatient voice summoned me rudely from my daydream. I looked up; Russell Gipf was addressing me crisply from the platform. My feminine eye noted that he was still a spiffy dresser, a regular up-to-the-minute gink.

"Will you please answer the question, Miss Hornbostel?"

"I—I didn't hear it," I quavered.

"Well, Miss 'Lame Brain'," he retorted sardonically, "maybe you had better stop galvanizing around nights and pay attention!" A cold fury welled up in me and I longed to hang one on his lug for his insolence. I was seething but he could not see it, for several of my girl chums were seething in front of me. A moment later the bell tolling in ivy-covered Hoffenstein brought the class to a close. Slipping my pencil box and pen wipers into my corsage I approached his desk, a plan fermenting in my brain.

"Yes, Miss Hornbostel?" Russel Gipf's eyes were dancing with fun.

"Oh, Mr. Gipf," I began, "I hardly know how to say this. It—it's so personal." His eyes stopped dancing with fun and began dancing with sex.

"Go on," he urged.

"I—I can't get the cap off my toothpaste," I faltered, a tear trembling on my nose. "If you could only help me . . ." I gazed out of my huge bedroom eyes appealingly.

"Well, now—ahem—this is serious," he said slowly. "No wonder you weren't prepared in class just now. Naturally, you were upset."

"And you were cruel," I said.

"I'm sorry," he added Quigley.

"Why did you add Quigley?" I begged him. He apologized and subtracted Quigley, then divided Hogan. We hastily dipped the slices of Hogan into Karo, poured sugar over them, and ate them with relish.

"Tell me," said Gipf, as he wiped his mouth on the tail of his shirt, "about this toothpaste: if you could bring the tube to my office . . ."

I explained hurriedly that it was too heavy to carry and that he would have to come up to my dormitory room that evening after "lights out." He readily fell in with my wish and promised. As we walked across the campus toward ivy-covered Lapidus, I drew him out craftily. He had been in the north of Scotland that summer shooting bob-tail flushes, and he was full of his subject. Although I hated him, I had to confess that his smile made my pulses sing, and I gladly would have leaped through a hoop had he asked me to. He must have been aware of it, for he suddenly reached into his green baize bag and produced a hoop.

"Here, leap through this hoop, you," he ordered. I did so and he flicked me lightly with his whip. I saw his face go dark with passion. "Dolores—I love you!" he whispered, his hand closing over mine. Mine in turn closed over his. In an instant we had chosen up sides, it was my turn at bats, and I knocked a sizzling bunt to Pipgrass in the daisies.

"Ah, *cara mia,* giz a kiz," panted Russell. I tried to resist his overtures, but he plied me with symphonies, quartets, chamber music and cantatas. I felt myself softening, but I was determined to go through with my plan.

"Are you mad, Russell?" I stopped him haughtily. He bit his lip in a manner which immediately awakened my maternal sympathy, and I helped him bite it. Foolish man! In a trice the animal in him rose to the surface again. He caught my arm in a vice-like grip and drew me to him, but with a blow I sent him groveling. In ten minutes he was back with a basket of appetizing fresh-picked grovels. We squeezed them and drank the piquant juice thirstily. Then I blew him an airy kiss.

"Tonight—at ten-thirty, *mon désir!*" I flung at him over my shoulder. Even in my room I could hear him panting four floors below on the campus as I changed to a flimsy negligee and began to cold-cream my glowing cheeks.

The dim glow of shaded lamps and the heady intoxication of incense had transformed my room into a veritable Oriental bower when Russell Gipf knocked cautiously on my door at ten-thirty. From the ostermoor where I was stretched out lazily, I murmured an inviting "Come in!"

"Come in!" I murmured invitingly. He entered shaking himself vigorously. There had been a heavy fall of talcum several hours before and as far as the ground could see the eye was white. I offered Russell a dish of soap flakes, but despite my attempts to put him at his ease he seemed nervous.

"The—the toothpaste," he began, looking about suspiciously. I indicated the bathroom with a lazy finger. In a moment he reappeared, his face haggard and his eyes like burning holes in the snow.

"Yes," I shot at him coldly, "I tricked you. No, it's useless to try the door—and it's a four-story drop straight down from those windows, Mr. Russell Gipf. Perhaps you're wondering what I intend to do now." I picked up the telephone, my voice a snarl. "In five minutes the faculty will break in and find you in a co-ed's room. What will your wealthy old father Prosper Gipf, president of the Absconders' and Defaulters' National Bank, say to that?" He backed away from me whimpering piteously. But I was goading him on as only a raging woman can. "You humiliated me in front of all my classmates today. Now—you shall pay." My hand was lifting the receiver when a faint scratching sounded at the door, followed by stertorous breathing. I threw it open. Dean Fothergill, his face that of a man mad with desire, lunged at me.

"Dolores," he implored, "you adorable little witch—I've been following you with my eyes—I . . ."

"You rotter!" I turned in surprise at Russell Gipf's voice as he flashed past me and drove a decisive blow into the aged roué's kidneys. The two men grappled, their teeth bared. Russell's head snapped back as Dean Fothergill, who I forgot to say was once amateur light-heavyweight boxing champion of University of California at Los Angeles, drove a decisive blow to the Gipf kidneys. The noise of fist on kidneys rang out in the still air. I watched the spectacle unmoved. After all, tomorrow I would have to pass my law exam; I opened *Fist on Kidneys* and was deep in it when I heard a groan. I looked up. There, manacled to Russell Gipf, stood Dean Fothergill, a hangdog expression on his face.

"Well, Miss Hornbostel," he admitted shamefacedly, "I guess the jig is up."

"Tell her, you swine!" grunted Russell menacingly, pounding his windward kidney.

"I—I am Jim the Penman," said Fothergill with bowed head. "I forged the notes which sent your father, Harry Trefusis, to the cooler."

"Then you are Donald Fenstermacher, Russell?" I queried, dazed. He put his strong young arms about me and nodded shyly.

"Now may I ask you that question?" he blushed.

"Yes, Donald," I told him, hiding my scarlet face in his shoulder. Outside, the insupportable sweetness of a guitar cleft the warm summer air and bewhiskered, beflanneled, bejasused and bejabbered undergraduates strolled under the hoary elms. The Splendid Wayfarer had come home.

House Party

FROM *The New Yorker*

Walter Bernstein wrote for The New Yorker *during the war from overseas command posts. He was the first American correspondent to interview Marshal Tito of Yugoslavia, after an overland march from the Dalmatian coast with a group of fifty partisans.*

"House Party" has the same quality of spare, lean reporting of an engagement that marked Bernstein's war reportage; the locale is somewhat more peaceful but the strategy and tactics follow the classic military pattern, designed to disable the opponent before striking.

THE small room was crowded, but the boy managed to get through without spilling the drink he held in his hand.

"Hello," he said to the girl on the window seat. "Here's your drink."

The girl looked at him and then looked at her watch. "You're late," she said. "Last time you were faster."

"I couldn't help it," the boy said. "The place is filling up."

The girl accepted the glass and took a long drink. She looked up at the boy and took another drink. Then she set the glass down. "What do they put this Scotch in with—an eye dropper?" she asked.

"I'll get you some more."

"No, never mind." She turned to look out of the window.

"That's the library," the boy said.

"Your friend told me. I guess he wanted me to get the idea. He told me five times. Look," she said, "there's a clock on the other side of that tower, too, isn't there?"

"Sure," said the boy. "Four of them."

"Does it keep the same time as this one?"

"Sure."

The girl looked triumphant. "How do you know?" she asked.

"Well—" the boy said. He was a trifle uneasy. "Well, I guess it does."

"You ought to find out," the girl insisted. "You really ought to find out. That clock on the other side might be slow. If you can only see one clock at a time, how do you know it isn't slow?"

"I guess you don't know," said the boy. "You have to take their word for it."

"I'd find out if I were you," said the girl, shaking her head slowly. She took another drink. "You really ought to know." She looked out of the window, then turned back to the boy. "What do they call this place again?"

"Dartmouth," said the boy.

"That's a silly name," said the girl. She finished her drink. "Do you think you could get me another one of these with some Scotch in it?"

"Sure," said the boy. He took the glass and started through the crowd. The girl put her nose against the pane and looked out of the window.

After a while, the boy came back, holding the drink above his head so it wouldn't be spilled. He tapped the girl on the shoulder. "Hello," he said. "I'm back."

The girl looked at him. "Go away," she said. "I never heard of you."

"I'm your date," said the boy. "I'm bringing you another drink."

The girl peered at him. "So you are," she said. She took the drink and returned to the window.

"I got a little more Scotch this time," the boy said.

The girl turned around. "You're cute," she said.

The boy blushed. "Look," he said, "are you having a good time?"

"I'm having a wonderful time," the girl said. "I am having a simply wonderful time." Her eyes were very large and bright.

"I'm glad," said the boy. He sat down and took hold of her hand. The girl looked at his hand holding hers and then up at his face. She looked at his hand again and took another drink. The boy held on to her hand and leaned forward. "Do you really dance in a chorus?" he said.

"When I'm working," the girl said. "They call us chorus girls." She put her head next to his. "Who squealed?"

"Oh, no one." The boy was emphatic. "My sister told me. Remember? You know my sister. She introduced us in New York."

The girl nodded. "I know your sister." She hiccuped gently. "Little bitch."

The boy released her hand and sat up straight. Seeing his startled expression, the girl put her fingers to her mouth. "There I go again, always belching in public," she said. She leaned toward the boy. "Pardon me."

"Sure," said the boy. "Sure." He sat up very straight.

The girl was beating out a rhythm on the glass with her fingernails, watching the crowd. "How long do you have to stay in this place?" she asked.

"No special time," said the boy. "We can leave now if you want."

"Not here," said the girl. "I mean in college."

"Oh. Four years. I have one to go."

"That's a long run." She drained her glass and looked at the boy. "You're cute," she said. She put down the glass and took up his hands. "You have nice hands."

The boy gave her hands a slight squeeze. "So have you," he said, but the girl had turned away.

"You touch that glass," she was saying to a girl about to sit down, "and I'll lay you out like a rug." She retrieved the glass and held it out to the boy. "How about another drink?"

"Sure," said the boy. He took the glass and moved into the crowd. As he was pouring the liquor, another boy came over and put an arm around his shoulders.

"How're you doing?" he asked.

The boy spilled a little soda into the glass and started back toward the window.

"Fine," he called back. "Fine." He dodged someone carrying a tray. "She's a cinch," he said.

GEORGE MARTIN LANE

Harvard 1846—Professor of Latin

The Lay of
the Lone Fish Ball

FROM *Harvard Classics: Ballad Series, No. 1*

"This," said an anonymous annotator, "is a truthful Narration of what happened to a Professor of Mathematicks in those simple ante-Bellum days when it is said that all who attained a place on the Harvard Faculty were dignified and sensitive Gentlemen." From the same source, we learn that the ballad was the theme for an Italian operetta, "Il Pesceballo," rendered into English by James Russell Lowell, another son of Harvard, and given its first and only performance in 1861 by a Harvard cast before a much-amused Harvard audience.

When the ballad was resurrected, to sweep the country as a pop song, some ten years ago, the lone fish ball had turned into one meat ball.

THERE was a Man went round the Town,
To hunt a Supper up and down:
For he had been right far away
And nothing had to eat that Day.
He feels his Cash to count his Pence,
And all he had was just Six Cents.
"Wretch that I am, it happens meet,
"Why did I leave my Kirkland Street!
"None but a Fool a Wife forsakes,
"Who Raspberry Jam and Waffles makes.

"If I were now safe out of Town,
"I'd give my bran new Dressing Gown.

"But yet I'll make a start and try
"To see what my Six Cents will buy."

He finds at last a Right Cheap Place,
And stealeth in with bashful Face.

The Bill of Fare he runneth through,
To see what his Six Cents will do.

The cheapest of the Viands all,
Was 12½ for Two Fish Ball'.

The Waiter he to him doth call,
And whispers softly "One Fishball."

The Waiter roars it through the Hall;
The Guests they start at "One Fish Ball!!"

The Waiter brings One Fish Ball on,
The Guest he looks abashed down.

The Scantness of the Fare he sees;
"A Piece of Bread now; if you please."

The Waiter roars it through the Hall,
"We don't give Bread with One Fish Ball."
Then whoso orders One Fish Ball
Must get Bread first or not at all.

And who would Two with Fixin's eat,
Should get some Friend to stand a Treat.

J. P. MARQUAND

The Right Sort of Person

FROM *H. M. Pulham, Esquire*

> This suave insight into upper-class Boston society comes from the Marquand
> novel whose central character is H. M. Pulham, Esquire. As class secretary,
> Pulham writes a twenty-fifth-anniversary report for his college class and
> evaluates his own college years.
>
> Marquand is Harvard 1915, and has drawn heavily and pointedly on
> his Harvard-Boston background for many of his books. "Beneath the
> smooth bright surface of his fiction," says the critic Granville Hicks, "there
> is a rich vein of social irony."

I ALWAYS say that Harvard is the most democratic institution in the
world, but secretly I do not believe it, because all my friends, with the ex-
ception of Bill King, were the friends I made at school. For instance, even
today when I see a man who is too carefully groomed my emotions move in
an old instinctive groove. Again, if I meet a man who is too anxious to
please I feel that he is trying to "suck up." There was nothing more undesirable back at Harvard than to be someone who "sucked up." You did
not have to do it if you were the right sort of person.

Joe Bingham and I roomed together all through Harvard. We were in
Randolph during our freshman year and other members of our form at
St. Swithin's lived in the same entry. Bo-jo Brown and Sam Green were
right across the hall and they used to pass a football to each other every
morning. Sam, even when he studied, used to balance a football in his hand.
That was why his forward passing came to be phenomenal in his last two
years at college. Steve Rawley was in that entry too, and was the sort of
person the book agents were always after. He bought Balzac's *Droll Stories*
and *The Human Comedy* bound in silk and sets of Fielding and Smollett
and Edgar Allan Poe. He used to hide in our room when the book agents

came to collect their installments. Then there were Bob Carroll and Pink Stevens. Bob had been the funny boy of our crowd. He used to wrap himself in bath towels and recite "Horatius at the Bridge" and how the Highwayman came riding up to the old inn door and how Gunga Din hoped you liked your drink. He could also play all the songs from "The Pink Lady" and "The Quaker Girl."

It is rather startling to go to Harvard now and see what has happened to Mt. Auburn Street. I wonder if the street Arabs scramble for pennies any more. The old eating places are gone and most of the shops are changed. Harvard's bright color has faded in my memory. It has been washed out like my childhood, very flat.

What I remember best about it is Bill King, and Bill too is entirely different now. It has always amazed me that I ever got to know him, that is, very well. I was alone in my room one autumn afternoon our freshman year, finishing my daily theme for English A, when he knocked. The door was opened by a thin boy in a gray suit who was a complete stranger. It was unusual for strangers to appear in our entry. His clothes were perfectly all right and so were his soft shirt and tie. It must have been his manner that told me he had not gone to one of the larger schools.

"Is your name Pulham?" he asked.

"Yes," I said.

"Oh, well, to hell with it," he said. "Do you mind if I sit down?"

I did not mind if he sat down, exactly. Yet at the same time I did not know what good it would do. He was not my type of person.

"Did you want to see me?" I asked.

He kept looking at me as if he could not find an answer. We were both half grown up then and correspondingly inadequate.

"No," he said. "I've been looking for people whose names begin with P for two hours, and to hell with it."

"Oh," I said, "you mean you're out for something."

"That's what they call it, isn't it," he answered, " 'out for something'? They say the way to get to know people here is to go out for something. I'm asking everybody whose name begins with P if he'd like to act in the Dramatic Club."

"Oh, I couldn't do that," I said. It seemed to end the conversation, but he still sat there.

"You don't mind if I sit here, do you?" he asked. "I just want to talk to someone. I've been around here for two months and no one's spoken to me."

"Where did you go to school?" I asked.

"In New Jersey," he said.

"Oh," I said, "New Jersey."

"Well, what the hell's wrong with that?" he asked.

"Aren't there any other people from your school?" I asked him.

"No," he said, "not anybody. And I've always heard what a good time you had at college."

"What's your name?" I asked.

"King," he said, "Bill King."

"It's just that you don't know anybody," I said.

"Well, what I'm asking you," he answered, "is how I get to know anybody in this place? Will you come in town with me and go to dinner?"

Before I could answer he continued speaking, quickly.

"I know a lot of places in town. I spend a lot of time down in the North End. There's an old hotel where they have a parrot and a dog in the dining room. Listen, is there anything wrong in my asking you to go down there to dinner? Well, never mind. I just asked you."

Then something in the way he said it made me ashamed of myself.

"Thanks," I said. "I'd like to go."

He stood up.

"That's nice of you," he said. He paused and swallowed. "You're the first person I've seen here who isn't a nickel-plated son of a bitch."

I had an uneasy feeling that I was doing something out of the ordinary, that I was associating with someone dubious, but still I was pleased.

Joe Bingham came in a moment later and looked at Bill King distrustfully, just as I had looked at him.

"This is a friend of mine, Mr. King," I said.

"Oh," Joe said, "hello."

Then Bo-jo Brown came in.

"Hello, you bastards," he began, but of course he stopped when he saw Bill King.

"This is a friend of mine, Mr. King," I said.

"Oh," said Bo-jo, "I thought it was the book salesman. Are you any relation to Kinkey King?"

Bill King shook his head.

"All right," Bo-jo said. "I didn't think you were. Who the hell are you anyway? I've never seen you anywhere."

Then Steve Rawley came in, and Bob Carroll. They both looked at Bill King too, but I don't think they ever knew that I did not really know him, for now it was too late to tell them.

I had never known anything exactly like that evening with Bill King. We went to a part of Boston that was entirely new to me, off Scollay Square and through the crowded streets of the North End. Once he was there Bill seemed entirely at home. The New England House, which has disappeared long ago, was downtown beyond the dimly lighted market district. Downstairs where they had sawdust on the floor men were drinking ale in soiled butchers' aprons, and upstairs in the dining room an old lady sat in a corner behind a desk with a gray parrot hanging above her, and a fat, mangy dog sniffed at you. There were long tables with bread and butter and jars of pickles in the center, and big waitresses who shrieked orders down the dumbwaiters into the kitchen. I had never seen anything like it, but Bill King seemed to know it very well. Afterwards we went to a place where we drank ale out of pewter mugs, and after that we went to a moving picture and vaudeville show, where there was a man who did tricks on roller skates and where the audience joined in singing popular songs.

Bill could get on perfectly well anywhere, even when I took him home to Sunday dinner. The anxiety of my parents to meet my friends often caused me a profound embarrassment, for I knew how I felt about most of my friends' parents when I saw them. They were almost invariably peculiar, presenting a display of uncouth mannerisms and inanities of thought. I did not want anyone to feel that way about my family, but Father and Mother kept insisting that I bring some friend home for Sunday lunch. My main reason for bringing Bill King must have been that he did not know anyone and that his opinion would be harmless.

I took him to the house on Marlborough Street, after the family had moved in from Westwood for the winter. Hugh opened the door and smiled at me and said, "Good morning, Master Harry," and then he added in a tone that had certain implications, "You look tired. You must have been studying hard all week."

I knew that I looked tired, because I had been on what was known as a "party" with Pink Stevens the night before. I had not been able to eat my breakfast and I had no appetite for lunch.

"I'm not tired," I said.

"You'd better have some spirits of ammonia before your father sees you, Master Harry. You have no idea how you look, a horrible sight," Hugh said.

I took Bill into the downstairs parlor, where the Inness landscape hung over the mantelpiece and where the French chairs always stood in uncomfortable rows.

"Hugh is always that way," I said to Bill. "I don't look badly, do I?"

I often wished that the family did not have a butler. It was too ostentatious, too much like the parlor. Bill and I stood there, looking at the little tables and the pictures, and then I heard steps on the stairs. Mother came in first in a billowy purple dress with a very high neck.

"Kiss me, dear," she said. "Harry darling, you look so tired. Sometimes we really think that Harry tries to conceal us from his friends, Mr. King. Do you try to conceal your mother from your friends?"

"My mother's dead," Bill said.

"Oh," Mother said, "oh," and she sat down on the settle beside the fireplace where the cannel coal was burning. "Sit beside me, Harry, and do sit down, Mr. King. Do you think Harry works too hard?"

"He's been studying a good deal," Bill said.

"Harry, dear," she said, and she took my hand. "I'm sorry you lost your mother, Mr. King. Mothers mean so much. Harry and I have always been such friends."

I think she really meant it. I knew it was what she had always wanted. Bill King sat down carefully on one of the French chairs.

"You don't have to tell me what you've been doing all the week," Mother said to me, "because I know. Mrs. Motford said you danced with Kay twice on Thursday night—and now I have a surprise for you. Kay's coming to lunch."

"Coming to lunch?" I repeated. "Coming to lunch here?"

"Why, you act as though you weren't pleased, darling," Mother said. "I don't see what gets into boys. Do you know Kay Motford, Mr. King?"

"No," Bill said, "I'm afraid I don't."

"She's such a dear," Mother said, "a dear, sensible girl. She's one of those girls who doesn't think about herself, or think about her looks. She thinks of other people."

"She must be very nice," Bill said. "That's a beautiful Inness, Mrs. Pulham."

"Oh," Mother said, "do you know about pictures, Mr. King? I've always loved that picture, I've always loved the sky." And then she was talking to Bill King about Inness. It seemed incredible to me that Bill King should wish to talk about Inness, but from Inness he went on to Mr. Sargent, and then Father came downstairs.

"What are we waiting for?" Father asked. "Where's lunch? Where's Mary?" and he walked out into the hall.

"Mary," he shouted. I winced slightly. I had hoped that he would not shout.

"John," Mother said, "this is Mr. King. We're waiting lunch because Cornelia Motford's coming."

"Oh," said Father, "hello, King. Who in blazes is Cornelia Motford?"

"She's a friend of Harry's, dear," Mother said. "You remember Cornelia, the Cecil Motfords' girl."

Father began to blow his nose loudly. I wished that he would not blow his nose.

"She isn't a friend of mine," I said. "I just happen to know her, that's all."

Father began to laugh knowingly.

"She isn't a friend of yours," he said, "but you asked her to lunch?"

"I didn't know she was coming to lunch," I said. "Kay Motford is a lemon, if you want to know."

"Then why is she coming to lunch?" he asked.

"I don't know why," I said, "except Mother asked her."

"Well, I don't see what all the fuss is about," Father said, and he blew his nose. "Where's Hugh? Where's the sherry?"

"John—" Mother began.

"I guess Harry and Mr. King are old enough to have a glass of sherry," my father said. "All the boys at Harvard drink, don't they, Mr. King?"

Then Mary came downstairs. She had pigtails and a white dress halfway below her knees and her complexion was bad. She curtsied when she was introduced to Bill, and then she looked at me and grinned.

"Harry's girl is coming to lunch," she said.

"Mary," my mother said, "Mary!"

"Look here," I began, "if you want to know—" I stopped because the doorbell rang, and I felt like the victim of a hideous conspiracy.

Kay looked like an illustration of "The Little Colonel When Her Knight Came Riding." Her hair was pulled back tight in a bun, her shirt waist was as stiffly starched as a nurse's uniform. She was thin, too thin, but her face was pudgy, and her brown eyes were bright and her nose was shining.

"Hello, Mrs. Pulham," she said. "I've been out walking with the dogs."

Then Hugh came in with some glasses on his silver tray, and five minutes later we were in the dining room.

"Well," Father called when we sat down, "what are we waiting for?"

"Grace, dear," Mother said. "You forgot it."

"Oh, yes," Father said. "For what we are about to receive may the Lord make us truly thankful. For Christ's sake. Amen."

It has always seemed to me that family luncheons have nothing to do with anything else in existence. We were all acting, speaking set lines all the time we were at table, and it was the same in the library upstairs. I know the way Father felt now. First he tried to talk about football and then about how different Harvard was when he was there; and then he hit upon the subject of President Taft and Theodore Roosevelt. Father was saying that Theodore Roosevelt was a social menace and that his attack upon self-respecting men, who had made the nation what it was, broke down confidence. Bill agreed, but I do not think he meant it. Bill was always looking at people and listening.

"Now, that's a sensible boy," my father told me afterward, "the first sensible friend you've ever brought around."

I could not see why, because Bill had not said anything.

"He's such a gentleman," Mother said. "He's the nicest boy I've seen."

I don't know why she thought he was nice, except that he spoke about Inness in the parlor.

It was my definite conviction that the family had never behaved worse, that they had never been more obtuse and dull. I explained to Bill that Sunday lunch was always awful.

"It's like home," Bill said, "it's like home anywhere."

"Is it that way where you live?" I asked.

"It's that way anywhere. God Almighty, it's sad."

"Why is it sad?" I asked.

"It's sad," Bill said, "because they try so hard. It's sad because we don't like anything they do. We're thinking about one sort of thing, and they're thinking about something else."

It was the first time I realized that Bill was clever.

"Your mother thought she could make you happy by asking that little what's-her-name to lunch," he went on.

That is the way Bill referred to Kay, as a little what's-her-name.

"It's sad," Bill King said, "because your father is so fond of you that he's shy. It's sad because it's all the way that everything goes."

Bill would actually have got on very well at Harvard, I think, if he had cared about trying. It was true that he did not have any connections, but if he had gone out for something besides the Dramatic Club, such as the *Lampoon* or even the *Crimson,* and if he had bothered with the people to whom I introduced him and who usually liked him, he would very possibly have made a Club. The trouble was that he did not seem to care to make the effort. When Kay Motford asked him to her coming-out party at the Somerset, for instance, he refused the invitation, and it was the same when he was asked to the Bradburys'. At the time when everyone was worrying about Clubs he never bothered to be seen with the right people; he never bothered to do the right thing.

That attitude of his made me very angry once shortly after Bo-jo Brown had thrown out his hip in the game with Dartmouth our junior year. Bo-jo would hobble down on his crutch to watch the football practice, but he knew that he would not be well enough to play against Yale. Everyone in our entry felt very badly for him. Bo-jo would sit in his room with his crutch beside him and watch Sam Green balancing a football in his hand while he studied for his hour examinations, and if anybody came in Bo-jo would tell exactly how it happened.

"Listen, boys," he would say, "I want you to get this straight. There isn't anyone in the world, not anyone, who could wrench the ligaments in my hip if I was ready for them. That Dartmouth bastard didn't like me. He was out to get me. He said he was. No one living can hurt me when I'm ready."

"That's right, Bo-jo," everybody said. "That's the boy, Bo-jo."

"Now, listen," Bo-jo said. "Here's the way it happened, and if you don't believe it, Sam Green will tell you. You saw it, Sam."

"That's right," said Sam. "I saw it, Bo-jo. We were right on the ten-yard line."

We were all on the ten-yard line as soon as Bo-jo and Sam began talking.

"And Max called the play through me. He always calls it through me if he wants first down, and I got that slob off his feet and we made five yards. We'd have made ten yards, Sam, if you'd been carrying the ball."

"Oh, no," said Sam. "I don't think so, Bo-jo."

"You would have. There was a hole a mile wide. Well, the whistle blew. The play was over. I was just standing up, relaxed, perfectly relaxed, and he pulled my leg and I went down on top of him."

"How do you mean, he pulled your leg?" I asked.

"My God," said Bo-jo, "don't you understand English? I was standing up, perfectly relaxed, and I started to step over him, and he said I stamped on him. You know damn well I didn't stamp on him, did I, Sam? I was just stepping over him to get out of his way."

"That's right, Bo-jo," said Sam. "He was laid out flat. Why should you want to stamp on him?"

"Listen, boys," Bo-jo said. "I was just walking over him, relaxed, and he grabbed my leg. He got me off my balance, and then the ligaments went, and I sat down on his head. I could feel the whole hip go, just because I wasn't ready for him. And then do you know what he did?"

"What?" I asked. Bo-jo always wanted somebody to ask him.

"He bit me," he said. "That's what they do at Dartmouth."

"Bit you?" someone repeated, and that was what Bo-jo wanted.

"You don't believe it, do you? Well, his teeth marks are still there. Take my pants down if you don't believe it. Somebody help me take down my pants." It was an interesting exhibit. There was no doubt that someone had bitten him.

"Well, that's the way it is, boys," Bo-jo said. "And I don't know what's going to happen now with Yale."

Those were the days when it was important to beat Yale, and the night before the game an unusual thing happened. Bo-jo shouted through the entry at seven in the evening.

"Hey," Bo-jo shouted, "everyone come in here."

Bill King was in my room at the time and he came too. Bo-jo was sitting in his morris chair and Sam Green was standing beside him.

"Hello, boys," Bo-jo said. "Hello, King. You don't have to go away. The team is coming up. Sammy Lee's bringing them, and I'd sort of like my friends around."

We all stood against the wall, looking at Bo-jo Brown. We all knew that it was an unusual honor. It was a privilege to be standing there, a privilege to be asked to witness such a scene.

"It's a lot of bunk, of course," Bo-jo said, "but I'd sort of like you boys around."

"Maybe I'd better go," Bill King suggested. "There'll be a lot of people."

"Hell, no," said Bo-jo. "Stay around as long as you're here."

"They're coming now," said Sam.

We could hear the footsteps in the entry, and the hall and Bo-jo's room were filled with people. The assistant coach, Sammy Lee, came first, an older man who had a beefy square face and blue eyes and very short hair.

"How's it going, Bo-jo?" he said. "I brought the boys around to see you." He put his hand on Bo-jo's shoulder and turned and addressed the group.

"Well, men," he said, "here's Bo-jo Brown, and I guess we all know how we feel about Bo-jo Brown. We all know that Bo-jo won't be in there with us tomorrow, and we all know what that means. But there's one thing that all of you men can do. I want you all to go up and shake hands with Bo-jo Brown and tell him that we're going to beat the living hell out of Yale tomorrow, even if he isn't there. All right, men. Shake hands."

I felt my breath catch and I felt a lump in my throat. It was hard not to be moved by the simple solemnity of the scene. As the team filed past him, mumbling a few broken words, Bo-jo's face grew red.

"Do you want to say something to them, Bo-jo?" Sam Lee asked.

Bo-jo seized his crutch and stood up and leaned against it. It seemed hardly decent to be present, because his eyes were bright with tears.

"All I can say is," Bo-jo said, "give 'em hell. To hell with Yale." And then his voice broke in a sob, and he sat down and covered his face.

"Men," Sam Lee said, "I guess we know how we all feel. How about it? Three times three for Brown!"

I do not know if they have such scenes now, but I know that I was weeping and that I was not ashamed of it any more than Bo-jo. We tiptoed away, softly and reverently, and I found myself in my own room with Joe Bingham and Bill King.

"God," Joe Bingham said, "that's something I'll never forget."

Bill King lighted a cigarette.

"I won't forget it either," he said. "It makes me want to puke."

"What?" I said. "What do you mean, Bill?"

"It makes me want to puke," Bill said.

I was looking at Joe Bingham; his face was blank and shocked. Bill King puffed at his cigarette.

"Now, wait a minute before you speak," he said. "Wait and try to think what there is to cry about. Bo-jo Brown isn't going to die, is he? What is there to cry about? Suppose we don't beat Yale, what difference does it make? It's only a football game."

Joe Bingham found his voice first.

"I never thought," Joe said, "that you were such a son of a bitch. And if you don't like what I say, we can finish it off right now."

Bill King flicked the ash from his cigarette.

"He doesn't really mean that, Joe," I said. "You're just trying to get a rise out of us, aren't you, Bill?"

"You know damn well I'm right," Bill said. "What difference does it make?"

"It makes a lot of difference if anyone goes around talking like that," I said. "People won't like you, Bill. You'll get in wrong. You'll make a fool of yourself."

"You know I'm right," Bill King said. "Both of you really know it."

"It isn't the right spirit," I said.

"To hell with it," Bill King said. "Good night, boys."

Joe Bingham and I must have been glad of each other's company after Bill King had left.

"Harry," Joe said.

"What?" I asked.

"Why don't you say something?"

"I'm thinking," I said.

"Do you know what I think?" Joe Bingham said. "I think he's a sorehead."

"Maybe he is," I said.

"My God," Joe Bingham said. "I wish we'd had him at school. I wish the Skipper could have heard him. We'd have paddled his tail off and put him under the pump."

"Yes," I said, "I guess we would have."

"But I suppose there are a lot of radical bastards all over the place who aren't getting anything out of college," he added, "who just don't know what it means. Harry, do you know I'm kind of sorry for him? He'd have been all right if he'd had hell beaten out of him in some good school."

Football Girl

FROM *Other Women*

The apparent moral of Katherine Brush's "Football Girl" is plain enough: you can't mix football with the tender passion. As to whether the picture is either fair or typical, one may argue that, after all, a woman wrote it and who should know better?

Katherine Brush was a product of the Jazz Age generation and one of its most keenly observing reporters in fiction. Her first published writing was for the college magazine of the '20s, College Humor. *Her novels were best sellers and many of her stories are sharp, acid comments on that hectic era in American social history. However, during the period of her greatest success, her more durable qualities were overshadowed by her reputation for "sophisticated glamour"—which often meant an emphasis on glittery romances and adultery.*

"IT'S cold in this stadium," said the girl behind me.

She had a slow little voice, clear and sweet, with a trace of Southern accent. Just a trace. You thought perhaps she visited in Macon or in Memphis—it was that much of an accent and no more. She had just arrived at her seat, escorted by a long-legged undergraduate in a ponderous black bearskin coat. They were late. The game had begun some moments before.

I knew what she looked like though I did not turn around. I had watched her coming up the steps. Everybody in thirty rows had watched her. She was that sort of girl. Little she was, and slim in a coat of soft tan fur, belted tight at the waist with broad brown leather. The collar of the coat was high and puffy and immense: it held her face as velvet holds a jewel. She was very young. She could not have been more than sixteen or seventeen. An exquisite child, with black hair curling below a tilted patch of hat, with a spoiled red mouth, with extravagant dark-blue eyes. The eyes were older than the girl. They were adult with self-assurance. They had a lazy stare for the staring world.

The boy was mad about her. He had looked it, coming up the steps— though he had tried hard not to, he had looked almost fatuously proud. Now, when she remarked that it was cold in this stadium, he repeated, "Cold?" in instantaneous alarm.

"Wait!" he said. "Wait'll I get this ole robe unfolded. You won't be cold with this ole robe around you."

"My face will be," she said.

On the field a halfback made a gain of thirteen yards.

"Lift your feet a minute," said the boy, "while I tuck it under. There! How's that? Okay?"

"I guess so."

"Warm enough now?"

"Maybe I will be in a minute," she said doubtfully.

In a minute she said, "It's cold underneath, that's the trouble. It's sitting on this icy cold stone."

"Well, here," said the boy. "Sit on one of these programs. Get up a minute—— Now, try that."

"That's slick," said the girl. "And let's put the other one under where my feet are, humm'm, Tom? Because my feet always practically freeze."

"They're so little," the boy said, in the voice of one bent double. "There now!" he added more clearly. "Now you're all set."

"Um-hmm. Now I am. What's the score?"

"Nothing to nothing."

"Oh," said the girl, "then we're not really late. You kept saying we were going to be late."

"Well, we were, a little."

"I'm never late," the girl said dreamily.

The boy did not answer. *"Watch that pass!"* he shouted hoarsely instead. *"Watch it!"*

"Look," said the girl. "Before you get all excited, may I please have one of your cigarettes?"

"Ye-e-eah!" the boy was yelling. "Get 'im! Nail 'im! *Ye-e-eah!* What's trouble, baby?" he added softly.

"I want a cigarette."

"Oh, gosh," said the boy, "now where did I—Wait a minute."

"Ye-e-eah!" he cried again, but faintly now.

He began a subdued muttering. "Wallet," he said. "Keys. Lighter. Handkerchief. 'Nother handkerchief. Powder—here's your powder gadget, Jill. And here's your purse, and here's your comb. And your rouge or whatnot. But where in hell're the cigarettes?"

"Isn't my lipstick there?" the girl asked anxiously.

"I'll look."

"I never saw so many pockets."

The cigarettes were finally found, but the rejoicing was halfhearted. The lipstick, it appeared, was missing still.

"It was one I bought in Paris," the girl said sadly. "And now it's gone goodness knows where through a hole in your pocket."

"But I tell you it couldn't 've, honey! This is a new suit!"

"It was a new lipstick. It was a bra——"

"Here it is!" he crowed triumphantly. "I've got it!"

"Oh, good. I'm so glad."

"Here, take it," said the boy. "Don't you want it?"

"Uh-uh," said the girl. "Not now. I just wanted to be sure it wasn't lost. . . . Look, Tom. This lighter won't light in this wind."

"Sure it will. Give it here."

"I told you," the girl said presently. "Haven't you got some matches?"

Matches were borrowed, and many were scratched in succession. This took some time, and a touchdown was meanwhile made by the visiting team. In the accompanying tumult the girl's small voice was lost to me. I thought she was saying, "Try putting your head inside your coat and lighting it, why don't you?" But I could not be sure.

The first quarter ended shortly. The boy, withdrawing his gaze from the sky, where he had been urged to direct it with a view to determining whether it wasn't really terribly, terribly dangerous for that plane to be swooping down so low over all these people—the boy remarked the end of the first quarter with surprise.

"Say," he said, "it's the quarter already."

"Oh, is it?" said the girl. "Well, now's our chance to fix this robe. I didn't tell you, but I've been getting chillier by the minute."

"Say! You haven't!"

"Oh, it'll be all right when we fix it," she assured him soothingly. "The trouble is that it's *over* me and then tucked under, instead of *under* me and then wrapped *over*. Do you see what I mean?"

He did. He was able to fix it in a little less than four minutes.

"There!" said the girl. "That's marvelous! I won't be cold now. . . . Oh, look, they're all playing down our end of the field."

"You bet they are!" said the boy. "And we're going to score—we're gonna *sco-o-ore—There* you GO!" he howled. "THERE YOU—oh, tough. Tough. *Hard luck, Red, old boy! Next time!*" He beat his hollowed gloved palms together once, making a loud report. "*Come on,* TEAM!"

"Tom," said the girl. "I smell something burning."

"What?"

"I smell something burning. I think the robe must be on fire. I think," said the girl, "we must have wrapped my cigarette up in it."

It turned out after a wild interval that she was partly right, though only partly. It was her cigarette, but it was the robe of the gentleman next her.

"What a time!" she sighed exhaustedly, when it was all over and the boy was carefully wrapping her up again. "After that, I'll have to have my make-up, please, Tom. Not the rouge. Just the powder and the lipstick."

"You look all right," he demurred. "You look great."

"Oh, no I don't. I'm all hot and bothered. Such a horrid mean old man I never did see in all my days," she added clearly.

"Hush!" said the boy. "Here! Here're your things."

"And may I have your hanky? Because mine must have blown away."

Her next remark was about a cheerleader. It was her most enthusiastic remark so far, though it was brief. It was, "Oh, looky! Who's *he?*"

"Who?"

"That cheerleader!"

"Oh, him," said the boy. "I believe his name's Adams or something. Or maybe it's Andrews. Something like that."

"But I want to *know*, Tom!"

"What for?" Tom asked suspiciously.

"I just do. Listen, wouldn't he be in the program somewhere?"

The boy didn't think so.

"Well, look and *see*, silly!" the girl suggested sweetly, adding, "You can take the one that's under my feet. It isn't keeping them a bit warm anyway."

The search for the cheerleader occupied the boy for quite a while. He said nothing, but he was to be heard turning pages rapidly. "Don't go so fast," the girl said once, and once she accused him of skipping. She had previously explained that she herself would look through the program "—only my hands would freeze if I didn't keep them in my sleeves."

There were several interruptions. Once the girl sneezed, a tiny sneeze like a little cat's, and the boy was obliged to produce his handkerchief again in a hurry. "And the powder again too," said the girl. "Oh, and the lipstick! Because look, it all rubbed off on your handkerchief."

Somewhat later she said suddenly and pitifully, "I'm hungry."

The boy stopped turning pages. "Hungry?" he said. "But you just had lunch!"

"I didn't have anything but that old salad."

"Well," said the boy, "can you wait till between the halves? I can get you a hot dog or something then."

"I suppose I can if I have to," the girl said. "But I'm awfully hungry."

"Well, shall I go out now and try to find something? I will if you say so, only you'll be all alone——"

"No," sighed the girl. "I'll wait."

"But I'm awfully hungry," she added low, a moment later.

"Smoke another cigarette," said the boy. "Maybe that'll help."

"All right," said the girl. "You light me one."

The intermittent hissing of matches began again.

"Look at that child," the girl observed, in the midst of it.

"Where?"

"Two rows down. Climbing all over his father's lap. Can't you see him?"

It was a little bundled red-faced boy about five years old, with the feather of his father's alma mater in his cap.

"Imagine bringing a child that age to a football game!" the girl said. "Imagine *bothering!*"

The youth agreed with her. It was plain from his tone that he wagged his head.

"Can you beat it?" he demanded solemnly.

Third Down—A Drama

FROM *College Humor*

Here is Benchley again, this time with a "collegiate drama of love and mid-years," in four acts and a light delirium. His equally phrenetic reminiscence of his college days appears earlier in this book.

CAST

"Bud" Kenyon .... Captain of the crew
"Fatty" Lipschutz .... His chum
"Fatty" Hofnagle .... Their chum
"Fatty" Teeple .... Captain of the crew
Dorothy Lapf .... "Bud's" fiancée and captain of
the brassiere team
Helen Gazump .... Her chum
Marian Heef .... Anybody's chum
Professor Halbtoit .... Captain of the crew
College-boys, policemen, fried egg-sandwiches, members of the
Faculty and prom girls.

ACT 1

The scene is in the college room of "Bud" Kenyon in Howzis Hall. There are banners on the wall reading "Harvard," "Yale," "Princeton," "Humboldt," "U. of J." and "Bridal Veil Falls, N. Y." Over the door is an oar crossed with a basket-ball, with "29-0" written under them. In one corner of the room hangs a mathematics professor, quite cold by now.

(Enter Bud.)

(He is singing "Bright College Years" in four-part harmony and carries a tennis-racquet, a golf-bag and a catcher's mitt. He is about forty-five years old.)

254

BUD

Hello, everybody! I have just passed an exam! Now for some fun!

FATTY

What luck! And today is the day that Dorothy and Marian are coming
to tea. I am the happiest boy in the world now that Dorothy has promised to
marry me.

BUD

Marry you in a pig's eye! She is going to marry *me* if we win the big
race today from Nutley Commercial College.

FATTY

Yes, but how can you win a race at five o'clock today if you have that
appendicitis operation at two-thirty?

BUD

The doctor says that I will be up and about by four. That gives me a
whole hour for practice before the race. And if do-or-die spirit counts for
anything in this world, we are going to win over Nutley Commercial by a
comfortable margin. . . . But here come the girls now! Hurry down to the
spring and fetch up a bucket of gin.
(*Enter* DOROTHY, HELEN, *and* MARIAN.)

DOROTHY

Well, boys! This is the day of the big race. How about a song?

ALL

A song! A song! Let's have a jolly song!
(*They sing "Aunt Dinah's Quilting Party" and "Solomon Levi."*)

MARIAN

And now a toast! May the best man win Dorothy, president of the Senior
Class!

FATTY (*as the toast is drunk*)

We shall see. We shall see.
(*Curtain*)

ACT 2

Scene 1

*The scene is in the college infirmary. There are banners on the wall
reading "Harvard," "Yale," "Princeton" and "N. Y. College of Physicians
and Surgeons." The doctors wear sweaters with their class numerals on them
and are humming "Dear Old Elms" in close harmony as the curtain rises.*

Doctor "Skinny" Watrous

This is a very important operation we have on hand today, boys. It is "Bud" Kenyon the captain of the crew. He must be out in time to row the big race this afternoon with Nutley Commercial. It is up to us to guard the name and fame of old Humboldt, may we ever loyal be, and sing thy praises to the sky, for old H-U-M-B-O-L-D-T. Rah!

Doctor "Ted" Lattles

Here he comes now! Everybody up and give a short team for Kenyon.

All

Kenyon-Kenyon-Kenyon-Team-Team-Team!

Bud

Thank you, Doctors. I am sure I did nothing that any fellow wouldn't do for old Humboldt. And remember, we still have our big race ahead of us. . . . All right, Doctors!

(Bud *rips off his sweater and climbs up on the operating table. As he does so,* Fatty *is disclosed to the audience, hiding under the table and holding a key in his hand.*)

Fatty (*sotto voce*)

Ha-ha-ha!

(*Curtain*)

ACT 3

Scene 2

The boat-house. Four-thirty that afternoon. The scene is one of great confusion. Members of the crew are running about in their street clothes, members of the faculty tear past in their academic robes and mortar-boards, prom-girls huddle in corners crying. Bud *enters, looking pale but game.*

Bud

Well, fellows! What's the matter? Why aren't you out rehearsing in the boat?

Tom

Matter enough, Bud, old man. Someone has taken the key to the locker-room and we can't get in to get our suits. And, as they are the only suits which have our college letters on the jerseys, we can't row without them.

Bud

By George, I know where the key is!

All

Where, Bud, old man?

BUD

Inside me! I remember it all now as plain as day. As I was lying on the operating table, Fatty suddenly appeared and called the doctors' attention to a yellow warbler which was flying past the infirmary window. They all ran to look, and I remember now that Fatty dropped something into my incision. I thought at the time that it was a dime or something nice, and so said nothing. Then they came back and sewed me up, and, boys, the key to the locker-room is sewed up inside me!

(*The crew from the Nutley Commercial College enter, all dressed for rowing with big "N's" on their jerseys.*)

NUTLEY CAPTAIN

Well, Kenyon. Are you ready?

BUD

I don't know what to say. You see, we can't row without our varsity letters and our varsity letters are locked up where we can't get at them.

NUTLEY CAPTAIN

Then we win the race by default, nine to nothing.
(*Enter* DOROTHY, HELEN *and* MARIAN.)

DOROTHY

Oh, no, you don't! We girls have made eight "H's" out of our petticoats and our boys can pin them onto their sweater vests and go out and row the race for dear old Humboldt in their street clothes.

ALL

Humboldt! Rah-rah-rah! Team-team-team! Petticoats-petticoats!

FATTY (*slinking off in a corner*)

It can't be true. Girls don't wear petticoats nowadays.
(*Curtain*)

ACT 4

Back in BUD's *room again. Late that evening. The members of the crew are there and all the Faculty and the girls. They are all very gloomy.*

BUD

Well, even though Nutley Commercial won the race by nine lengths, I hope that you will still marry me, Dorothy.

DOROTHY

I can't, Bud. I married Fatty on the street-car coming home from the race.

Professor Halbtoit

I have just come from correcting the examination papers, and I am sorry
to announce that everyone in this room has flunked; so we shall have to
close the college.

All (*sing in harmony*)

Hail to thee, dear old Humboldt!

Our Alma Mater, true.

We'll ever sing thy praises, on gridiron, track and gridiron,

And hope that you are the same.

H-U-M-B-O-L-D-T. That spells Apple-sauce to me!

Team-team-team!

(*Curtain*)

HERBERT GOLD

Fraternity Brothers

FROM *Playboy*

At this writing the young Midwest author, Herbert Gold, has three novels and a considerable body of critical and evaluative writing to his credit. This is testimony not only to his skill and energy, but also to the efficacy with which grants and fellowships are assigned and perform the functions intended by their founders—for it is likely that Gold has been awarded more of these, and exploited them to better advantage, than any other successful author of his generation. As journalist and fictioneer, Gold has appeared in the most recherché little magazines and in the so-called slicks and mass magazines. His first two novels were Birth of a Hero *and* The Prospect Before Us. *His third,* The Man Who Was Not With It, *was generally well received, but encountered a somewhat puzzling reception in some quarters. The critics were almost unanimous on the writer's extraordinary gift for language, character, and dialogue, but some were disturbed that he had selected such "unpleasant" people to write about—a curious judgment. Gold has the uncommon faculty for intimately involving the reader in the lives of his characters—even the "unpleasant" ones, as is evident in this story of a fraternity's attempt to impose group mores on a member's private feelings. As will be seen, Gold is a serious writer: however entertainingly he writes, he has something to say as well as a story to tell.*

ALLEN TURNER, a busy man with creamy cheeks and a rapid, decisive speech, tempered his hard duty by smiling with the steadiness of a clock. The face supporting the smile broadened magnificently with approval of his words. He smiled past a missing tooth. "You don't play poker? OK," he said to Dan Shaper, "you don't have to. This is the free democratic world. You don't like the programs the fellows all like? Okay, the TV isn't a law, just for rec-ration. You had a ticket to the last game and you didn't go? It's your prillege. But boy," he added mournfully, "you don't *ever* play poker."

259

Dan Shaper bowed his head before this correction, just and measured as it was, administered by the President of the Chapter. Modestly he showed Allen the ridges of his scalp. His hair was growing back in little pinfeathers after their ritual shaving. He no longer wore the beanie.

Very friendly and fraternal, Allen went on with Allen's important phrases: Prepare for positive living . . . develop the social side . . . getting along, being well-liked, and good contacts . . . Allen had risen to high office in his junior year. The voice faded in strongly: "We got Monsanto men who listen to us, we got G.M. men. We got Allis-Chalmers in our pocket, boy."

He paused. Now it was up to Dan to say something. Smiling, nodding, pulling the lobe of one ear, all excellent chapter spirit, Allen encouraged him to confess error and forthrightly resolve upon virtue. Allen put his tongue in the empty socket where he had lost a tooth. Patiently he sucked. He waited.

Skinny, quick, carefully controlled, Dan Shaper had searched about, hungering, during his first year at college. The winter had been sad—like his own vacant, fatherless home. The first spring had been desperate—like the mood of his mother when she remembered love. Watching the fraternity boys in easy fellowship with each other, or strolling confidently with their girls, Dan had gritted his teeth to say, *No, no, stop!* He would not carry his isolation through college with him.

The hungering shone in his eyes as ardent energy. He was both clever and shy, and yet had a touch of the easy lounging manners of the father he barely remembered. Before long he was asked again, and this time he joined, and now he wanted to be liked by these friends who had tested him for virtue and performance, approved him for display, and finally initiated him into brotherhood. They depended upon him to be one of the group. It was nice to be needed. He turned from the dark panels of the rec room to the strained leather couches, the collapsing ping-pong table, and the familiar lounging forms before the TV at one end of the long room and about the study table at the other end. It was an easy place, warm as kitchen life. His loneliness had been a terrible thing.

Allen abruptly stopped waiting. "Well? What's there to think about?"

"I wish," said Dan, and let Allen interrupt him.

"Don't think I'm telling you this just because I'm responsible for the whole Chapter," Allen said. "I'm speaking as a friend, duty aside. I voted for you personly."

With an effort Dan raised his eyes to Allen's. "I really appreciate how you took me in. I never expected——"

"Don't misunnerstand me, boy," Allen insisted. "We like you to be serrus, a scholship student. How much your old man has in the bank or sound common stocks don't matter so much. The war changed all that. We need balance in the Chapter—we already had athletes, old-type families, big men in activities like me, that element there. We *need* you the way you are, Danny boy! But one and the same, you got to show your true colors for being one of us——"

"I know, I'm learning," Dan said to this very mature young man.

"Let me finish, please." For the first time Allen's voice turned sharp and cold and the smile froze into a quirk of tonguing the empty socket. "I was talking to you, boy, so you listen here to me now. Your individellism goes too far. It is not c'structive. If you want to be a loner, like I mean dating townies like that girl, you didn't have to join the Chapter. Nobody twisted your arm. In this moddun free world, we all do whatever we want, but when we decide, we got to take the consekences." The smile returned with his moral calm. He patted Dan on the back. "That's all I have to say, boy." He nodded encouragingly. "Now you talk."

Allen gave him this moment for confession and repentance. To humiliate himself just a bit would establish the old good-feeling, that sense of responsibility to a group upon which every mortal man's health depends. Allen was big enough to forgive and forget on behalf of all the boys, and say no more about it, if only Dan could find the right words—shy and modest ones, but stalwart all the same, in the best traditions of the fraternity. Again Dan tried to meet his eyes, failed again, and said in haste and unsuccessfully, wishing only that Allen would stop sucking the empty socket in his gums:

"All right, all right, I'll play poker with the fellows next time."

*   *   *

Lucille lived below the hill from campus. To save bus fare Dan made the long walk on foot down that coppery strewn slope toward the darker town autumn with its leaves frayed in the gutters. His trouble made the walk seem less long. He wanted time to think out Allen Turner and the fraternity and why he needed them.

At the curb part way into town someone was vainly trying to start an automobile, working the sick battery, *roo*-hum, *roo*-hum, while a thick blanket of wet leaves clung to the roof and other stray leaves mottled the hood. The man inside, mouth working, feet and hands punching, sweating ferociously in his topcoat, punished the starter button and gas pedal without mercy.

Dan shook his head, scuffing through leaves and tasting their acid burning. He would do anything to hold on now. He could give up Allen and the others, yes, he could do that; but he could not let them give *him* up.

The mark of the Yankee, he thought wryly. And smiled at his self-conscious college-boy naming of the thought. At home they wouldn't call themselves Yankees: they were just stubborn was all. Besides, the warmth and laughter of the House was something for which he had been parched since the news came that his father had gone down over Calais.

The evening stroll with Lucille went badly. "What's the matter with you?" she demanded almost at once, knowing that he was not all for her tonight.

Despite her lovely, pale, almost silvery hair, worn unfashionably long, despite her huge eyes of that magical blue which can change in an instant from a wintery withdrawal to an ardent summer sky azure, she was gawky and shy herself, needing great tenderness from him before she could give him any of her own. A townie, grown up to warnings about the college boys on the hill. They only want what they want, and then they marry back home or one of the sorority girls. "Dan? Don't you like me tonight?" she asked. "You thinking about someone else?"

"No, no. I like you very much." How could he like anyone but this tall, long-waisted, silvery and quiet girl?

"You don't even look at me or call me Lucille. I'm tired. I need to go to bed early tonight."

"Lucille, let's not go back yet. Please."

"I want to go home, Dan. You don't even say you like my dress. I worked on it all day. I wanted something new to wear for Saturday."

"Lucille, wait, you're not giving me a chance about anything."

"I'm sorry. I guess I'm just tired. I thought you could make me feel better."

He heard the pleading shrillness of his own voice: "Then let me try,"— and knew it was no good. "Would you like to stop for——?"

"I want to go home right now, Dan."

She permitted her hand to rest in his without gripping it. He did not let her go, fearing the moment when she would no longer be with him, even in this bad way with him. And almost her last words were, as he fumbled and pressed clumsily against her at the door, his shyness turned to pushing, his need brutally excluding her, turning her away as he wrestled like any stupid youth: "What *is* the matter with you?"

"Nothing you can't help!"

For the time of a single failing breath beneath his mouth, her body went soft and split, like a ripe plum under the midsummer blaze—then she gasped, stiffening her reply to mere anger and elbows. She beat at his chest with both fists. He fell away.

"I'm sorry. I'm not myself, Lucille. I'm sorry."

She was furious, aroused despite herself, shivering in her new dress, and made still more cold and distant by fright at her secret ache of response to his strange violence. "Stop it! Is this the way they tell you to handle the

townies? Oh I know you,"—and she used a girlish word which he hated:
"Do you have to get grabby? Now stop it."

I, I, I, he started to say, wanting to tell her of his trouble, trouble up on
the hill at the House and now trouble in town with her, but he lost the
strength for explanations. A girl is a mystery, and says *grabby* when you turn
all the way to her because you are a stranger to yourself.

He had shown disrespect to his date. All right, then give her a dose of
courtesy.

"I'm sorry," he said.

She relented at the return of his shyness. She worked against her own
heavy breathing. "That's all right. Please don't say it like that. I wish . . .
Never mind."

"Good night, Lucille."

She gave him her lips chastely to kiss. He leaned forward, lightly encircling her shoulders in his arms, with only the heat of his mouth reminiscent
of the brutal straining of a few moments ago. Despite herself, Lucille regretted that harsh secret person so abruptly fled, but she could only ask once
more, "Dan, whatever is the matter with you tonight?"

On his long walk back up the hill, the sleek sweat started again under his
new suit, and the chill breezes made him feel feverish. Yes, it's true that
trouble, once finding a door, sprawls and breathes foully in every corner of
a man's life. Trouble with Allen and the Chapter led to trouble with Lucille,
and these troubles made it hard to study, and troubles with his scholarship
were surely due. All this made it difficult to write home—thus trouble with
his mother. And the thought of it turned him hot, turned him cold, and
what if he caught some disease, the flu or something, and had to take to bed?

No! he decided. He would not look for release by illness. He resolved to
stop perspiring in this stop-and-start way, not to catch a germ, not to do it.
He paused near the car with the bad battery, glistening under its wet
fringe of leaves, unmoved, shut, abandoned beneath the streetlight. Someone had cursed; someone had failed and gone away. He made himself smile.

Better, better. He would call Lucille tomorrow, and maybe send her a
box of candy with a note composed now, before bed, to tell her how he felt
about her. It must be earnest but elegant, something she might even want to
whisper over proudly with her best friend—and yet it would take its lonely
sense from their gathered memories together of a fine dark autumn. (One
night, after walking so late that it was dawn when they stopped, they had
gone to have breakfast together in a steaming early morning restaurant.
Very precisely caring for him, she had buttered his toast, sliced it, and offered
him the warm bread with a smile which, more than any other gesture, promised that she might someday be his.) As he wrote, he thought of her tender,
tilted grace when she buttered toast for him. She would understand his

stammering. Wanting him as he needed her, the someday was already and now. Or so they might both feel.

The letter was painfully made up, working to tell the truth without spoiling it, difficult. Writing to her helped him to remember and hold on.

He sat awhile at the table downstairs in the rec room. Most of the men were still out on their Saturday dates, but the few who were playing cards left him in peace. He was grateful for that, said goodnight without interrupting their game, and went up to bed.

*   *   *

Usually the brothers lay slugabed on Sunday mornings, but when Dan went to the House kitchen to make his coffee, he found Allen long awake, waiting for him near the stove, dressed, combed with much water, his face cheerful at the cheeks and wet at the temples.

"Had a good date?" Allen asked. "The fellows say you got in before midnight. What's the matter, that girl of yours having her sick days? Why you in bed so long? Dreaming? Or were you awake and thinking, boy?"

"Thinking about what?" Dan flushed. He had tossed hotly, unwilling to begin Sunday, yes, and thinking of Lucille.

"About what I said—my frenly advice."

"Sure," Dan agreed, dryly working this around into a joke, "sure." His longing for Lucille was a tightness of chest and belly every morning unless the alarm routed him out for a class. *I joined the fraternity because I was alone,* he would explain. *Well, I'm just another townie,* she would say, *I wouldn't know about that. You feel better now?* And he would answer very simply, responsible to her need: *I've met you, Lucille.* And she would say . . .

Allen elbowed the fantasy away. "Well, thinking isn't enough in this moddun world," he continued. "When I anlized your problem for you, boy, I wasn't just bulling around—issue of the uttermost portance. You got to straighten up and fly right. I'm telling you brother to broth, not because I'm Presdent of the Chapt."

"OK, you're right, I will," Dan said, much too fast. He needed the coffee and wanted privacy for warming his hands over the cup and figuring out Lucille.

Allen did not go. He blocked the way, his body settling without moving. His face darkened. Hiding the vacant gum, the small full mouth stopped smiling. Easy victories did not please Allen. The glitter at his forehead was no longer water from combing; perspiration swelled in little droplets. "Just a sec, Shaper," he said. "Way-tup. Not so fast, boy."

Dan watched this pensiveness with an unreasoning flutter of panic in his stomach. It was a long Sunday for quarreling. He didn't like that part of brotherhood; it was too much like his own meddling relatives. The bland false faces that appeared abruptly at the several doors to the kitchen were ready. It had all been arranged, and Allen's solemnity was another sham, part of the play.

His trial, conducted along lines of strict democracy in the fine old mansion, was scheduled for that very afternoon. He had the right to choose a defense attorney. Only Allen, as President, could not serve—he regretted, he had to be judge—but anyone else Dan wanted. In a democratic way, the Chapter as a whole would sit as jury.

Dan looked at his brothers. They watched without speaking. "I'll defend myself," Dan said.

"That's your prillege, of course." Allen shrugged. *"Privilege.* But our procedure is merely to p'tect you from yourself, Dan, you should know that. We're all your brothers."

"I'm not afraid."

"We're a demcratic club. Maybe you want to be alone now to think things through?" The gap in his teeth abruptly disappeared and reappeared. The plump body leaned solicitously toward Dan. "You prolly have lots to think over, fella."

"Yes."

"Any questions?"

"May I know what I'm accused of?"

Allen smiled and touched his arm, sorrowing at the duty to report such grave charges: "Natch, this is a d'mocracy. Billy Kay, our pre-law senior, has put the complaint in correct form, but I speak as man to man." He paused before pronouncing the accusation, very careful, giving every syllable its value: "Arrogance. Lack of Brotherhood. Insufficient Belongingness. Lone Wolfism. Any further questions?"

There were none.

The Chapter sat whispering away the morning, giving Dan his right to quiet alone in his room while he thought through the charge. To plead guilty would indicate an almost perfect humility and might earn special forgiveness from the brothers. "It's the *right kind* of pride," Billy Kay told him, "the kind the fellows would appreciate." Curled in a tight arch as he lay fully clothed on the unmade bed, Dan admitted his guilt to himself, felt it and felt punished, but did not know if he could admit it in the mock seriousness of a mock trial. He tried thinking of Lucille to make himself strong. He needed strength to take her; he could not draw on her while she too was mysteriously not yet his. Stiff and pale, he imagined kissing her hair, her distant eyes, the full mouth which once swelled under his teeth—but he was not yet sure of her. Perhaps he really did suffer under the wrong kind of pride.

* * *

The first unfavorable impression made by Dan's neglecting to shave, shower, and dress in his best charcoal grays was dissipated by his pale, modest, bowed tonsure as he heard the charge and the testimony.

ITEM: Alleged sarcastic attitude for card-playing. *(I don't care, it's a matter of taste, I don't have the money.)*

ITEM: Quitting after winning one game of ping pong, without giving Billy Kay a return match. *(I had to study, and besides, he could never beat me with that weak backhand of his.)*

ITEM: Persistent silence, hasty eating, and running to his room after meals. *(Yes, I like my room. How can I explain that I feel less lonely with you all in the house, but still need privacy?)*

ITEM: On the day of the Greenville game, when the House chartered a bus so that all could go together . . . *(Guilty, I wanted to spend that last Indian summer Saturday with Lucille.)*

Item, item, item.

Guilty, guilty, guilty. Dan assented to the judgment. But he liked them anyway, he did; he wanted them to like him. With a long dwelling together, couldn't the group come to understand?

And now came his most serious symptom: Lucille. Weren't the college girls good enough? Didn't he know the traditions of the Chapter—that the sorority across the hill counted on each of them? This year there were several extra girls; he had no excuse. Couldn't he understand that using a townie was an insult to the honor of the club?

I'm not *using* her, Dan thought, gritting his teeth as he listened.

"Defense?" Allen inquired.

"What?"

"Defend yourself, boy."

"Nothing to say."

"Were you listening?"

"Yes."

The voice rose fiercely: "And you still don't have anything to say, boy? Listen here now—you admit everything?" Then there was no need for the jury to vote. He denied nothing. Just sentence him.

Allen considered. The born leader, he knew how to impose his silences upon a group. Dan looked at the walls of the rec and study room, finding comfort in their familiar closeness even at this moment, remembering his year of helpless loneliness before the Chapter took him in. He could be grateful for the punishment which would cleanse him of guilt and put him in good standing.

They would not expel him. He had paid for his room and meals, and it was inconvenient to refund the money—this the practical reason. It would also be a scandal. They needed his record as an honor student. The duties of leadership and the weight of decision lay heavily on Allen's shoulders. Responsibility—what would a senator do? How would the director of a great corporation behave? Where lay Justice and Security?

Allen started suddenly as if waking from a dream, as if thinking: *Mercy!* Repentance, Forgiveness, Honest Reform—these words now flowed freely from his lips. He made a brief but statesmanlike appeal. The applause was spontaneous. Billy Kay led it. Allen modestly raised his hands for silence.

"Is it greeable to you, Dan?" he asked mildly. If Dan would submit to a little further initiation, this would put him back in good standing, cement his place in brotherhood, give proof of sincerity.

Having passed successfully through the initiation only a few months ago, Dan found this most generous—and yet he began to shiver. He could not understand his delayed anger and fright after such unexpected clemency. He managed to reply yes, and to nod yes, and to stand to say, "Yes, thank you, brothers."

The ceremony was for that very evening. Close the business, declare peace and harmony for the new week . . .

Allen patted him reassuringly on the back and invited him up for a drink from his personal bottle. "Buck up, boy," he said, "it's not so bad. I don't even know what it'll be myself. You know how busy I been with you? I haven't made my d'cision."

*　　　*　　　*

They kept Dan in his room. Allen, very busy, bustling, arranging, and managing, popped his head through the doorway to say, "You OK? Don't you worry about a thing." It was a pleasure not to jitter through another dull Sunday evening. Even in his liquored detachment, Dan sensed something like gratitude to him for the sin which they could all celebrate together.

There was a conference downstairs, but judging by the way his good friend Allen kept running in and running out, showing his blank tooth and smiling his orders, Dan understood that the decisions were executive ones. Allen would take the responsibility. Well, that was all right. Allen was his friend, his good brother, President of the Chapter.

"Put on your pajamas,"—and Allen ducked out. Dan got undressed while Billy Kay watched him. Billy, plump and friendly, and a bottle, friendly and plump, had been delegated to keep Dan company. Allen didn't want him to worry. Billy watched curiously while he undressed and dressed in the dullest, brownest pajamas he owned.

"Wait just ten more minutes, fella,"—and Allen disappeared. Dan could wait. He folded the top inside and pulled the drawstring. Billy filled his glass, but this time he shook his head. He could take anything. He was ready.

"Is the brother all set?"

"Yes, Allen."

"OK, just a sec." He looked sternly to Billy. "It's now tenna-ten. S'chronize your watch. Bring him down to the rec hall at ezzackly ten o'cla," —and the door slammed to. Allen was a preparing person tonight. An automobile pulled into the driveway and there was hubbub downstairs. Dan found it odd that, this last time, Allen had not spoken to him. *Bring him down.* It was as if he were an object or an animal.

"Let's go."

Barefooted, tipsy, cool and sure within, Dan moved under Billy's command. He followed obediently down the carpeted stairways—the tufted wool pleasant on his bare toes—across the linoleum of the kitchen—slippery and cold it was—and into the basement from the back way. As instructed, Billy led him into the laundry room.

A large unshaded bulb filled the place with light—sink, soap, pails, brick, a heap of old tennis shoes in the corner. Lounging and easy with himself, his healthy chops pink with smiling, Allen waited to greet him. He put out his hand, and then said to Billy, "OK, you go in now. Go on. I'll explain it to the brother." Billy started through the door. Allen put a hand on his arm, saying, "Thank you, Billy," making it personal, making it something done for Allen.

Alone with Dan, Allen went on nodding and smiling. It was his way of showing that nothing worried him. Others were always filling up empty spaces; Allen Turner did not need to talk. Naked under flimsy pajamas, Dan found it difficult to meet the eyes of this fully-dressed man. He needed a belt. He wanted shoes. Finally Allen spoke: "Don't you worry now, boy."

"I'm not," Dan said.

"It's nothing much. It's just for the form."

"I'm all right. I'm ready."

"Here, boy, put away a bit of my bottle."

Dan took it. He had never drunk so much in one day. It was generous of his pal, Allen.

Allen smiled, then steadied him, backing him against the automatic washer. "Now listen," he began. Dan barely understood.

He listened to Allen with a beautiful smile. The fellows were all swell. They were a swell bunch of fellows. It would all be over soon. Dan was happy in his new brotherhood. Allen approved of him.

But just for the form, like he said, just to make sure, just not to back out now, they wanted him to pass one more little initiation rite. It was nothing serious. He had nothing to fear if his loyalty was perfect. "Take off the pajamas."

Dan stripped, shivering in the chill cement dampness of the laundry room. He stood naked before Allen, sobering dizzily, pulling his wrists together in front.

"Stand up like a man."

Dan tried to pull his shoulders straight, as in ROTC drill.

"You're among your sworn brothers. Don't look so damn chicken."

Dan fixed his teeth to stop the chattering. He was alone with Allen, but secure among his brothers. Over soon. He was not frightened, but being without clothes in the cold basement, with everyone else dressed, obscurely troubled him. He had dreamt of times like this, and never believed the dreams.

From the rec room, through the door, Dan heard the phonograph playing. They all were waiting for him. The record was some cornball Hawaiian tune, aloah-oh, with many guitars and a sickly jogging rhythm. Allen explained, talking rapidly while, around Dan's middle, he tied an Indian headdress, part of the Chapter's stock of souvenirs.

The feathers behind and the front bare-naked. The feathers tickled the back of his legs. They hung and scratched at his flanks as he moved. "Now you go out there and do a hoola dance for the boys," Allen said.

"Wh-*what?*"

Allen nodded encouragingly.

"Like this?" *But these feathers—I'm naked—I'm worse than . . .* The stiff working of his mouth meant protest; his voice—joining the group—already—did not work for him and he could not speak out.

"It's nothing at all, boy, you heard me, and then it'll be all over. A nice little hoola-hoola kootchie-kootchie, that's all. Now you just wait here a sec."

"No!"

"Listen here, c'trol yourself, boy. I'll go up front and call you when we're ready. OK?"

Dan nodded his head yes.

Alone again, he wished that Allen had remained until it was time. He needed to talk. He tried moving the way he had to, and the prickly feathers tickled him. He knew that he could not hide himself with his hands or the fellows would hoot and complain. He had to throw himself into the joke. All right, he would show them. He knew them! He knew himself! He punished himself for his own failures, first of all for his awful loneliness last year, by offering this tribute to belonging before he took his stand on the outside. For stubbornness, for punishing pride, for perverse justification of all his differences, he would conform now in order to stand afterward more firmly apart.

"Brother Dan! Hey, Brother Dan!" It was Billy Kay's voice.

Dan emerged, blinking, into the rec hall. The ping pong table had been dismantled. They burst into applause and cheers: he turned to let them see the feathers and fluffed them up behind and they shouted and clapped their hands. Someone turned up the music. He was suddenly very drunk and victorious.

"Dance! Dance now!"

He began slowly undulating, keeping his back to them, arching it, giving them what they wanted, calm both in contempt for the watchers and victory over his own feelings. He held to this sense, dancing furiously, even bumping and grinding to their cheers, flipping the stiff feathers and letting them fly. Aloah-ho, aloah-oh, sliding and moving. Now, still dancing, he turned.

Many of the faces were not watching him. Odd. He danced, but they were craned around, staring at the door. Allen had come in through the front door of the long room. He was standing with someone. She had a round, astonished, terrified face, and her eyes were fixed on him with an expression so strange, so fixed, and finally so cold even in her fright, that for a moment he did not recognize Lucille.

Allen had promised her a surprise party, and maybe said it was his birthday—*a sprize potty for g'dold Dan?* Understanding at once, in the single act of his rush through the audience while the music screeched and whined, Dan felt completely clothed, not at all naked, winged and feathered by rage as he flew toward Lucille. He did not touch her, however. He fell on Allen, flailing, punching, kicking, working deliberately toward Allen's bad teeth, and it took Billy Kay and two others to pull him off.

Looking at Allen's aggrieved face, white and stiff in the unexpected, not having counted on this, the mouth already puffing and swelling, Dan Shaper felt that he had come a long way toward his education. You have to make your own terms, he decided, even for fellowship. Lucille had slipped out alone. The girl could not now be Lucille; having committed herself to his disgrace, even by mistake, she should have stayed with him until the end; but after this evening, with the next girl, Dan and everything else would be different.

And Allen's lip would stay broken for awhile.

RICHARD M. DORSON

Campus Folklore

FROM *The American Mercury*

Here are gags and anecdotes, tall tales and legends, bawdy ballads and sentimental songs, born on campus and in classroom, in bull sessions and at beer busts. They make the rounds of a hundred campuses, changing a little each time to suit the time, place and circumstance. They are all a part of collegiate folklore, says Richard M. Dorson, even the corny ones.

Dorson teaches American history at Michigan State College and collects folklore as a pleasant avocation.

WHEN she comes tripping by, stone lions will bark. A Revolutionary War cannon will fire out. Two facing statues will solemnly dismount from their pedestals, walk to the center of the courtyard, and clasp hands in congratulation. A series of boulders, delicately balanced atop each other by nature's art, will suddenly collapse. When she gazes their way, the Flattop Mountains will turn purple with rage.

On college campuses throughout the country these various signs will greet her achievement. For she will be the first virgin to graduate from the University. One report states that the teetering rocks on the University of Alabama campus did once topple to the earth, when an undefiled soul passed by. It belonged to a young man.

The variations are legion, but the theme is national, for undergraduates from Florida to Oregon inherit the same general traditions, adjusted of course to local deans and professors and coaches. We usually associate folklore with cowboys and lumberjacks, but college students also tell stories and sing songs that they learn purely by word of mouth.

Consider for instance the gags about the absent-minded or eccentric professor. Every college and university in the land possesses some odd faculty member whose behavior makes legends. At Exeter I remember hearing

271

tales about an extremely cross-eyed Latin master, whom we called "Squint" among ourselves. Enraged in class one time, Squint glared at a squirming student and roared, "Look out, I've got my eye on you!" "Which eye?" the student asked innocently. In another irate mood Squint commanded, "You in the back row, stand up," transfixing a malefactor with his wrathful gaze. Thereupon six students stood up. I always accepted these stories as gospel until recently, when I began to investigate the ways of college folklore.

At Harvard a number of anecdotes cluster around the historian, Albert Bushnell Hart, who kept pottering about the library after his retirement. Folklore says that from force of habit he took careful notes on all the books he handled each afternoon, and then tore up all the notes before going home. A curious librarian noticed him browsing in the fine-arts section for several days, and examined the books Hart had been using. Around every nude figure he found a penciled circle—proof of Hart's ever-youthful outlook. Resurrected to present a paper at the installation of a high school principal, Hart (still according to the folklore) dutifully read the speech his secretary had typed for him, including the two carbon copies she had forgotten to remove.

Everyone knows that professors live in another world, and campus yarns prove the point. A University of Texas professor of ichthyology, walking across the campus with a colleague, was greeted cordially by a student, whom he answered impersonally. "How come you don't know the name of that friendly student?" asked the colleague. "I have made it a point," replied the ichthyologist, "never to learn the names of my students. Whenever I remember a student I forget a fish."

College folklore cherishes the tale of Professor Brown's visit to Professor Smith. The evening wore on, the guest showed no signs of leaving, and finally Brown said, "Harry, I'm awfully sorry but it's 2 A.M. and I must ask you to go. I have an 8 o'clock class in the morning." "Bill," said Harry, "you're in my house."

They also tell for true the story of the University of Illinois professor who invited a number of his associates to dinner. When the first guest showed up in a tuxedo, the host's wife motioned him upstairs to do a quick change into formal dress. The other guests arrived, but the host did not reappear. At length the frantic hostess excused herself and slipped up to his room. The professor snored in bed. Taking off his clothes to change, he had unconsciously put on his pajamas and gone to sleep.

II

The classic absent-minded-professor story concerns the pundit who drove his car to a destination, took a train back, and bawled out his wife for

Wesleyan

Culver

Vassar

Brown Brothers

Vassar

Culver

Brown Brothers

Wellesley

Brown Brothers

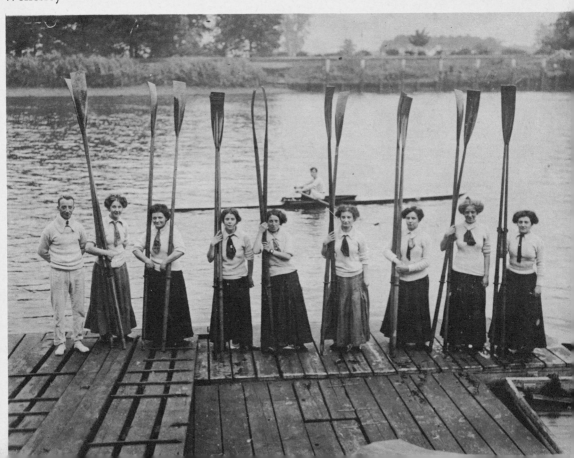

Yale

Hasty Pudding—Harvard

Class of 1870—Yale

Flag rush . . . and after

Chafing Dish Party

Home Ec

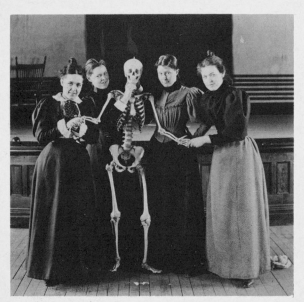

Seniors and Friend

Culver

Chem class at Vassar

Drafting at Cooper Union

not meeting him at the station with the auto. A variation on this theme recently appeared in the *Harvard Alumni Bulletin,* which reported that Professor William J. Cunningham, holder of the chair in transportation at the Business School, had dropped his wife at a mail box and then continued on his journey. Some time later he noticed her absence and informed the police. But I have heard the same story told on a mathematics professor at the University of Michigan, whose wife went to the rest room when he stopped for gas, and came out to find him gone. Worse yet, she had newly arrived in this country and could speak no English.

Professors are important, campus-wise, chiefly because they give grades. How they arrive at their decisions, folklore alone knows. The old story, of course, is that the prof throws the bluebooks down the stairs, and gives A's to those which land at the foot, F's to those at the head. Or he throws them at the ceiling, and whichever stick receive an A. A Harvard tale has chemistry professor J. P. Cooke distributing his papers to his family; he gave the E's himself, his son-in-law the D's, and so on up to the baby, who, being the slowest, marked the A's. From 'way back I recall the tale of the professor who customarily placed his papers in two heaps, representing the good and the bad students. When he came across an error by a good student he disregarded it, saying, "He knows better than that." When he saw a correct answer by a poor student he marked it wrong, saying, "He couldn't have meant that."

Examinations, the source of grades, provide more folktales. Around Harvard they still talk about Robert Benchley's feat in handling a question in American diplomatic history on rights to the Newfoundland fisheries. Benchley knew nothing about the matter, so he wrote, "This question has long been discussed from the American and British points of view, but has anyone ever considered the viewpoint of the fish?" He proceeded to give it, and was awarded, appropriately enough, a C. The chairman of the University of Minnesota's history department told me of a coed who showed up at the final exam with a few cocktails under her belt. She thought the questions looked a little strange, but went at them with a will. Some weeks later she received a grade of B for a course in American political science, in which she was not enrolled, and a statement of incomplete for the course in American literature in which she belonged.

A colleague of mine claims this is gospel. He caught a student cheating on an examination, and duly reported him to the dean. Ordinarily this meant expulsion, but the student had a relative on the governing board, and was let off with a reprimand. Some years later the professor entered a bank to cash a check, and saw this youth in the front office, scrutinizing the books. He held the post of state bank examiner.

III

There is a sheaf of stories about the dumb star athlete. His coach instructs him to sit next to the class grind for the crucial exam. Forty-nine questions the two answer identically. On the fiftieth the brilliant student writes, "I don't know the answer to this," so the athlete puts down, "I don't know the answer either." Then they tell of the football star who received such encomiums in the press that the dean asked the coach, "Won't all this praise go to his head?" "No," said the coach, "he can't read."

As the prof is lowly and comical, so the coach is lofty and admired. Which college president was it whose salary was raised to make it equal that of the football coach? Anyway, tales constantly spring up of coaches' magic. For instance, Adolph Rupp, the wizard basketball coach at the University of Kentucky, lays his luck to the fact that the door to his office is exactly six feet high. If an ambitious freshmen enters without stooping, Rupp doesn't even bother to stand up and shake his hand. Bernie Bierman of the University of Minnesota uses a similar technique in culling football talent. On a scouting trip he drives through a farm area until he comes to a young fellow plowing. He asks him, "Where is the University?" and if the young man points the direction with his hand, Bierman drives on. If, however, he lifts his plow to show the direction, Bierman stops to explain how attractive attendance at the University could be. This plow-lifting stunt, incidentally, is told on several European folk heroes.

Deans, too, grow into legends, and the Dean of Women leads all the rest. Her advice to new coeds echoes across the country. Never wear patent leather shoes on a date; they reflect. Never wear a red dress; it inflames. Don't eat olives; they're passion pills. Always carry along a telephone book (or a newspaper, or a copy of the *Saturday Evening Post*) in case your date asks you to sit on his lap. The bright street lamps erected in front of the dorms are known as Dean X's birth-control lights. A coed must turn the picture of her boy-friend to the wall before undressing at night.

In spite of these warnings, coeds do manage to have some fun. Just becoming a coed involves certain traditional procedures that the Lady Dean would be horrified to learn about. A mild one is that at Michigan State College, where a girl becomes a coed when kissed in the shadow of Beaumont Tower at the stroke of midnight. At Purdue the requirements are more demanding. Girl kisses boy under the arch of the clock tower at Havoline Hall, on the first stroke of the chimes at midnight. Then both race across campus to John Purdue's grave and commence more serious business before the last chimes strike.

Believed tales, or legends, can be found in college folklore. A macabre one that turns up in various forms is known as the Fatal Fraternity Initiation. The pledge is tied to a chair, blindfolded, and told that his arm is to be cut open. The back of the blade is pressed against his skin, while a wet towel is hung over a chair and drips into a bucket, to simulate the bleeding. The actives tell the pledge they will return later. When they come back, the boy is dead.

Sometimes the pledge is led blindfolded to the edge of a supposed cliff, and dropped two feet to die of shock. Or he is to be singed with a hot poker, which is pressed against raw meat at the same time that a piece of ice is held on the pledge's skin. He smells the burning meat, thinks it is his own flesh, and crumples up dead. In a sorority initiation, the pledge was blindfolded and told to shake the hand of a dead man. The actives thrust a pickled hand they had swiped from the laboratory into her hand then ran out of the room and locked the door. In the morning they found their sister with snow white hair, nibbling on the pickled hand.

Campus cries form still another aspect of collegiate tradition. At Harvard "Rinehart" rallies the mob for action, and thus memorializes a lonesome alumnus. Poor Rinehart, lacking friends, would go beneath his window and call out his own name, to make the neighbors think him popular. Some say that he actually was popular. At the University of California the cry is "Pedro," and the explanations are myriad. Pedro is the ghost of a student who dropped dead from the shock of getting all A's, and now assists cramming undergrads when they call him in their distress. Or he is the ghost of an Indian whose tepee was razed to build the library, and who still hangs angrily about. Or again he is the date of a girl who found herself locked out of the dorm and called after him in despair. Anyway, "Pedro" voices the soul yearnings of Berkeley bookworms on soft spring nights.

IV

Anyone who would penetrate the minds of American collegians must know their songs. The undergraduate inherits a spirited grab-bag of folk-song from upperclassmen, and sings them lustily at dorm bull sessions, beer busts, fraternity and sorority parties, or any other convivial occasion. The tunes are standard Tin Pan Alley stuff latched on to parodies and originals. The texts rise up spontaneously and spread mysteriously. Some classics seem to be familiar to college students everywhere; last fall, coming back from Europe on a ship carrying fourteen hundred assorted students, I saw casual groups form on deck and join into lyric after lyric without benefit of songbooks or prompters. Most of the songs wouldn't look well in print anyway.

The *leitmotif* in college balladry is love, but not Tin Pan Alley or

Hollywood brands of love. Dimpled, cherubic coeds sing the praises of an earthy, physical passion, of an insatiable sex mania. One group of their songs twines around Wicked Women and their lures: Flamin' Mamie, "a love scorcher and a human torture"; Mimi the College Widow, who taught the boys anatomy; Gumdrop Sal, the friendly Eskimo Queen, whose husband stayed out all night, in a land where the nights are six months long. But the chief beguiler, head and fins above the rest, is Minnie the Mermaid:

> *Many's the night I spent with Minnie the Mermaid,*
> *Down at the bottom of the sea.*
> *She forgot her morals, down among the corals,*
> *Gee but she was good to me.*
>
> *Many's the night when the pale moon was shining,*
> *Down on her bungalow.*
> *Ashes to ashes, dust to dust,*
> *Two twin beds and only one of them mussed.*
>
> *Oh it's easy to see she's not my mother,*
> *'Cause my mother's forty-nine.*
> *And it's easy to see she's not my sister,*
> *'Cause I'd never give my sister such a helluva good time.*
>
> *And it's easy to see she's not my sweetie,*
> *'Cause my sweetie's too refined.*
> *She's just a cute little kid who never knew what she did,*
> *She's just a personal friend of mine.*

In reverse plot stands the well-known fate of "The Lady in Red," begging a night's shelter under the bar. The moral to over-ambitious coeds: beware the ways of college men, "and how they come—and go."

The drinking songs assist men of mettle to drain their cups, stimulating them with sagas of mighty drunks, or providing due pauses for gulping purposes. Thus the popular Chug-A-Lug Song requires the rapid downing of a mugful of beer upon the completion of each verse, while the celebrated Whiffenpoof Song hymns a stately salute to the tavern hall.

There are various apostrophes to beer, gin, rum and whisky, and an epic ballad about an Irish wake:

> *The night that Paddy Murphy died*
> *I never shall forget,*
> *The whole damn town got stinkin' drunk,*
> *And some ain't sober yet.*

The only thing they did that night
That filled my heart with fear,
They took the ice right off the corpse
And put it in the beer.

Chorus

That's how they showed their respect for Paddy Murphy,
That's how they showed their honor and their pride,
Ho-ho-ho, that's how they showed their respect for Paddy Murphy,
On the night that Paddy died.

When they finished with the beer they started on the corpse.
They took him from his coffin and put him on the porch,
And then they went next door and stole a neighbor's pig
And brought it back to Paddy's house and tied it on his leg.

A college story about Paddy Murphy says that he came to the States from County Cork, spent his life cheating on, and beating up, his wife, and died of acute alcoholism. His relatives assembled for a handsome wake. They duly passed the body and kissed the forehead, when Cousin Maureen felt a movement and screamed to Mrs. Murphy, "He's hot, he's hot!" "Hot or cold, he goes out in the morning," said the grieving widow.

At Northwestern University the alcoholic exploits of Paddy Murphy receive each fall appropriate funeral rites, sponsored by the local Sigma Alpha Epsilon chapter. A procession three blocks long files from the chapter house to the outskirts of Evanston, the marchers festooned in green and tearfully draining beer bottles as they follow the corpse, itself composed of dead beer bottles, with a red lamp bulb for a nose. Upon reaching the grave, which has been dug by pledges, the mourners light candles and break into the Paddy Murphy song. An active attired in priestly robes renders the service, paying tribute to Paddy's inspiring and heroic drunks. En route to the grave the Sigma Chis attempt to purloin the corpse, and so seriously do the SAEs defend their honor that in 1945 one circled the procession in a plane to warn his fellow-actives of the enemy's approach.

The group loyalties of college folk get expressed in odes of sentiment and corny humor to fraternities and sororities, and to the alma mater. Serious songs of love and devotion are used to serenade the newly pinned coed, or to entertain a visiting sorority. They crawl with romantic clichés. But the undergrad has no scruples about parodying himself, and will compose such a slurring "Ode by a Sigma Chi" as this:

The girl of my dreams has bobbed her hair
And dyed it a fiery red.
She drinks, she smokes, and she tells dirty jokes,
She hasn't a brain in her head.
The girl of my dreams is a cigarette fiend,
She drinks more booze than I.
But the girl of my dreams is not what she seems,
She's the sweetheart of six other guys.

One must add to the stories and songs such other folk matter as the slang of the campus, and the festivals and customs that perforate college life. The enterprising folklorist doesn't need to journey into the back hills to scoop up tradition. He can set up his recording machine in the smokeshop or the college grill.

RUTH McKENNEY

Sock Hunt

FROM *My Sister Eileen*

Judging by the following account, Eileen's sister Ruth took her maiden steps into journalism in a rather unusual way. As "daisy-eyed star reporter" for the Ohio State University Lantern, *she may have achieved only minor success; since those days she's developed her rare gift for rueful and ludicrous humor into a fine tool for high comedy.*

Miss McKenney's education, she says, was spotty. Between classes at Ohio State she worked on a Columbus newspaper. "I never got a diploma, but on the other hand, I was a pretty good printer and had a union card." Perhaps the possession of that card led her to an interest in industrial and labor problems. At any rate, for a time her career was divided between humorous writing and sociological journalism. Her best-known work is, of course, My Sister Eileen, *which enjoyed a long and lucrative life as novel, Broadway play, motion picture and musical comedy. Short of selection by a book club or enshrinement in a time capsule, that would seem to be about everything good that could happen to one book.*

I SUPPOSE, what with the passing years and the girls he's met since, that young Mr. Randolph Churchill, the scion of the London Churchills, does not remember me. Still, looking back on it all, I should think he would. I certainly do. Precisely as I can never, for so long as I walk this earth, forget the time I fell down at my high-school senior prom, right smack in front of the orchestra with my best beau and only sprawled beside me, so can I never put aside the memory of young Mr. Churchill. My flesh still crawls. Not that Mr. Churchill is anything to make a girl's flesh crawl. Not at all. In a certain way, like the men in the breakfast-food ads, he is quite handsome.

Mr. Churchill and I met in a purely professional capacity. It was the late fall of 1930. He was touring America, speaking before literary clubs, Rotary

Clubs, university clubs, and the like on a variety of light topics, including "Fate of an Empire" and "Why I Am a Conservative." He was then nineteen, and I was the daisy-eyed star reporter on the *Ohio State Lantern*, a newspaper published daily, except Saturday and Sunday, by the students of journalism at Ohio State University.

Young Mr. Churchill arrived in Columbus, Ohio, on the flood tide of a lot of awe-struck advance notices. He was to address a local men's dinner club which for pure hauteur would make the Union Club look sick any day. All the speeches before this tony outfit were dead secret; no reporters allowed. Furthermore, celebrities who appeared before these hallowed few were never interviewed by the Columbus press. The editors of the papers were all members of the club, and that was that.

Well, my mouth watered to interview Mr. Churchill. I had never seen a real Englishman in the flesh, for one thing. For another thing, my deadly rival on the *Lantern* staff, a chap of considerable energy and no ethics, had publicly stated that he considered the feat of obtaining an interview with Mr. Churchill too great even for his remarkable talents. After this, nothing could hold me. I marched forward with determination to my doom.

I arrived at the hotel lobby at 4:35 P.M. and briskly set about finding out Mr. Churchill's room number. Then, with success almost in the hollow of my hand, I collapsed on a lobby lounge with an attack of acute panic. This lasted until 5:22 P.M., when a man insulted me. At least he came directly over to my lounge and said, in a chummy tone, "Waiting for somebody?"

This drove me to Mr. Churchill. I fled from my insulter and arrived at the forbidding door of Mr. Churchill's hotel room, still unnerved. I knocked valiantly. I had mapped out my strategy well in advance. When Mr. Churchill asked, "Who's there?" I intended to reply, "Maid, with towels." Then, when he opened the door, I planned to stick my foot in the crack and ask him a lot of questions very fast. I think a scene such as this had been in a newspaper film about that time.

Anyway, Mr. Churchill ruined my pretty plans by replying, to the knock, "Come in." I hesitated, getting a burning sensation in my throat. I was nineteen and lived with my grandmother, who would have been absolutely horrified at the thought of any young woman traipsing into a man's hotel room alone.

"Come IN!" roared Mr. Churchill from behind the door. He sounded rather angry. I kept telling myself that after I got out of school and got a real job on a newspaper, I would look back on this moment and laugh. As it turned out, however, in spite of a lot of jobs on newspapers, genuine daily ones, the mere thought of that frightful moment, with Mr. Churchill bellowing "Come IN" on one side of the door and me trembling on the other, has never brought even the sickliest of smiles to my face. It still makes my hair prickle.

Finally I opened the door very timidly indeed, and beheld Mr. Churchill, surely the blondest young man in the world, seated at a desk, writing. He wore a smoking jacket over his dinner trousers, black vest, and starched shirt front. His bare feet were stuck in floppy leather slippers. Mr. Churchill looked so very public-school English he was faintly incredible. Maybe he's grown out of that now, but in 1930 he was certainly breath of Empire. You could—or at least I could—just see him wolfing down supper off in the tropics, dressed to the teeth in tails and white tie. Mr. Churchill's eyes were a china blue and his smoking jacket was the same, overlaid, however, with old rose and gold.

I stood by the door for several seconds while Mr. Churchill continued to scratch away at his desk. Now, a cynical old interviewer of ripened years, I fear that Mr. Churchill was attempting to impress me. But on that trying evening I felt that I had intruded on the literary labors of a young genius. Finally Mr. Churchill lifted his blue eyes to mine.

"Ah," he said, leaping gallantly to his feet, "a lady! I beg your pardon. Pray do forgive me."

My mouth sagged. Mr. Churchill drew up a chair beside his desk and, with a cozy gesture, beckoned me over. I went.

"Pray excuse me," said Mr. Churchill. "I must finish this wireless message." On his desk lay eleven or twelve Western Union blanks covered with writing.

"What?" I said. The reason I said this was that I could not understand very much of what he said. His accent, which I had so longed to hear, a real, bona fide Oxford accent, was so broad that unfortunately he might as well have spoken French. I can get every other word a Frenchman says, too, which is fairly good, considering I studied French in the Ohio public schools for only eight years.

Young Mr. Churchill now turned to me and said in a fierce tone, "What would you say if you wanted to tell your manager you did not want ladies to give you flowers at lectures?" At least that is what I thought he said. It was so difficult for me to decipher Mr. Churchill's accent, and the question seemed so entirely improbable, that, after agonized reflection, I simply shook my head.

Mr. Churchill didn't note my silence. He apparently hit on just the right words, for he signed his name with a flourish I am sure no American operator ever spelled out, and turned briskly to me, saying, "Now, what may I do for you?"

I explained haltingly that I was a newspaper reporter. Mr. Churchill didn't ask, so I didn't find it necessary to tell him that the paper I was interviewing him for was only, alas, the university daily. I simply trotted out all my carefully prepared questions. I asked him about Ramsay Mac-Donald and Hoover and Briand and a few other such people. Mr. Churchill roundly denounced them all, for different reasons. MacDonald was too far left, and even Mr. Hoover was pretty much of a Socialist. I asked him about the future of English youth, and Mr. Churchill said that if only a few more young people of his class would awaken to their responsibility, the future of England was safe. I was slightly shaken at Mr. Churchill's firm Tory opinions. He seemed quite young to be so fierce.

However, I drew a breath and started off on the English public-school system. Just at this point Mr. Churchill created a diversion.

In an ordinary speaking voice, as distinguished from the voice in which he denounced Mr. Hoover or Mr. MacDonald, he said, "Would you care for a drink?"

This unnerved me again. I could explain the interview to Grandma and my conscience, but drinking with a total stranger in his hotel room certainly seemed excessive. In those days, most college students—at least at my school —still thought drinking, no matter where, was pretty darned daring. Mr. Churchill, however, had already unearthed from his suitcase a bottle of what he assured me was fine Scotch, straight from England.

I was no judge. Up to that very moment I had never tasted anything in alcoholic beverages except a variety of bootleg liquor distilled in some abandoned mines near New Straitsville, Ohio. New Straitsville corn burned your throat and made you sick. Also, it hurt so to choke down New Straits-ville corn that you were acutely conscious of every drink. It was the suave, sneaking quality of Mr. Churchill's fine liquor which undid me. You hardly knew you were drinking it, until afterward.

Mr. Churchill and I soon forgot serious topics. I asked him whether he really enjoyed lecturing about "Fate of an Empire." He said he did not, and also that he hated America and couldn't wait to get home. After a while Mr. Churchill thought we ought to eat something.

"I say," he said, "how about a spot of food, what?" He really talked just like that.

"O.K." I said. "Let me order, though. They can't understand you over the phone. You talk so funny."

Mr. Churchill glowered. He said I was the one who had a peculiar accent.

"You talk through your nose," he said, with truth, "and you pronounce all your 'r's. They aren't supposed to be pronounced."

"That's what you think," I said, feeling hilarious, "Old Mushmouth."

For some reason, Mr. Churchill thought that was very funny. " 'Mushmouth!' " he shouted joyously, amid peals of real upper-class English laughter, very high-pitched, like a whinny. " 'Mushmouth!' Deah me, I must remembaw that."

We ate lamb chops, a lot of them. "Tell them to send up a bally lot of them!" Mr. Churchill roared while I telephoned. "I want six lamp chops all for myself. After all, I must lecture on the 'Fate of an Empire.' "

While we were gnawing on lamb-chop bones we traded opinions on moving pictures. Mr. Churchill was a fan, and so was I. It turned out we both adored Vilma Banky. Suddenly Mr. Churchill said, "What about my lecture?"

"Well," I said, "what about it?"

"I won't do it," Mr. Churchill said. "Let the Empire go rot for tonight. Let's go to the cinema. You and I."

For a moment I was sorely tempted. Then I pictured the fearful scandal. The lecturer disappears. The town's leading citizens are left waiting. Among the leading citizens was the publisher of the Columbus *Dispatch*. I was the campus correspondent for the Columbus *Dispatch*, and I lived—in a very meager way, to be sure, but still I lived—on the weekly wages the *Dispatch* paid me. In my fancy I saw the publisher of the *Dispatch* discovering that his most minor employee had practically kidnapped young Mr. Churchill.

"No," I said firmly. "You have to make that speech."

Mr. Churchill sighed. "Well, then," he said, "I have to put on my dinner jacket." He found that all right; also his white scarf and his black overcoat and his two patent-leather pumps. But alas, as the hour approached nine, he could find only one black sock. The club was to send a committee at nine, to escort Mr. Churchill to the lecture hall.

"What shall I do?" Mr. Churchill inquired frantically. "I can't lecture with only one sock." I rose from the dinner table, still gnawing a bone, and cast a quick look over the room.

"Be calm," I said. "They'll never notice."

"Oh, yes, they will," Mr. Churchill said. "Besides, I won't go unless we find that sock. And I only have one black pair with me. The rest of them are in Pittsburgh."

"Wear another color," I said lightly. "What happened to the socks you had on this afternoon?"

"Tan socks," Mr. Churchill shouted, "with a dinner coat?"

I observed Mr. Churchill's frenzy with a motherly eye. "There, there," I said. "Relax. I'll find it."

Mr. Churchill sat down, putting a childish faith in me. I failed. I trotted around in circles, afraid to look in his luggage—for after all, that would hardly be proper—and unable to spot a stray black sock in the immediate surroundings.

Suddenly Mr. Churchill shouted, "I bet it's under the bed. I unpacked my things on the bed, and maybe it fell off on the floor." He threw himself down beside his bed and stuck his head under the springs.

"I can't see it," he said dismally, sounding muffled. "You have a look from the other side."

I obligingly sprawled out under the wall side of the bed, and peered around, coughing in the dust. At this moment precisely, there was a knock on the door.

"Come in!" bellowed Mr. Churchill, before he thought. I gave a faint scream, and too late Mr. Churchill considered the informality of his position. He tried to get up, too suddenly, and bumped his head severely on the bed slats. He relapsed, groaning, just as the committee of super-leading citizens walked in.

Fortunately, I do not now remember the names of those three well-starched, beautifully tailored citizens who marched in on that sock-hunting expedition. It would be frightful to be haunted all my life by their names as well as their faces.

"Mr. Churchill?" said the first leading citizen, in a tone of pained surprise.

Young Mr. Churchill showed the heritage of generations of gentlemen. Still reclining on the floor, he turned his head, nodded an acknowledgment, and said in a loud, belligerent voice, "I'm looking for my lost black sock." The second leading citizen went directly to the bureau and picked up the lost black sock.

"Your sock, sir," he said. Mr. Churchill rose, bowed slightly, and said, "I thank you very much." Then he shouted to me, "Get up! We've found it."

I hesitated. I wanted to stay under that bed and just die there peacefully, without ever having to rise and face those three leading citizens. I did get up, though, feeling the way you do in dreams when you have no clothes on at a gala performance of "Aïda" in the Metropolitan. I suppose, from the expression on the faces of the three leading citizens, that they had not realized until the moment my face slowly emerged from behind the bed that there was a young lady in the room. Each leading citizen did a combination gasp and snort.

"She's coming to hear my lecture," Mr. Churchill announced as he put on his sock. The purple staining my cheeks now rose to my hairline.

"I couldn't," I said weakly. "I couldn't indeed. It's private. They don't allow women in."

"Nevertheless," said Mr. Churchill briskly, "I don't speak unless you come."

The three leading citizens looked so grim I thought I should really faint, although I never had in my whole life. Mr. Churchill and I and the committee now left the room and boarded the elevator. All the way down, Mr. Churchill maintained his position. I was to come or he wouldn't speak. The three leading citizens took turns saying, "But that is impossible, Mr. Churchill. The rules of the club do not permit ladies."

As we got off the elevator, one of the leading citizens, a tall, white-haired man with a large stomach, managed to fall in step with me while the two other leading citizens took Mr. Churchill by the arms.

"Now," said my sudden escort, "you go away fast, and stop bothering Mr. Churchill."

"Me?" I said in honest astonishment. "I never bothered him."

The leading citizen did not stop to argue. "Go away," he hissed, giving me a slight push into the lobby. I went. I was never so glad to leave any place in my life. I wrote my interview that night, and it was a big success. My rival, Ernest, was a picture of jealous confusion when he read it next day. But even the sweet rewards of college fame and my colleagues' envy did not erase the memory of that hideous moment when I was caught, red-handed, looking for Mr. Churchill's sock. It is comparatively easy to recover from honest sorrows, but I wake up in the dead of night at least twice a year and my heart fills with agony, remembering that unspeakable moment when, like a rising moon, my face slowly appeared from behind Mr. Churchill's bed, to confound the three leading citizens of Columbus, Ohio.

Life can hold no further terrors for me.

OWEN JOHNSON

Three Cheers for Dink Stover

FROM *Stover at Yale*

Today, Owen Johnson's Stover at Yale, *the best-selling college novel of the 1900s and since then a perennial favorite with prospective Yale men, is an amusing—if unintentional—tintype. It is grandpa as a college boy, fully equipped with a "Y" and that do-or-die glaze in his eyes as he tears down the field for a touchdown.*

In this selection we meet Dink Stover early in his celebrated college career—a freshman, but even then a man of grit, grim determination and unblemished character; in a word, a real rooster, as they used to phrase it at Yale in those far-off happy days—winning the plaudits of his class at a freshman-sophomore wrestling match. Who knows—maybe it was like that then.

H ELLO, there, Stover!"

"Stover, over here!"

"Oh, Dink Stover, this way!"

Over the bared heads of the bobbing, shifting crowd he saw Hunter and McCarthy waving to him. He made his way through the strange assorted mass of freshmen to his friends, where already, instinctively, a certain picked element had coalesced. A dozen fellows, clean-cut, steady of head and eye, carrying a certain unmistakable, quiet assurance, came about him, gripping him warmly, welcoming him into the little knot with cordial acknowledgment. He felt the tribute, and he liked it. They were of his own kind, his friends to be, now and in the long reaches of life.

"Fall in, fall in!"

Ahead of them, the upper classes were already in rank. Behind, the freshmen, unorganized, distrustful, were being driven into lines of eight and ten by seniors, pipe in mouth, authoritative, quiet, fearfully enveloped in dignity. Cheers began to sound ahead, the familiar *brek-e-kek-kex* with the class numeral at the end. A cry went up:

"Here, we must have a cheer."

"Give us a cheer."

"Start her up."

"Lead a cheer, some one."

"Lead a cheer, Hunter."

"Lead the cheer, Gimbel."

"Lead the cheer, Stover."

"Come on, Stover!"

A dozen voices took up his name. He caught the infection. Without hesitating, he stepped by Hunter, who was hesitating, and cried:

"Now, fellows, all together—the first cheer for the class! Are you ready? Let her rip!"

The cheer, gathering momentum, went crashing above the noises of the street. The college burst into a mighty shout of acclaim—another class was born!

Suddenly ahead the dancing lights of the senior torches began to undulate. Through the mass a hoarse roar went rushing, and a sudden muscular tension.

"Grab hold of me."

"Catch my arm."

"Grip tight."

"Get in line."

"Move up."

"Get the swing."

Stover found himself, arms locked over one another's shoulders, between Schley, who had somehow kept persistently near him, and a powerful, smiling, blond-haired fellow who shouted to him:

"My name's Hungerford—Joe Hungerford. Glad to know you. Down from Groton."

It was a name known across the world for power in finance, and the arm about Stover's shoulder was taut with the same sentimental rush of emotion.

Down the moving line suddenly came surging the chant:

> "*Chi Rho Omega Lambda Chi!*
> *We meet to-night to celebrate*
> *The Omega Lambda Chi!*"

Grotesquely, lumbering, tripping and confused, they tried to imitate the forward classes, who were surging in the billowy rhythm of the elusive serpentine dance.

"How the deuce do they do it?"

"Get a skip to it, you ice-wagons."

"All to the left, now."

"No, to the right."

Gradually they found themselves; hoarse, laughing, struggling, sweeping inconsequentially on behind the singing, cheering college.

Before Dink knew it, the line had broken with a rush, and he was carried, struggling and pushing, into a vacant lot, where all at once, out of the tumult and the riot, a circle opened and spread under his eyes.

Seniors in varsity sweaters, with brief authoritative gestures, forced back the crowd, stationed the fretful lights, commanding and directing:

"First row, sit down."

"Down in front, there."

"Kneel behind."

"Freshmen over here."

"Get a move on!"

"Stop that shoving."

"How's the space, Cap?"

In the center, Captain Dana waited with an appraising eye.

"All right. Call out the lightweights."

Almost immediately, from the opposite sophomores, came a unanimous shout:

"Farquahar! Dick Farquahar!"

"Come on, Dick!"

"Get in the ring!"

Out into the ring stepped an agile, nervous figure, acclaimed by all his class.

"A cheer for Farquahar, fellows!"

"One, two, three!"

"Farquahar!"

"Candidate from the freshman class!"

"Candidate!"

"Robinson!"

"Teddy Robinson!"

"Harris!"

"No, Robinson—Robinson!"

Gimbel's voice dominated the outcry. There was a surging, and then a splitting of the crowd, and Robinson was slung into the ring.

In the midst of contending cheers, the antagonists stripped to the belt and stood forth to shake hands, their bared torsos shining in high lights against the mingled shadows of the audience.

The two, equally matched in skill, went tumbling and whirling over the matted sod, twisting and flopping, until by a sudden hold Robinson caught his adversary in a half nelson and for the brief part of a second had the two shoulders touching the ground. The second round likewise went to the freshman, who was triumphant after a struggle of twenty minutes.

"Middleweights!"

"Candidate from the sophomore class!"

"Candidate from the freshman!"

"Fisher!"

"Denny Fisher!"

The sophomore stepped forth, tall, angular, well knit. Among the freshmen a division of opinion arose:

"Say, Andover, who've you got?"

"Any one from Hotchkiss?"

"What's the matter with French?"

"He doesn't know a thing about wrestling."

"How about Doc White?"

"Not heavy enough."

The seniors began to be impatient.

"Hurry up, now, freshmen, hurry up!"

"Produce something!"

Still a hopeless indecision prevailed.

"I don't know any one."

"Jack's too heavy."

"Say, you Hill School fellows, haven't you got some one?"

"Some one's got to go out."

The sophomores, seizing the advantage, began to gibe at them:

"Don't be afraid, freshmen!"

"We won't hurt you."

"We'll let you down easy."

"Take it by default."

"Call time on them."

"I don't know a thing about it," said Stover, between his teeth, to Hungerford, his hands switching impatiently, his glance fixed hungrily on the provokingly amused face of the sophomore champion.

"I'm too heavy or I'd go."

"I've a mind to go, all the same."

McCarthy, who knew his impulses of old, seized him by the arm.

"Don't get excited, Dink, old boy; you don't know anything about wrestling."

"No, but I can *scrap!*"

The outcry became an uproar:

"Quitters!"

" 'Fraid cats!"

"Poor little freshmen!"

"They're in a funk."

"By George, I can't stand that," said Stover, setting his teeth, the old love of combat sweeping over him. "I'm going to have a chance at that duck myself!"

He thrust his way forward, shaking off McCarthy's hold, stepped over the reclining front ranks, and, springing into the ring, faced Dana.

"I'm no wrestler, sir, but if there's no one else I'll have a try at it."

There was a sudden hush, and then a chorus:

"Who is it?"

"Who's that fellow?"

"What's his name?"

"Oh, freshmen, who's your candidate?"

"Stover!"

"Stover, a football man!"

"Fellow from Lawrenceville!"

The seniors had him over in a corner, stripping him, talking excitedly.

"Say, Stover, what do you know about it?"

"Not a thing."

"Then go in and attack."

"All right."

"Don't wait for him."

"No."

"He's a clever wrestler, but you can get his nerve."

"His nerve?"

"Keep off the ground."

"Off the ground, yes."

"Go right in; right at him; tackle him hard; shake him up."

"All right," he said, for the tenth time. He had heard nothing that had been said. He was standing erect, looking in a dazed way at the hundreds of eyes that were dancing about him in the living, breathing pit in which he stood. He heard a jumble of roars and cheers, and one clear cry, Mc-Carthy crying:

"Good old Dink!"

Some one was rolling up his trousers to the knee; some one was flinging a sweater over his bared back; some one was whispering in his ear:

"Get right to him. Go for him—don't wait!"

"Already, there," said Captain Dana's quiet, matter-of-fact voice.

"Already, here."

"Shake hands!"

The night air swept over him with a sudden chill as the sweaters were pulled away. He went forth while Dana ran over the rules and regulations, which he did not understand at all. He stood then about five feet ten, in perfect condition, every muscle clearly outlined against the wiry, spare Yankee frame, shoulders and the sinews of his arms extraordinarily developed. From the moment he had stepped out, his eyes had never left Fisher's. Combat transformed his features, sending all the color from his face, narrowing the eyes, and drawing tense the lips. Combat was with him always an overmastering rage in the leash of a cold, nervous, pulsating logic, which by the very force of its passion gave to his expression an almost dispassionate cruelty—a look not easy to meet, that somehow, on the instant, impressed itself on the crowd with the terrific seriousness of the will behind.

"Wiry devil."

"Good shoulders."

"Great fighting face, eh?"

"Scrapper, all right."

"I'll bet he is."

"Shake hands!"

Stover caught the other's hand, looked into his eyes, read something there that told him, science aside, that he was the other's master; and suddenly, rushing forward, he caught him about the knees and, lifting him bodily in the air, hurled him through the circle in a terrific tackle.

The onslaught was so sudden that Fisher, unable to guard himself, went down with a crash, the fall broken by the bodies of the spectators.

A roar, half laughter, half hysteria, went up.

"Go for him!"

"Good boy, Stover!"

"Chew him up!"

"Is he a scrapper!"

"Say, this *is* a fight!"

"Wow!"

Dana, clapping them on the shoulders, brought them back to the center of the ring and restored them to the position in which they had fallen. Fisher, plainly shaken up, immediately worked himself into a defensive position, recovering his breath, while Stover frantically sought some instinctive hold with which to turn him over.

Suddenly an arm shot out, caught his head in chancery, and before he knew it he was underneath and the weight of Fisher's body was above, pressing him down. He staggered to his feet in a fury, maddened, unreasoning, and went down again, always with the dead weight above him.

"Here, that won't do," he said to himself savagely, recovering his clarity of vision; "I mustn't lose strength."

All at once, before he knew how it had been done, Fisher's arm was under his, cutting over his neck, and slowly but irresistibly his shoulders were turning toward the fatal touch. Every one was up, shouting:

"Turn him over!"

"Finish him up!"

"Hold out, freshman!"

"Hold out!"

"Flop over!"

"Don't give in!"

"Stick it out!"

With a sudden expenditure of strength, he checked the turning movement, desperately striving against the cruel hold.

"Good boy, Stover!"

"That's the stuff!"

"Show your grit!"

"Hold out!"

"Show your nerve!"

In a second he had reasoned it out. He was caught—he knew it. He could resist three minutes, five minutes, slowly sinking against his ebbing strength, frantically cheered for a spectacular resistance—and then what? If he had a chance, it was in preserving every ounce of his strength for the coming rounds.

"All right; you've got me this time," he said coldly, and, relaxing, let his shoulders drop.

Dana's hand fell stingingly on him, announcing the fall. He rose amid an angry chorus:

"What the deuce!"

"Say, I don't stand for that!"

"Thought he was game."

"Game nothing!"

"Lost his nerve."

"Sure he did."

"Well, I'll be damned."

"A quitter—a rank quitter!"

He walked to his seconds, angry at the misunderstanding.

"Here, I know what I'm doing," he said in short, quick breaths, forgetting that he, a freshman, was addressing the lords of creation. He was a captain again, his own captain, conducting his own battle. "I'll get him yet. Rub up this shoulder, quick."

"Keep off the ground," said one mentor.

"You bet I will."

"Why the deuce did you give in so easily?"

"Because there are two more rounds, and I'm going to use my head—hang it!"

"He's right, too," said the first senior, rubbing him fiercely with the towel. "Now, sport, don't monkey with him until you've jarred him up a couple of times!"

"That's what I'm going to do!"

"Time!" cried the voice of Dana.

This time he retreated slowly, drawing Fisher unwarily toward his edge of the ring, and then suddenly, as the sophomore lunged at him, shot forward again, in a tackle just below the waist, raised him clear off the ground, spun him around, and, putting all his force into his back as a wood-chopper swings an ax, brought him down crashing, clear across the ring. It was a fearful tackle, executed with every savage ounce of rage within him, the force of which momentarily stunned him. Fisher, groggy under the bruising impact, barely had time to turn on his stomach before Stover was upon him.

Dink immediately sprang up and back, waiting in the center of the ring. The sophomore, too dazed to reason clearly, yielding only to his anger at the sudden reversal, foolishly struggled to his feet and came staggering toward him. A second time Stover threw all his dynamic strength into another crashing tackle. This time Fisher went over on his back with a thump, and, though he turned instinctively, both shoulders had landed squarely on the turf, and, despite his frantic protests, a roar went up as Dana allotted the fall to Stover.

This time, as he went to his corner, it was amid pandemonium:

"You're a corker, freshman!"

"Oh, you bulldog!"

"Tear him up!"

"You're the stuff!"

"Good head, freshman!"

"Good brain-work!"

Several upper classmen came hurriedly over to his corner, slapping him on the back, volunteering advice.

"Clear out," said his mentor proudly. "This rooster can take care of himself."

Fisher came up for the third round, visibly groggy and shaken by the force of the tackles he had received, but game. Twice Stover, watching his chance, dove under the groping hands and flung him savagely to the ground. Once Fisher caught him, as they lay on the ground, in a hold that might have been decisive earlier in the match. As it was, Stover felt with a swift horror the arm slipping under his arm, half gripping his neck. The wet heat of the antagonistic body over his inflamed all the brute in him. The strength was now his. He tore himself free, scrambled to his feet, and hurled Fisher a last time clean through into the scattering crowd, where he lay stunned, too weak to resist the viselike hands that forced his shoulders to the ground.

Dana hauled Stover to his feet, a little groggy.

"Some tackling, freshman! Bout's yours! Call out the heavyweights!"

Scarcely realizing that it was his captain who had spoken, Dink stood staring down at Fisher, white and conquered, struggling to his feet in the grip of friends.

"I say, Fisher," he said impulsively, "I hope I didn't shake you up too much. I saw red; I didn't know what I was doing."

"You did me all right," said the sophomore, giving his hand. "That tackle of yours would break a horse in two. Shake!"

"Thank you," said Stover, flustered and almost ashamed before the other's perfect sportsmanship. "Thank you very much, sir!"

He went to his corner, smothered under frantic slaps and embraces, hearing his name resounding again and again on the thunders of his class-mates. The bout had been spectacular; every one was asking who he was.

"Stover, eh, of Lawrenceville!"

"Gee, what a fierce tackler!"

"Ridiculous for Fisher to be beaten!"

"Oh, is it? How'd you like to get a fall like that?"

"Played end."

"Captain at Lawrenceville."

"He ought to be a wonder."

"Say, did you see the face he got on him?"

"Enough to scare you to death."

"It got Fisher, all right."

While he was being rubbed down and having his clothes thrust upon him, shivering in every tense muscle, which, now the issue was decided, seemed to have broken from his control, suddenly a hand gripped his, and, looking up, he saw the face of Tompkins, ablaze with the fire of the pro-fessional spectator.

"I'm not shaking hands on your brutal old tackling," he said, with a look that belied his words. "It's the other thing—the losing the first fall. Good brain-work, boy; that's what'll count in football."

The grip of the veteran cut into his hand; in Tompkin's face also was a reminiscent flash of the fighting face that somehow, in any test, wins half the battle.

The third bout went to the sophomores, Regan, the choice of the class, being nowhere to be found. But the victory was with the freshmen, who, knit suddenly together by the consciousness of a power to rise to emergencies, carried home the candidates in triumph.

McCarthy, with his arms around Stover as he had done in the old school days after a grueling football contest, bore Dink up to their rooms with joyful, bearlike hugs. Other hands were on him, wafting him up the stairs as though riding a gale.

"Here, let me down will you, you galoots!" he cried vainly from time to time.

Hilariously they carried him into the room and dumped him down. Other freshmen, following, came to him, shaking his hand, pounding him on the back.

"Good boy, Stover!"

"What's the use of wrestling, anyhow?"

"You're it!"

"We're all for you!"

"The old sophomores thought they had it cinched."

"Three cheers for Dink Stover!"

"One more!"

"And again!"

"Yippi!"

McCarthy, doubled up with laughter, stood in front of him, gazing hilariously, proudly down.

"You old Dink, you, what right had you to go out for it?"

"None at all."

"How the deuce did you have the nerve?"

"How?" For the first time the question impressed itself on him. He scratched his head and said simply, unconscious of the wide application of what he said: "Gee! I didn't stop to think how rotten I was."

He went to bed, gorgeously happy with the first throbbing, satisfying intoxication of success. The whole world must be concerned with him now. He was no longer unknown; he had emerged, freed himself from the thralling oblivion of the mass.

What the College Incubator
Did to One Modest Lambkin

FROM *Breaking into Society*

   Among George Ade's relatively few abominations were "all persons who take themselves seriously." Most pre-eminently he did not. His turn-of-the-century fables in slang were for the reader who knew a laugh when he read one, even if the laugh was on himself.

   Ade was a graduate of Purdue and a member of Sigma Chi. He was active in fraternity affairs for a good portion of his life, was Grand Consul of the fraternity in 1909-11, wrote the Sigma Chi creed and financed the building of the Purdue Delta Chapter House.

ONE Autumn Afternoon a gray-haired Agriculturist took his youngest Olive Branch by the Hand and led him away to a Varsity. Wilbur was 18 and an Onion. He had outgrown his last year's tunic, and his Smalls were hardly on speaking terms with his Uppers. He had large warty Hands, which floated idly at his sides and his Wrists resembled extra Sets of Knuckles. When he walked, his Legs gave way at the Hinge and he Interfered. On his Head was a little Wideawake with a Buckle at the Side. Mother had bobbed his Hair and rubbed in a little goose grease to make it shine. The Collar that he wore was a size 13, and called the Rollo Shape. It rose to a Height of a half inch above his Neck-Band. For a Cravat he had a piece of watered Silk Ribbon with butterflies on it.

   Wilbur had his Money tied up in a Handkerchief and he carried a Paper Telescope, loaded down with one complete Change and a Catalogue of the Institution showing that the Necessary Expenses were not more than $3.40 per week.

As the train pulled away from Pewee Junction, Wilbur began to Leak. Salt Tears trickled down through the Archipelago of Freckles. He wanted to Crawfish, but Paw bought him a box of Crackerjack and told him that if he got an education and improved his Opportunities some day he might be County Superintendent of Schools and his $900 a year just like finding it. So Wilbur sparked up and said he would try and stick it out. He got out the Catalogue and read all of the copper-riveted Rules for the Moral Guidance of Students.

The Curriculum had him scared. He saw that in the next four years he would have to soak up practically all the Knowledge on the Market. But he was cheered to think that if he persevered and got through he would be entitled to wear an Alpaca Coat and a Lawn Tie and teach in the High School, so he took courage and began to notice the Scenery.

Wilbur was planted in a Boarding House guaranteed to provide Wholesome Food and Home Influence. Father went back after making a final Discourse on the importance of learning most everything in all of the Books.

Nine Months later they were down at the Depot to meet Wilbur. He had written several times, saying he could not find time to come Home, as he was in pursuit of Knowledge every Minute of the Day, and if he left the Track, Knowledge might gain several Laps on him. It looked reasonable, too, for the future Superintendent of Schools had spent $400 for Books, $200 for Scientific Apparatus, and something like $60 for Chemicals to be used in the Laboratory.

When the Train suddenly checked itself, to avoid running past the Town, there came out of the Parlor Car something that looked like Fitz, on account of the Padding in the Shoulders. Just above one ear he wore a dinky Cap about the size of a Postage Stamp. The Coat reached almost to the Hips and was buttoned below. The Trousers had enough material for a Suit. They were reefed to show feverish Socks of a zigzag design. The Shoes were very Bull-Dog and each had a wide Terrace running around it. Father held on to a Truck for Support. Never before had he seen a genuine case of the Inflammatory Rah-Rah.

Wilbur was smoking a dizzy little Pipe from which the Smoke curled upward, losing itself in a copious Forelock that moved gently in the Breeze. Instead of a Collar, Wilbur was wearing a Turkish Towel. He had the Harvard Walk down pat. With both Hands in his Pockets, the one who had been pursuing Knowledge Teetered toward the Author of his Being and said, "How are you, Governor?"

Father was always a Lightning Calculator, and as he stood there trying to grasp and comprehend and mentally close in, as it were, on the Burlap

Suit and the Coon Shirt, and the sassy Pipe, something told him that Wilbur would have to Switch if he expected to be County Superintendent of Schools.

"Here are my Checks," said Wilbur, handing over the Brasses. "Have my Trunks, my Golf Clubs, my portable Punching Bag, the Suit-Case, and Hat Boxes sent up to the House right away. Then drive me Home by the Outside Road, because I don't want to meet all those Yaps. They annoy me."

"You'd better git out of that Rig mighty quick if you don't want to be joshed," said his Parent. "Folks around here won't stand for any such fool Regalia, and if you walk like a frozen-toed Hen you'll get some Hot Shots or I miss my Calkilcations."

"Say, Papa, I've been eating Raw Meat and drinking Blood at the Training Table, and I'm on Edge," said Wilbur, expanding his Chest until it bulged out like a Thornton Squash. "If any of these local Georgie Glues try to shoot their Pink Conversation at me I'll toss them up into the trees and let them hang there. I'm the Gazabo that Puts the Shot. Anyone who can trim a Policeman and chuck a Hackman right back into his own Hack and drive off with him doesn't ask for any sweeter Tapioca than one of these Gaffer Greens. The Plowboy who is muscle-bound and full of Pastry will have a Proud Chance any time that he struts across my Pathway. In my Trunks I have 8 suits a little warmer than this one and 47 pairs of passionate Hose. I'm out here to give the Cornfields a Touch of High Life. It's about time that your Chaws had a Glimpse of the Great Outside World. Anyone who gets Fussy about the Color Combinations that I spring from Day to Day will be chopped up and served for Lunch. To begin with, I'm going to teach you and Mother to play Golf. If these Mutts come and lean over the Fence and start to get off their Colored Weekly Jokes we'll fan the Hillside with them."

"What do they teach you up at your School—besides Murder?" inquired the Father. "I thought you wanted to be County Superintendent of Schools?"

"I've outgrown all those two-by-four Ambitions," was the Reply. "I'm going to be on the Eleven next Fall. What more could you ask?"

That very week Wilbur organized a Ball Team that walloped Hickory Creek, Sand Ridge, and Sozzinsville. He had the whole Township with him. Every Cub at Pewee Junction began to wear a Turkish Towel for a Collar and practice the Harvard Walk.

MORAL: A Boy never blossoms into his Full Possibilities until he strikes an Atmosphere of Culture.

MORRIS BISHOP

The Crusty Professor's Song

FROM *The New Yorker*

Morris Bishop alternates the writing of light verse—of which this selection is a happy example—with biography, his chief writing interest.

Bishop is a Cornell man, class of Frank Sullivan, E. B. White and "other friends of wit, lovers of the shining phrase, foes of spiritual bombast." At Cornell, writes Bishop, "I was much influenced by Professor Martin Wright Sampson, who inspired the malleable young men in his Manuscript Club to control the wild fancy, to love reason, to laugh at folly." What better training for a writer of light verse?

ONCE in days of yore
  All the college scholars
Resolutely swore
  To give up stand-up collars.
Students never wore
  Stand-up collars, stand-up collars,
    Never any more.

They discarded cuff-links,
  And the cuffs likewise;
They abandoned tie-pins
  And dispensed with ties.
Students never wore
  Cuff-links, cuffs, tie-pins, ties,
  Stand-up collars, stand-up collars,
    Never any more.

307

They rejected headgear,
　Threw away their hats,
Eliminated garters,
　Extirpated spats.
Students never wore
　Caps and hats, garters, spats,
　Cuff-links, cuffs, tie-pins, ties,
　Stand-up collars, stand-up collars,
　　Never any more.

They renounced the jacket,
　They abjured the vest;
They undid the buttons
　To display the chest.
Students never wore
　Jackets, coats, waistcoats, vests,
　Caps and hats, garters, spats,
　Cuff-links, cuffs, tie-pins, ties,
　Stand-up collars, stand-up collars,
　　Never any more.

Maybe time will banish
　Sweat-shirts, dirty jeans;
Maybe these will vanish
　From collegiate scenes.
Students will not wear
　Dirty sweat-shirts, dirty jeans,
　Jackets, coats, waistcoats, vests,
　Caps and hats, garters, spats,
　Cuff-links, cuffs, tie-pins, ties,
　Stand-up collars, stand-up collars—
　　Then what *will* they wear?

A Team that Never Was

FROM *The New York Herald Tribune*

In a preface to his true story of this "team that never was," Bob Cooke, sports writer, says it was "a college football team second to none. It was never beaten, never tied. It had no coaches, no stadium, no customers. Yet it captured the fancy of a nation back in 1941."

THE entire football world was saddened the other day when Morris Newburger announced his retirement from football. Oh, you've heard of Knute Rockne, Walter Camp, Alonzo Stagg, and the like, but I'll make a bet you never thought of putting Newburger up there on the list. Fact is, I'll wager you never heard of Newburger.

Football was blessed with Newburger many years after Rockne, Stagg, Camp, and their kind had become famous in song and story. It remained for Newburger, a citizen of quiet renown, to provide an everlasting memorial to the game as we know it today.

Newburger was always a fellow who shied away from praise. He never played football. He is not a spotlight seeker. Yet, the advent of a football season, with no mention of Newburger, is more than a fan can stand.

Newburger once coached a team that was never beaten, never tied. He needed no assistant coaches, no stadium, no customers, and no players.

It was in the fall of 1941 when Newburger was seized by an uncontrollable desire to build an undefeated eleven.

So he created one which he called Plainfield State Teachers. Sounds like a college, doesn't it? Newburger thought so, and so did a number of metropolitan sports writers.

Having founded Plainfield State, Newburger needed only a schedule to get his season started. Swiftly he improvised some "tough opposition," not to mention "traditional rivals." When he had completed his work, Plainfield

State had an eight-game itinerary against such teams as Scott, Chesterton, Fox, Randolph Tech, Ingersoll, Benson, Appalachian, and Harmony U (home-coming).

The above institutions were as mythical as Plainfield State, but they appeared to be football teams. Newburger, working fiendishly, had given them names which carried a trace of the familiar thus leading to the illusion of the authentic.

In the opener against Scott, Plainfield State got off to a "terrific" start by whipping its "bigger opponents," 20–0. At this stage of the game, Newburger displayed a talent amounting to genius.

After he'd phoned the result of the Plainfield State-Scott game to the New York *Herald Tribune,* the New York *Times,* The Associated Press, and other news media, he created the celebrated fullback, John Chung.

"Can't have a miracle team without a miracle player," Newburger whispered to himself as he began to make an accounting of Chung's assets.

Chung was a 205-pound, full-blooded Chinese fullback. He was the star of the Plainfield State team, the crowbar which pried victory from defeat, the shining white horse on which the team rode forth to battle. According to Plainfield State's statistics, Chung gained an average of nine and three-tenths yards every time he carried the ball, due largely, so Newburger said, to Chung's habit of eating rice between the halves.

Herb Allan, former sports writer on the New York *Post,* received a publicity release on Chung and wrote a glowing feature about the star of the Orient. This was one week prior to the revelation that neither Chung nor Plainfield State existed.

Six victories had been recorded before Caswell Adams, then of the *Herald Tribune,* scooped the town with his story of the Plainfield State hoax.

Plainfield had trampled on Scott, Chesterton, Fox, Randolph Tech, Ingersoll, and Benson. Appalachian was to have been beaten, 20–2. Then, in the final, Harmony was to put up a great game but was to succumb to Chung's wizardry, 40–27, before an enthusiastic home-coming crowd.

The cancellation of the games against Appalachian and Harmony saddened Mr. Newburger. He was also downhearted over the sudden end to the career of John Chung, the indestructible Chinese. So retirement has claimed Mr. Newburger.

Always and forever, Newburger will recall the time he telephoned a local paper with the score of the Plainfield State-Randolph Tech game. The score was Plainfield State Teachers 35, Tech 0.

"Where's Plainfield State?" asked the rewrite man. "In Plainfield, New Jersey?"

"No, just outside," said Newburger and hung up.

SHIRLEY JACKSON

How to Be a Faculty Wife

FROM *Raising Demons*

As Shirley Jackson describes the profession of faculty wife, knowing how to be one is no small art, especially in the light of her definition of the term: "A faculty wife is a person married to a faculty."

The Hymans (Miss Jackson's husband is Professor Stanley Edgar Hyman, of Bennington, Vermont) live in a small rural community happily removed from city life. "Our major exports," she says, "are books and children, both of which we produce in abundance." This selection is from Raising Demons, *the engaging biography of her abundant family.*

MY HUSBAND had been teaching for several months, and I was slowly becoming aware of a wholly new element in the usual uneasy tenor of our days; I was a faculty wife. A faculty wife is a person who is married to a faculty. She has frequently read at least one good book lately, she has one "nice" black dress to wear to student parties, and she is always just the teensiest bit in the way, particularly in a girls' college such as the one where my husband taught. She is presumed to have pressing and wholly absorbing interests at home, to which, when out, she is always anxious to return and, when at home, reluctant to leave. It is considered probable that ten years or so ago she had a face and a personality of her own, but if she has it still, she is expected to keep it decently to herself. She will ask students questions like "And what did you do during vacation?" and answer in return questions like "How old is your little boy now?" Her little pastimes, conducted in a respectably anonymous and furtive manner, are presumed to include such activities as knitting, hemming dish towels, and perhaps sketching wild flowers or doing water colors of her children.

I was not bitter about being a faculty wife, very much, although it *did* occur to me once or twice that young men who were apt to go on and be-

311

come college teachers someday ought to be required to show some clearly distinguishable characteristic, or perhaps even wear some large kind of identi-
fying badge, for the protection of innocent young girls who might in that
case go on to be the contented wives of furniture repairmen or disc jockeys
or even car salesmen. The way it is now, almost any girl is apt to find herself
hardening slowly into a faculty wife when all she actually thought she was
doing was just getting married.

I put in four good years at college, and managed to pass almost everything, and got my degree and all, and I think it was a little bit unkind of
fate to send me back to college the hard way, but of course there *were*
things I might have done—or, put it, people I might have married—which
would have landed me in worse positions. Bluebeard, anyway.

The three big thorns in the faculty wife's ointment are her husband, her
husband's colleagues, and her husband's students. Naturally a husband
presents enormous irritations no matter what he is doing, and I think it is
unreasonable to regard a teaching husband as necessarily more faulty than,
say, a plumbing husband, but there is no question but what the ego of a
teaching husband is going to be more vividly developed, particularly if he
teaches in a girls' college. For instance, when I accompanied my husband to a
student party and we were greeted at the door by a laughing group of students who surrounded him, calling out, "Hello, there," and, "You *did* wear
the orange tie, after all," and, "Class was simply *super* this morning," I could
figure, as I stood alone in the hall moodily looking for a place to put my
coat, that it was going to be proportionately more difficult, once home, to
persuade my husband to put up the new shelves in the kitchen. He was
going to lie back in his chair, flaunting the orange tie, and tell me to get a
boy for things like that.

Well, I suppose husbands are all alike, at least the husbands of my friends
were. Before my husband commenced professor many of my friends had
been from the group of faculty wives, although they were in general under-
standably reluctant to wander out of their proper setting, and it was pleasant, now, to meet them as a colleague. We usually made a comfortable little
group as we gathered in the corner just to the right of the doorway at student parties. "Hello," we cried gaily to one another, "you here *too? How*
are the children? Did you get to that perfectly ripping affair last night at
that other student house? Are the children well? Is there any news of a raise
in faculty salaries? And the children—how are *they?*"

Of course, if one of us ever happened to mention that she was getting a
new refrigerator, or that her husband had just had an article published in
the *Wiltshire Archeological and Natural History Journal,* or that they were
turning in the old car on a new convertible, a certain coolness was apt to
arise. Someone might come out with the story of a woman *she* knew who

got herself hopelessly tangled in the descending top of *her* convertible and was late for a Trustee Tea, or someone would tell about what happened to some friends of hers with their new refrigerator the night they went out and left it alone for the first time, or we might mention with becoming modesty the articles *our* husbands have had in the *Journal of American Ethnobotany,* or the *Physical Culture Quarterly.* These coolnesses developed easily into open quarrels, with consequent feuds and taking sides and the comparative merits of publication in Wiltshire and East Lansing openly discussed, and the husbands bowing distantly in the faculty lounge.

I found, however, that there *were* sizable advantages to our connection with a college community. It was easier to get a piano tuner, for instance, and information, such as how to lay out a basketball court, or how to figure compound interest on a mortgage, was easily obtainable from the reference books in the library. Once, when my husband was out of town and I wanted to start the little wood-burning hot-water heater which was attached to our furnace, I took advantage of living in a seat of learning, and called the chemistry professor and asked him how you started a little wood-burning hot-water heater. He said that he personally lived in a college house which had electricity laid on, but why didn't I try the logic professor, who was accustomed to working out problems and things? The logic professor said that his work was purely theoretical, and the person I really wanted was the natural science man who ought to know how to start fires from camping out looking at ferns and stuff. The natural science man said that everyone knew that forest fires destroyed millions of dollars of animal life every year and if I wanted to start a fire I ought to get hold of the painting teacher who could probably bring over some turpentine and old canvases. The painting teacher said well, he *knew* turpentine was no good, but one of the literature teachers had been at Yaddo once, and *he* ought to know something, after all. The literature professor said that aside from washing himself in steep-down gulfs of liquid fire he managed to keep pretty well away from the stuff. I finally called the college president and he said he had the same sort of gadget in *his* house, and he came down and started it, but it went out.

Unlike faculty wives, students are nice girls who have come to college to get an education. The students I encountered had very little concern with anything outside of getting an education and so could not be expected to waste much time investigating the home lives of their teachers. I never, for instance, met a student who was the least bit interested in my sketches of wild flowers, and their anxiety to know the ages of my children was, to say the least, perfunctory. On the other hand, almost all the students I met were well mannered, civil, and nicely brought up. They were extremely thoughtful, and courteous to the point of chivalry. They were kind to children and to animals. If they slammed a door, it was never knowingly in the face of

a stray puppy or a small baby. If they knocked someone down, it was inconceivable that it should be a teacher or another student. If they brought up
some date who played professionally for the Green Bay Packers, he would
carefully avoid practicing his inside blocking on someone's roommate's
mother. I can say, categorically, that I never saw any student, of whatever
year, kick a sick cat. They were, as I say, neat, well mannered, and demure.
Their clothes were subdued, sometimes so much so as to be invisible. When
they gave parties they took pains to invite only the most congenial people,
such as their teachers and selected other students. I never, for my own part,
found any difficulty in declining an invitation to a student party, if I got
one at all, or in leaving, once I was there. I learned to have nothing but admiration for the student's faith in her teachers, and the kind of innocent
devotion which was frequently so touching; I am reminded of the student
who crept up, one spring dawning, to leave a basket of fresh strawberries
upon her teacher's pillow. Or the student who resolutely refused to remove a
lilac sweater her teacher had once admired, and became known, by her
junior year, as "The Purple Kid," although she dropped out, abruptly, during one Christmas vacation and was only seen once thereafter, in Paris with
a retired manufacturer of pinball machines.

Perhaps the only quarrel the faculty wife might have with her husband's students is their spirit of pure scientific inquiry; they were very apt
to throw out the baby, as it were, with the bathwater, particularly when
baby-sitting. As a matter of fact, I once had a conversation with a student
upon this very topic; it was rather late at night, and we were among the
dregs of a student party. She was there because she was a hostess and I was
there because it was beginning to look as though there were no good way of
getting my husband home. I was wearing my "nice" black dress and holding
a glass of ginger ale and she was wearing a strapless short evening dress,
pink, with gardenias in her hair, and holding and perhaps even drinking a
glass of the punch they had been serving at the party, made of equal parts of
sweet vermouth, vodka, and cold cocoa. We were sitting on the floor and I
had already asked her about her vacation and she had told me she spent six
weeks working as a feather duster in a museum, sometimes dusting feathers
and sometimes feathering dusters, and that she had found the work very
constructive and very useful in influencing her in the eventual choice of her
senior program, and I had told her that my little boy was three now. After
a short, agonized silence, broken only by the harmonies of six voices doing
something from La Bohème in another corner of the room, she turned to me
and asked, "Listen, when you were young—I mean, before you kind of settled
down and all, when you were—well, younger, that is—did you ever figure
you'd end up like this?" She waved her hand vaguely at the student living

room, my "nice" black dress, and my glass of ginger ale. "Like *this?*" she said.

"Certainly," I said. "My only desire was to be a faculty wife. I used to sit at my casement window, half embroidering, half dreaming, and long for Professor Right."

"I suppose," she said, "that you *are* better off than you would have been. Not married at all or anything."

"I was a penniless governess in a big house," I said. "I was ready to take anything that moved."

"And of course you *do* make a nice home for your husband. Someplace to come back to, and everything so neat."

"My spinning lacks finesse," I said. "But I yield to no one on my stone-ground meal."

"And *he's* lucky, too, of course. So many men who marry young silly women find themselves always going to parties and things for their wives' sake. An older woman—"

"He was only a boy," I said. "How well I remember his eager, youthful charm; 'Lad,' I used to say, fondly touching his wanton curls, 'lad, youth calls to youth, and what *you* need—' "

"He's *still* terribly boyish, don't you think?" She bent a tender glance upon my husband, who was waving a cigar and telling an enthralled group of students an expurgated story of how he graded examination papers. "He's always so full of vitality."

"You should see him at home," I said. "We never have a dull moment *there,* I can tell you. Absolutely nothing but boyish vitality and youthful charm all over the place. He's positively faunlike. Why, I could tell you things—"

"I don't suppose," she said, blushing slightly and studying her fingernails, "that he talks much about us students at home, does he?"

"He babbles about you all the time," I assured her, and rose and went over to the noisy group of which my husband was the center. "Hail, ruddy stripling," I said.

"What?" he said, startled.

"Never mind," I said. "You leaving now or do I have to carry you home?"

I decided that I was going to fewer student parties after I ripped part of the sleeve out of my black dress helping a freshman climb a fence. By the end of the first semester, what I wanted to do most in the world was invite a few of my husband's students over for tea and drop them down the well.

An Extra Large Boat Race

FROM *Money From Home*

⌂ *Those familiar with* Guys and Dolls *will recognize as old friends such Damon Runyon characters as Sam the Gonoph and Society Max, who figure in this story of a boat race between the Harvards and the Yales.*

It is occasionally given to us to read a writer in the role of his own most cogent critic. Here is Runyon reviewing a book by Runyon. "As a study in the art of carrying water on both shoulders, of sophistry, of writing with tongue-in-cheek, and of intellectual dishonesty, I think it has no superior since the beginning of time. . . . I tell you Runyon has subtlety, but it is the considered opinion of this reviewer that it is a great pity the guy did not remain a rebel out-and-out, even at the cost of a good position at the feed trough."

ONE hot morning in June, I am standing in front of the Mohican Hotel in the city of New London, Conn., and the reason I am in such a surprising spot is something that makes a long story quite a bit longer.

It goes back to a couple of nights before, when I am walking along Broadway and I run into Sam the Gonoph, the ticket speculator, who seems to have a very sour expression on his puss, although, even when Sam the Gonoph is looking good-natured his puss is nothing much to see.

Now Sam the Gonoph is an old friend of mine, and in fact I sometimes join up with him and his crew to hustle duckets to one thing and another when he is short-handed, so I give him a big hello, and he stops and the following conversation ensues:

"How is it going with you, Sam?" I say to Sam the Gonoph, although of course I do not really care two pins how it is going with him. "You look as if you are all sored up at somebody."

"No," Sam says, "I am not sored up at anybody. I am never sored up at

316

anybody in my life, except maybe Society Max, and of course everybody knows I have a perfect right to be sored up at Society Max, because look at what he does to me."

Well, what Sam the Gonoph says is very true, because what Society Max does to Sam is to steal Sam's fiancée off of him a couple of years before this, and marry her before Sam has time to think. This fiancée is a doll by the name of Sonia, who resides up in the Bronx, and Sam the Gonoph is engaged to her since the year of the Dempsey-Firpo fight, and is contemplating marrying her almost any time, when Society Max bobs up.

Many citizens afterwards claim that Max does Sam the Gonoph a rare favor, because Sonia is commencing to fat up in spots, but it breaks Sam's heart just the same, especially when he learns that Sonia's papa gives the happy young couple twenty big G's in old-fashioned folding money that nobody ever knows the papa has, and Sam figures that Max must get an inside tip on this dough and that he takes an unfair advantage of the situation.

"But," Sam the Gonoph says, "I am not looking sored up at this time because of Society Max, although of course it is well known to one and all that I am under oath to knock his ears down the first time I catch up with him. As a matter of fact, I do not as much as think of Society Max for a year or more, although I hear he deserts poor Sonia out in Cincinnati after spending her dough and leading her a dog's life, including a few off-hand pastings —not that I am claiming Sonia may not need a pasting now and then.

"What I am looking sored up about," Sam says, "is because I must get up into Connecticut tomorrow to a spot that is called New London to dispose of a line of merchandise."

"Why, Sam," I say, "what can be doing in such a place?"

"Oh," Sam says, "a large boat race is coming up between the Harvards and the Yales. It comes up at New London every year, and is quite an interesting event from what I read in the papers about it, but the reason I am sored up about going tomorrow is because I wish to spend the week-end on my farm in New Jersey to see how my onions are doing. Since I buy this farm in New Jersey, I can scarcely wait to get over there on week-ends to watch my onions grow.

"But," Sam the Gonoph says, "this is an extra large boat race this year, and I am in possession of many choice duckets, and am sure to make plenty of black ink for myself, and business before pleasure is what I always say. By the way," Sam says, "do you ever see a boat race?"

Well, I say that the only boat races I ever see are those that come off around the race-tracks, such a race being a race that is all fixed up in advance, and some of them are pretty raw, if you ask me, and I am by no means in favor of things of this kind unless I am in, but Sam the Gonoph says these races are by no manner of means the same thing as the boat races he is talking about.

"I never personally witness one myself," Sam says, "but the way I understand it is a number of the Harvards and the Yales, without any clothes on, get in row boats and row, and row, and row until their tongues hang out, and they are all half-dead. Why they tucker themselves out in this fashion I do not know and," Sam says, "I am too old to start trying to find out why these college guys do a lot of things to themselves.

"But," Sam says, "boat racing is a wonderful sport, and I always have a nice trade at New London, Conn., and if you wish to accompany me and Benny South Street and Liverlips and maybe collect a few bobs for yourself, you are as welcome as the flowers in May."

So there I am in front of the Mohican Hotel in New London, Conn., with Sam the Gonoph and Benny South Street and old Liverlips, who are Sam the Gonoph's best hustlers, and all around and about is a very interesting sight, to be sure, as large numbers of the Harvards and the Yales are passing in and out of the hotel and walking up and down and back and forth, and making very merry, one way and another.

Well, after we are hustling our duckets for a couple of hours and it is coming on noon, Benny South Street goes into the hotel lobby to buy some cigarettes, and by and by he comes out looking somewhat excited, and states as follows:

"Say," Benny says, "there's a guy inside with his hands full of money offering to lay three to one that the Yales win the boat race. He says he has fifteen G's cash with him to wager at the price stated."

"Are there any takers?" Sam the Gonoph asks.

"No, not many," Benny says. "From all I hear, the Yales figure. In fact, all the handicappers I speak with have them on top, so the Harvards do not care for any part of the guy's play. But," Benny says, "there he is, offering three to one."

"Three to one?" Sam the Gonoph says, as if he is mentioning these terms to himself. "Three to one, eh? It is a nice price."

"It is a lovely price," old Liverlips puts in.

Well, Sam the Gonoph stands there as if he is thinking, and Benny South Street seems to be thinking, too, and even old Liverlips seems to be thinking, and by and by I even find myself thinking, and finally Sam the Gonoph says like this:

"I do not know anything about boat races," Sam says, "and the Yales may figure as you say, but nothing between human beings is one to three. In fact," Sam the Gonoph says, "I long ago come to the conclusion that all life is six to five against. And anyway," he says, "how can anybody let such odds as these get away from them? I think I will take a small nibble at this proposition. What about you, Benny?"

"I will also nibble," Benny South Street says. "I will never forgive myself in this world if I let this inviting offer go and it turns out the Harvards win."

Well, we all go into the hotel lobby, and there is a big, gray-haired guy in a white cap and white pants standing in the center of a bunch of other guys, and he has money in both hands. I hear somebody say he is one of the real old-time Yales, and he is speaking in a loud voice as follows:

"Why," he says, "what is the matter, Harvards, are you cowards, or are you just broke? If you are broke, I will take your markers and let you pay me on the installment plan. But," he says, "bet me. That is all, just bet me."

Personally, I have a notion to let on I am one of the Harvards and slip the guy a nice marker, but I am afraid he may request some identification and I do not have anything on me to prove I am a college guy, so I stand back and watch Sam the Gonoph shove his way through the crowd with a couple of C notes in his hand, and Benny South Street is right behind him.

"I will take a small portion of the Harvards at the market," Sam the Gonoph says, as he offers the gray-haired guy his dough.

"Thank you, my friend," the guy says, "but I do not think we are acquainted," he says. "Who do you wish to hold the stakes?"

"You hold them yourself, Mr. Campbell," Sam the Gonoph says. "I know you, although you do not know me, and I will gladly trust you with my dough. Furthermore, my friend here, who also wishes a portion of the Harvards, will trust you."

So the gray-haired guy says that both Sam the Gonoph and Benny South Street are on at 3 to 1, and thanks again to them, at that, and when we get outside, Sam explains that he recognizes the guy as nobody but Mr. Hammond Campbell, who is a very important party in every respect and who has more dough than Uncle Sam has bad debts. In fact, Sam the Gonoph seems to feel that he is greatly honored in getting to bet with Mr. Hammond Campbell, although from the way Mr. Campbell takes their dough, I figure he thinks that the pleasure is all his.

Well, we go on hustling our duckets but neither Sam the Gonoph nor Benny South Street seem to have much heart in their work, and every now and then I see one or the other slip into the hotel lobby, and it comes out that they are still nibbling at the 3 to 1, and finally I slip in myself and take a little teensy nibble for twenty bobs myself, because the way I look at it, anything that is good enough for Sam the Gonoph is good enough for me.

Now Sam the Gonoph always carries quite a little ready money on his body, and nobody will deny that Sam will send it along if he likes a proposition, and by and by he is down for a G on the Harvards, and Benny South Street has four C's going for him, and there is my double saw, and even old

Liverlips weakens and goes for a pound note, and ordinarily Liverlips will not bet a pound that he is alive.

Furthermore, Mr. Hammond Campbell says we are about the only guys in town that do bet him and that we ought to get degrees off the Harvards for our loyalty to them, but of course what we are really loyal to is the 3 to 1. Finally, Mr. Campbell says he has to go to lunch, but if we feel like betting him any more we can find him on board his yacht, the *Hibiscus,* out in the river, and maybe he will boost the price up to 3½ to 1.

So I go into the hotel and get a little lunch myself, and when I am coming out a nice-looking young doll who is walking along in front of me accidentally drops her poke from under her arm, and keeps right on walking. Naturally, I pick it up, but several parties who are standing around in the lobby see me do it, so I call to the young doll and when she turns around I hand her the poke, and she is very grateful to me, to be sure. In fact, she thanks me several times, though once will do, and then all of a sudden she says to me like this:

"Pardon me," the young doll says, "but are you not one of the gentlemen I see wagering with my papa that the Harvards will win the boat race?"

"Yes," I say, "and what is more, we may keep on wagering him. In fact," I say, "a friend of mine by the name of Sam the Gonoph is just now contemplating wiring home for another G to accept your papa's generous offer of three-and-a-half to one."

"Oh," the young doll says, "do not do it. You are only throwing your money away. The Harvards have no chance whatever of winning the boat race. My papa is never wrong on boat races. I only wish he is today."

And with this she sits down in a chair in the lobby and begins crying boo-hoo until her mascara is running down her cheeks, and naturally I am greatly embarrassed by this situation, as I am afraid somebody may come along and think maybe she is my step-child and that I am just after chastising her.

"You see," the young doll says, "a boy I like a very, very great deal belongs to the Harvards' crew and when I tell him a couple of weeks ago that my papa says the Yales are bound to win, he grows very angry and says what does my papa know about it, and who is my papa but an old money-bags, anyway, and to the dickens with my papa. Then when I tell him my papa always knows about these things, Quentin grows still angrier, and we quarrel and he says all right, if the Harvards lose he will never, never, never see me again as long as he lives. And Quentin is a very obstinate and unreasonable boy, and life is very sad for me."

Well, who comes along about now but Sam the Gonoph and naturally he is somewhat surprised by the scene that is presented to his eyes, so I explain to him, and Sam is greatly touched and very sympathetic, for one thing about Sam is he is very tender-hearted when it comes to dolls who are in trouble.

"Well," Sam says, "I will certainly be greatly pleased to see the Harvards win the boat race myself, and in fact," he says, "I am just making a few cautious inquiries around here and there to see if there is any chance of stiffening a couple of the Yales, so we can have a little help in the race.

"But," Sam says, "one great trouble with these college propositions is they are always leveling, though I cannot see why it is necessary. Anyway," he says, "it looks as if we cannot hope to do any business with the Yales, but you dry your eyes, little miss, and maybe old Sam can think up something."

At this the young doll stops her bawling and I am very glad of it, as there is nothing I loathe and despise so much as a doll bawling, and she looks up at Sam with a wet smile and says to him like this:

"Oh, do you really think you can help the Harvards win the boat race?"

Well, naturally Sam the Gonoph is not in a position to make any promises on this point, but he is such a guy as will tell a doll in distress anything whatever if he thinks it will give her a little pleasure for a minute, so he replies as follows:

"Why, who knows?" Sam says. "Who knows, to be sure? But anyway do not bawl any more, and old Sam will give this matter further consideration."

And with this Sam pats the young doll on the back so hard he pats all the breath out of her and she cannot bawl any more even if she wishes to, and she gets up and goes away looking very happy, but before she goes she says:

"Well, I hear somebody say that from the way you gentlemen are betting on the Harvards you must know something and," she says, "I am very glad to have the courage to talk to you. It will be a wonderful favor to Quentin and me if you help the Harvards win, even though it costs my papa money. Love is more than gold," she says.

Personally, I consider it very wrong for Sam the Gonoph to be holding out hope to a young doll that he is unable to guarantee, but Sam says he does not really promise anything and that he always figures if he can bring a little joy into any life, no matter how, he is doing a wonderful deed, and that anyway we will never see the young doll again, and furthermore, what of it?

Well, I cannot think what of it just off-hand, and anyway I am glad to be rid of the young doll, so we go back to disposing of the duckets we have left.

Now the large boat race between the Harvards and the Yales takes place in the early evening, and when it comes on time for the race one and all seem to be headed in the direction of the river, including all the young guys with the stir haircuts, and many beautiful young dolls wearing blue and red flowers, and old guys in sports pants and flat straw hats, and old dolls who walk as if their feet hurt them, and the chances are they do, at that.

Well, nothing will do Sam the Gonoph but we must see the boat race, too, so we go down to the railroad station to take the very train for which we are hustling duckets all day, but by the time we get there the race train is pulling out, so Benny South Street says the next best thing for us to do is to go down to the dock and hire a boat to take us out on the river.

But when we get to the dock, it seems that all the boats around are hired and are already out on the river, but there is an old pappy guy with a chin whisker sitting in a rickety-looking little motor-boat at the dock, and this old guy says he will take us out where we can get a good peek at the race for a buck apiece.

Personally, I do not care for the looks of the boat, and neither does Benny South Street nor old Liverlips, but Sam the Gonoph is so anxious to see the race that finally we all get into the boat and the old guy heads her out into the river, which seems to be filled with all kinds of boats decorated with flags and one thing and another, and with guys and dolls walking back and forth on these boats.

Anybody must admit that it is quite a sight, and I am commencing to be glad I am present, especially when Benny South Street tells me that these guys and dolls on the boats are very fine people and worth plenty of money. Furthermore, Benny South Street points out many big white boats that he says are private yachts, and he tells me that what it costs to keep up these private yachts is a sin and a shame when you start to figure out the number of people in the world who are looking for breakfast money. But then Benny South Street is always talking of things of this kind, and sometimes I think maybe he is a dynamiter at heart.

We go putt-putting along under a big bridge and into a sort of lane of boats, and Benny South Street says we are now at the finish line of the large boat race and that the Harvards and the Yales row down this lane from away up the river, and that it is here that they have their tongues hanging out and are nearly all half-dead.

Well, it seems that we are in the way, because guys start yelling at us from different boats and shaking their fists at us, and it is a good thing for some of them that they are not close enough for us to get a pop at them, but the old pappy guy keeps the motor-boat putt-putting and sliding in and out among the boats until we come to a spot that he says is about a hundred yards above the finish and a great spot to see the best part of the race.

We are slipping alongside of a big white boat that Benny South Street says is a private yacht and that has a little set of stair steps running down one side almost into the water, when all of a sudden Sam the Gonoph notices his feet are wet, and he looks down and sees that the motor-boat is half-full of water and furthermore that the boat is commencing to sink.

Now this is quite a predicament, and naturally Sam the Gonoph lets out a slight beef and wishes to know what kind of accommodations we are paying for, anyway, and then the old pappy guy notices the water and the sinking, and he seems somewhat put out about the matter, especially as the water is getting up around his chin whiskers.

So he steers the boat up against the stair steps on the yacht and all of us, including the old pappy guy, climb out on to the stairs just as the motor-boat gives a last snort and sinks from sight. The last I see of the motor-boat is the hind end sticking up in the air a second before it disappears, and I remember the name that is painted on the hind end. The name is *Baby Mine*.

Well, Sam the Gonoph leads the way up the stairs to the deck of the yacht, and who meets us at the head of the stairs but Mr. Hammond Campbell in person, and who is right behind him but the young doll I am talking with in the hotel lobby, and at first Mr. Campbell thinks that we come out to his yacht to pick up a little of his 3½ to 1, and he is greatly disappointed when he learns that such is by no means our purpose and that we are merely the victims of disaster.

As for the young doll, whose name turns out to be Clarice, she gazes at Sam the Gonoph and me with her eyes full of questions, but we do not get a chance to talk to her as things begin occurring at once.

There are quite a number of guys and dolls on the yacht, and it is a very gay scene to be sure, as they walk around laughing and chatting, when all of a sudden I see Sam the Gonoph staring at a guy and doll who are leaning over the rail talking very earnestly and paying no attention to what is going on around and about them.

The guy is a tall, dark-complected young guy with a little mustache, and he is wearing white flannel pants and a blue coat with brass buttons, and white shoes, and he is a very foreign-looking guy, to be sure. The doll is not such a young doll, being maybe around middle age, giving her a few points the best of it, but she is a fine-looking doll, at that, especially if you like dolls with gray hair, which personally I am not so much in favor of.

I am close enough to Sam the Gonoph to hear him breathing heavily as he stares at this guy and doll, and finally the dark-complected young guy looks up and sees Sam and at the same instant Sam starts for him, and as Sam starts the young guy turns and takes to running in the other direction from Sam along the deck, but before he takes to running I can see that it is nobody but Society Max.

Naturally, I am somewhat surprised at seeing Society Max at a boat race between the Harvards and the Yales, because I never figure him such a guy as will be interested in matters of this kind, although I remember that Society Max is once a life guard at Coney Island, and in fact it is at Coney Island that Sonia gets her first peek at his shape and is lost forever to Sam the Gonoph, so I get to thinking that maybe Society Max is fond of all aquatic events.

Now of course the spectacle of Sam the Gonoph pursuing Society Max along the deck is quite surprising to one and all, except Benny South Street and old Liverlips and myself, who are aware of the reason, and Mr. Hammond Campbell wishes to know what kind of game they are playing, especially after they round the deck twice, with Society Max showing much foot, but none of us feel called on to explain. Finally the other guys and dolls on the yacht enter into the spirit of the chase, even though they do not know what it is all about, and they shout encouragement to both Sam the Gonoph and Society Max, although Max is really the favorite.

There is no doubt but what Society Max is easily best in a sprint, especially as Sam the Gonoph's pants legs are wet from the sinking motor-boat and he is carrying extra weight, but Sam is a wonderful doer over a route, and on the third trip around the deck, anybody can see that he is cutting down Max's lead.

Well, every time they pass the gray-haired doll that Society Max is talking to when we come on the yacht she asks what is the matter, Max, and where are you going, Max, and other questions that seem trivial at such a time, but Max never has an opportunity to answer, as he has to save all his breath to keep ahead of Sam the Gonoph, and in fact Sam the Gonoph stops talking, too, and just keeps plugging along with a very determined expression on his puss.

Well, now all the whistles on the boats in the river around us start blowing, and it seems this is because the large boat race between the Harvards and the Yales is now approaching the finish, and one and all on our yacht rush to the side of the yacht to see it, forgetting about everything else, and the side they rush to is the same side the stair steps are on.

But I am too much interested in Sam the Gonoph's pursuit of Society Max to pay any attention to the boat race, and as they come around the deck the fifth or sixth time, I can see that Sam will have Max in the next few jumps, when all of a sudden Society Max runs right down the stairs and dives off into the river, and he does it so fast that nobody seems to notice him except Sam the Gonoph and me and the gray-haired doll, and I am the only one that notices her fall in a big faint on the deck as Max dives.

Naturally, this is not a time to be bothering with fainting dolls, so Sam the Gonoph and me run to the side of the yacht and watch the water to see where Society Max comes up, but he does not appear at once, and I remember hearing he is a wonderful diver when he is a life guard, so I figure he is going to keep under water until he is pretty sure he is too far away for Sam the Gonoph to hit him with anything, such as maybe a slug from a Betsy.

Of course Sam the Gonoph does not happen to have a Betsy on him, but

Society Max can scarcely be expected to know this, because the chances are he remembers that Sam often has such an article in his pants pocket when he is around New York, so I suppose Society Max plays it as safe as possible.

Anyway, we do not see hide or hair of him, and in the meantime the excitement over the large boat race between the Harvards and the Yales is now so terrific that I forget Society Max and try to get a peek at it.

But all I remember is seeing the young doll, Clarice, kissing Sam the Gonoph smack-dab on his homely puss, and jumping up and down in considerable glee, and stating that she knows all along that Sam will figure out some way for the Harvards to win, although she does not know yet how he does it, and hearing Mr. Hammond Campbell using language even worse than Sam the Gonoph employs when he is pursuing Society Max, and saying he never see such a this-and-that boat race in all his born days.

Then I get to thinking about the gray-haired doll, and I go over and pick her up and she is still about two-thirds out and is saying to herself, as follows:

"Max, oh, my dear, dear Max."

Well, by and by Mr. Hammond Campbell takes Sam the Gonoph into a room on the yacht and pays him what is coming to all of us on the race, and then he takes to asking about Society Max, and when Sam the Gonoph explains how Max is a terrible fink and what he does to Sonia and all, Mr. Hammond Campbell hands Sam five large G's extra, and states to him as follows:

"This," he says, "is for preventing my sister, Emma, from making a fool of herself. She picks this Max up somewhere in Europe and he puts himself away with her as a Russian nobleman, and she is going to marry him next week, although from what you tell me it will be bigamy on his part. By the way," Mr. Hammond Campbell says, "not that it makes any difference, but I wonder whatever becomes of the guy?"

I am wondering this somewhat myself, not that I really care what becomes of Society Max, but I do not find out until later in the evening when I am at the Western Union office in New London, Conn., sending a telegram for Sam the Gonoph to the guy who runs his farm in New Jersey telling the guy to be sure and watch the onions, and I hear a newspaper scribe talking about the large boat race.

"Yes," the newspaper scribe says, "the Yales are leading by a boat length up to the last hundred yards and going easy, and they seem to be an absolute cinch to win, when No. 6 man in their boat hits something in the water and breaks his oar, throwing the rest of the crew out of kilter long enough for the Harvards to slip past and win. It is the most terrible upset of the dope in history," he says.

"Now," the scribe says, "of course a broken oar is not unheard of in a

naked, staring at him, his mouth open. "Go ahead," Manley said, giving him a push toward the door.

When his roommate had gone, Manley stood in the middle of the room brooding for a minute. His head was throbbing. He picked up the phone and called his almost-fiancée at Smith. "So what if I did get you out of bed, fats?" he said into the phone. "By the looks of you, you ought to be out weight-lifting, instead of lying around in bed all day. . . . I just wanted to tell you that I won't be up this weekend after all. . . . No, it's not because I have to study (this a falsetto mimic). . . . It's simply because I can't stand your stupid laughter. . . . Who's being funny? . . . God, don't start talking like your mother. . . . Yes, I would insult your mother, but why bring the Civil War into this? . . . What? . . . I know you were a perfect fool when you got engaged to me, but I didn't know it at the time."

He hung up, got dressed, and went over to his club for breakfast. While he was eating at a corner table by himself, having snubbed all the members, the leading candidate for the club's presidency came over and sat down. "Well, John," he said brightly, "all ready for the election tonight?"

Manley put down his fork. "Brinkwood," he said slowly, "I wouldn't vote for you for the president of this club if your running mate were one of those red-rumped, blue-faced baboons you see in the zoo. So please stop bothering me and go eat your soggy toast elsewhere." Manley finished his fried eggs and went out. It was time for his English class. He had planned to cut it, but now he decided to go.

Old Lindlump, the professor, was discussing Milton. Manley listened for a while, then he raised his hand. "Yes, Mr. Manley?" said Old Lindlump, smiling benevolently. "Old Lindlump," said Manley, "I just wanted to tell you that you fascinate me no end. I have never before met a man who, every time he opened his mouth, could be so consistently wrong on every possible subject." Manley got up and went toward the door. "I don't know why I've stood it so long. I suppose it's because I couldn't bring myself to stop staring at your fantastically silly face." He closed the door behind him as the class gazed in silence.

Manley went home and took a nap. His roommate was reading a book and listening to the radio when he came in, but Manley gave him a look and he went out. When he awoke it was lunch time and he trudged over to the college dining hall. He was feeling fouler than ever. His roommate was sitting by a window, chewing on a grilled cheese sandwich. Manley went over to him with his lunch and sat down next to him in silence. "Gee," said his roommate, "you have liver and onions. They had grilled cheese sandwiches when I went through the line."

Manley looked at him. "You'd prefer liver and onions to grilled cheese sandwiches?" he asked coldly. "Er . . . I guess so," said his roommate, a little afraid of the look in Manley's eye. He took a sip of milk and added, "I like liver and onions."

"So you like liver and onions, eh?" said Manley, his voice loud. "So you like liver and onions?" He picked up his piece of liver and pushed it flat and hard in his roommate's face. Then he wiped his hands on the napkin and walked out of the dining hall.

Later in the afternoon, when Manley entered his adviser's office, he found him leaning back in his chair and staring at the ceiling. "And how are we feeling today?" he asked smilingly when he saw Manley. Manley suddenly flipped over the fire extinguisher that hung on the wall and set the hose steadily on his adviser. "Cripes!" yelled the adviser, trying frantically to shield himself from the blast with his hands.

Manley went to a movie and then went home. His roommate had gotten a birthday cake from his mother that morning. Manley set the cake in the middle of the floor and then stepped on it. Then he went to bed. "I hope to hell I feel better in the morning," he said, setting the alarm and remembering he had to wake his roommate.

Reflections and Inquiries

4

"WE do not know what education can do for us, because we have never tried it," said Robert Hutchins when he was the youthful and iconoclastic president of the University of Chicago. He was delivering an address on "The Atomic Bomb Versus Civilization." The title gives explosive meaning to his curious comment.

What is a liberal education? And what are we educating for? And whom? And why? What is the role of the university in the life of its students, and what is the role of the university man in the life of his nation and of the world? To what end does he study? How and to what purpose can the myriad subjects of the university curriculum be employed? Is there such a thing as knowledge for its own sake; if so, can it be deemed to have some ultimate meaningfulness for mankind? These are not new questions. They have been asked and answered, argued and debated endlessly. But they have a new urgency now, with time running short.

In these writings, selected out of the vast numbers of questions and replies, those have been chosen which seem to have most relevance to our time, our place, and our future.

Of Studies

FROM *Essays*

The intellectual world in which Francis Bacon grew to manhood was dominated by Scholastic philosophy, which argued from authority and shunned originality. Much of Bacon's life was devoted to an attempt to revise this system of thought and to replace it with the inquiring mind of reason and experimentation. A versatile and brilliant scholar, he had what today would amount to a full career in at least four disciplines: writing, philosophy, science, statesmanship. Of all the minds of the Middle Ages, his stands out as having most dedicatedly and fearlessly sought the truth.

Bacon entered Trinity College in Cambridge at the age of thirteen, not at all an uncommon thing in the sixteenth century, which demanded an earlier maturity than our more indulgent times. After his second year he moved to Gray's Inn to study for the Bar. He rose to become Lord Chancellor of England.

STUDIES serve for delight, for ornament, and for ability. Their chief use for delight is in privateness and retiring; for ornament, is in discourse; and for ability, is in the judgment and disposition of business; for expert men can execute, and perhaps judge of particulars, one by one; but the general counsels, and the plots and marshaling of affairs come best from those that are learned. To spend too much time in studies is sloth; to use them too much for ornament is affection; to make judgment wholly by their rules is the humor of a scholar. They perfect nature, and are perfected by experience; for natural abilities are like natural plants, that need pruning by study; and studies themselves do give forth directions too much at large, except they be bounded in by experience. Crafty men contemn studies, simple men admire them, and wise men use them; for they teach not their own use; but that is a wisdom without them and above them, won by observation. Read not to contradict and confute, nor to believe and take for granted, nor to find talk and discourse, but to weigh and consider. Some books are to be tasted, others to be swallowed, and some few to be chewed and digested; that is, some books are to be read only in parts; others to be read but not curiously, and some few to be read wholly, and with diligence and attention. Some books also may be read by deputy, and extracts made of them by others; but that would be only in the less important arguments and the meaner sort of books; else distilled books are, like common distilled waters, flashy things. Reading maketh a full man; conference a ready man; and writing an exact man. And, therefore, if a man write little, he had need have a great memory; if he confer little, he had need have a present wit; and if he read little, he had need have much cunning, to seem to know that he doth not. Histories make men wise; poets, witty; the mathematics, subtle; natural philosophy, deep; moral, grave; logic and rhetoric, able to contend: *Abeunt studia in mores!* Nay, there is no stand or impediment in the wit but may be wrought out by fit studies; like as diseases of the body may have appropriate exercises. Bowling is good for the stone and reins, shooting for the lungs and breast, gentle walking for the stomach, riding for the head, and the like. So if a man's wit be wandering, let him study the mathematics; for in demonstrations, if his wit be called away never so little, he must begin again. If his wit be not apt to distinguish or find differences, let him study the schoolmen; for they are *cymini sectores!* If he be not apt to beat over matters, and to call up one thing to prove and illustrate another, let him study the lawyers' cases. So every defect of the mind may have a special receipt.

JOHN MILTON

A Complete and Generous Education

FROM *Of Education: To Master Samuel Hartlib*

John Milton was, in his own words, an "indocile student." He studied at Christ's College, Cambridge, had difficulties with his tutor, and left the university for a short period.

For most of his hard and tragic life—he became blind in early middle age—he was a rebel. Raised an Anglican, he became a Puritan and a potent polemicist of the Puritan ethic. When Charles II came to the throne, Milton's pamphlets and books were burned by the public hangman, and he himself barely escaped the gallows. In addition to his poetry he left a body of prose which promulgated many ideas far in advance of the thinking of his time. This selection, from an epistle "to Master Samuel Hartlib," on what should constitute a liberal education, is a notable example.

I CALL a complete and generous education that which fits a man to perform justly, skilfully, and magnanimously all the offices both private and public of peace and war. And how all this may be done between twelve and one and twenty, less time than is now bestowed in pure trifling at grammar and sophistry, is to be thus ordered.

First, to find out a spacious house and ground about it fit for an academy, and big enough to lodge a hundred and fifty persons, whereof twenty or thereabout may be attendants, all under the government of one, who shall be thought of desert sufficient and ability either to do all or wisely to direct and oversee it done. This place should be at once both school and university, not needing a remove to any other house of scholarship, except it be some peculiar college of law, or physic, where they mean to be practitioners; but as for those general studies which take up all our time from Lily to the commencing, as they term it, Master of Art, it should be absolute. After this pattern, as many edifices may be converted to this use as shall be needful in every city throughout this land, which would tend much to the increase of learning and civility everywhere. This number, less or more thus collected, to the convenience of a foot company, or interchangeably two troops of cavalry, should divide their day's work into three parts as it lies orderly. Their studies, their exercise, and their diet.

For their studies: First, they should begin with the chief and necessary rules of some good grammar, either that now used or any better; and while this is doing, their speech is to be fashioned to a distinct and clear pronunciation, as near as may be to the Italian, especially in the vowels. For we Englishmen being far northerly, do not open our mouths in the cold air wide enough to grace a Southern tongue; but are observed by all other nations to speak exceeding close and inward: so that to smatter Latin with an English mouth is as ill a hearing as law French. Next, to make them expert in the usefullest points of grammar, and withal to season them and win them early to the love of virtue and true labor, ere any flattering seducement or vain principle seize them wandering, some easy and delightful book of education would be read to them; whereof the Greeks have store, as Cebes, Plutarch, and other Socratic discourses. But in Latin we have none of classic authority extant, except the two or three first books of Quintilian and some select pieces elsewhere.

But here the main skill and groundwork will be to temper them such lectures and explanations, upon every opportunity, as may lead and draw them in willing obedience, inflamed with the study of learning and the admiration of virtue; stirred up with high hopes of living to be brave men and worthy patriots, dear to God and famous to all ages. That they may despise and scorn all their childish and ill-taught qualities, to delight in manly and liberal exercises: which he who hath the art and proper eloquence to catch them with, what with mild and effectual persuasions, and what with the intimation of some fear, if need be, but chiefly by his own example, might in a short space gain them to an incredible diligence and courage, infusing into their young breasts such an ingenuous and noble ardor, as would not fail to make many of them renowned and matchless men. At the same time, some other hour of the day, might be taught them the rules of arithmetic, and soon after the elements of geometry, even playing, as the old manner was. After evening repast, till bedtime their thoughts will be best taken up in the easy grounds of religion and the story of Scripture.

The next step would be to the authors of agriculture, Cato, Varro, and Columella, for the matter is most easy, and if the language be difficult, so much the better, it is not a difficulty above their years. And here will be an occasion of inciting and enabling them hereafter to improve the tillage of their country, to recover the bad soil, and to remedy the waste that is made of good: for this was one of Hercules' praises. Ere half these authors be read —which will soon be with plying hard and daily—they cannot choose but be masters of any ordinary prose. So that it will be then seasonable for them to learn in any modern author the use of the globes, and all the maps, first with the old names, and then with the new; or they might be then capable to read any compendious method of natural philosophy. And at the same time might be entering into the Greek tongue, after the same manner as was before prescribed in the Latin; whereby the difficulties of grammar being soon overcome, all the historical physiology of Aristotle and Theophrastus are open before them, and, as I may say, under contribution. The like access will be to Vitruvius, to Seneca's natural questions, to Mela, Celsus, Pliny, or Solinus. And having thus passed the principles of arithmetic, geometry, astronomy, and geography, with a general compact of physics, they may descend in mathematics to the instrumental science of trigonometry, and from thence to fortification, architecture, enginery, or navigation. And in natural philosophy they may proceed leisurely from the history of meteors, minerals, plants, and living creatures, as far as anatomy.

Then also in course might be read to them out of some not tedious writer the institution of physic; that they may know the tempers, the humors, the seasons, and how to manage a crudity: which he who can wisely and timely do, is not only a great physician to himself and to his friends, but also may at some time or other save an army by this frugal and expenseless means only; and not let the healthy and stout bodies of young men rot away under him for want of this discipline; which is a great pity, and no less a shame to the commander. To set forward all these proceedings in nature and mathematics, what hinders but that they may procure, as oft as shall be needful, the helpful experiences of hunters, fowlers, fishermen, shepherds, gardeners, apothecaries; and in other sciences, architects, engineers, mariners, anatomists; who doubtless would be ready, some for reward and some to favor such a hopeful seminary. And this will give them such a real tincture of natural knowledge as they shall never forget, but daily augment with delight. Then also those poets which are now counted most hard, will be both facile and pleasant, Orpheus, Hesiod, Theocritus, Aratus, Nicander, Oppian, Dionysius; and in Latin, Lucretius, Manilius, and the rural part of Virgil.

By this time, years and good general precepts will have furnished them more distinctly with that act of reason which in ethics is called Proairesis; that they may with some judgment contemplate upon moral good and evil. Then will be required a special reinforcement of constant and sound indoctrinating to set them right and firm, instructing them more amply in the knowledge of virtue and the hatred of vice; while their young and pliant affections are led through all the moral works of Plato, Xenophon, Cicero, Plutarch, Laertius, and those Locrian remnants; but still to be reduced in their nightward studies wherewith they close the day's work, under the determinate sentence of David, or Solomon, or the Evangels and Apostolic Scriptures. Being perfect in the knowledge of personal duty, they may then begin the study of economies. And either now or before this they may have easily learnt at any odd hour the Italian tongue. And soon after, but with wariness and good antidote, it would be wholesome enough to let them taste some choice comedies, Greek, Latin, or Italian; those tragedies also that treat of household matters, as *Trachiniae, Alcestis,* and the like.

The next remove must be to the study of politics; to know the beginning, end, and reasons of political societies; that they may not in a dangerous fit of the commonwealth be such poor, shaken, uncertain reeds, of such a tottering conscience, as many of our great counsellors have lately shown themselves, but steadfast pillars of the state. After this they are to dive into the grounds of law and legal justice; delivered first and with best warrant by Moses; and as far as humane prudence can be trusted, in those extolled remains of Grecian lawgivers, Lycurgus, Solon, Zaleucus, Charondas, and thence to all the Roman edicts and tables with their Justinian; and so down to the Saxon and common laws of England, and the statutes.

Sundays also and every evening may be now understandingly spent in the highest matters of theology, and church history ancient and modern; and ere this time the Hebrew tongue at a set hour might have been gained, that the Scriptures may be now read in their own original; whereto it would be no impossibility to add the Chaldee and the Syrian dialect. When all these employments are well conquered, then will the choice histories, heroic poems, and Attic tragedies of stateliest and most regal argument, with all the famous political orations, offer themselves; which if they were not only read, but some of them got by memory, and solemnly pronounced with right accent and grace, as might be taught, would endue them even with the spirit and vigor of Demosthenes or Cicero, Euripides or Sophocles.

And now, lastly, will be the time to read with them those organic arts which enable men to discourse and write perspicuously, elegantly, and according to the fitted style, of lofty, mean, or lowly. Logic, therefore, so much as is useful, is to be referred to this due place with all her well-couched heads and topics, until it be time to open her contracted palm into a graceful and ornate rhetoric, taught out of the rule of Plato, Aristotle, Phalereus, Cicero, Hermogenes, Longinus. To which poetry would be made subsequent, or indeed rather precedent, as being less subtle and fine, but more simple, sensuous, and passionate. I mean not here the prosody of a verse, which they could not but have hit on before among the rudiments of grammar; but that sublime art which in Aristotle's *Poetics,* in Horace, and the Italian commentaries of Castlevetro, Tasso, Mazzoni, and others, teaches what the laws are of a true epic poem, what of a dramatic, what of a lyric; what decorum is, which is the grand masterpiece to observe. This would make them soon perceive what despicable creatures our common rhymers and play-writers be, and show them what religious, what glorious and magnificent use might be made of poetry, both in divine and humane things.

From hence, and not till now, will be the right season of forming them to be able writers and composers in every excellent matter, when they shall be thus fraught with an universal insight into things. Or whether they be to speak in parliament or council, honor and attention would be waiting on their lips.

DANIEL DEFOE

A Woman Well Taught

FROM *An Essay upon Projects*

🏛 *As is evident from this plea for colleges for women to be established throughout seventeenth-century England, Daniel Defoe was no believer in coeducation. His opinions on the subject and its coincident and related problems of sex are, if not flattering to either gender, at least impartial. It is not that he distrusts the women more, it is that he trusts the men less.*

Most readers know little of Defoe's writings other than Robinson Crusoe *and* Moll Flanders, *but as journalist and pamphleteer for a variety of periodicals, and editor of a political review, he wrote articles on most current issues of his time. One of them, "The Shortest Way With Dissenters," a satirical commentary on Church of England practices, landed him in Newgate Prison for fifteen months.*

THE capacities of women are supposed to be greater and their senses quicker than those of the men; and what they might be capable of being bred to is plain from some instances of female wit which this age is not without; which upbraids us with injustice, and looks as if we denied women the advantages of education for fear they should vie with the men in their improvements.

To remove this objection, and that women might have at least a needful opportunity of education in all sorts of useful learning, I propose the draught of an academy for that purpose.

I know 'tis dangerous to make public appearances of the sex; they are not either to be confined or exposed; the first will disagree with their inclinations, and the last with their reputations; and therefore it is somewhat difficult; and I doubt a method proposed by an ingenious lady, in a little book called *Advice to the Ladies,* would be found impracticable. For, saving my respect to the sex, the levity which perhaps is a little peculiar to them, at least in their youth, will not bear the restraint; and I am satisfied nothing

340

but the heighth of bigotry can keep up a nunnery. Women are extravagantly desirous of going to heaven, and will punish their pretty bodies to get thither; but nothing else will do it; and even in that case sometimes it falls out that *Nature will prevail.*

When I talk therefore of an academy for women, I mean both the model, the teaching, and the government; different from what is proposed by that ingenious lady, for whose proposal I have a very great esteem, and also a great opinion of her wit; different, too, from all sorts of religious confinement, and above all from *vows of celibacy.*

Wherefore the academy I propose should differ but little from public schools, wherein such ladies as were willing to study should have all the advantages of learning suitable to their genius.

But since some severities of discipline more than ordinary would be absolutely necessary to preserve the reputation of the house, that persons of quality and fortune might not be afraid to venture their children thither, I shall venture to make a small scheme by way of essay.

The house I would have built in a form by itself, as well as in a place by itself.

The building should be of three plain fronts, without any jettings or bearing-work, that the eye might at a glance see from one coin to the other; the gardens walled in the same triangular figure, with a large moat and but one entrance.

When thus every part of the situation was contrived as well as might be for discovery, and to render intriguing dangerous, I would have no guards, no eyes, no spies set over the ladies, but shall expect them to be tried by the principles of honor and strict virtue.

And if I am asked, "Why?" I must ask pardon of my own sex for giving this reason for it:

I am so much in charity with women, and so well acquainted with men, that 'tis my opinion there needs no other care to prevent intriguing than to keep the men effectually away. For though inclination, which we prettily call love, does sometimes move a little too visibly in the sex, and frailty often follows, yet I think verily custom, which we miscall modesty, has so far the ascendant over the sex that solicitation always goes before it. . . .

Upon this ground I am persuaded such measures might be taken that the ladies might have all the freedom in the world within their own walls, and yet no intriguing, no indecencies, nor scandalous affairs happen; and, in order to this, the following customs and laws should be observed in the colleges, of which I would propose one at least in every county in England, and about ten for the city of London.

After the regulation of the form of the building as before:

1. All the ladies who enter into the house should set their hands to the orders of the house, to signify their consent to submit to them.

2. As no woman should be received but who declared herself willing, and that it was the act of her choice to enter herself, so no person should be confined to continue there a moment longer than the same voluntary choice inclined her.

3. The charges of the house being to be paid by the ladies, every one that entered should have only this encumbrance: that she should pay for the whole year, though her mind should change as to her continuance.

4. An act of Parliament should make it felony, without clergy, for any man to enter by force or fraud into the house, or to solicit any woman, *though it were to marry,* while she was in the house. And this law would by no means be severe; because any woman who was willing to receive the addresses of a man might discharge herself of the house when she pleased; and, on the contrary, any woman who had occasion might discharge herself of the impertinent addresses of any person she had an aversion to, by entering the house.

In this house the persons who enter should be taught all sorts of breeding suitable to both their genius and their quality; and, in particular, music and dancing, which it would be cruelty to bar the sex of, because they are their darlings; but, besides this, they should be taught languages, as particularly French and Italian, and I would venture the injury of giving a woman more tongues than one.

They should, as a particular study, be taught all the graces of speech and all the necessary air of conversation, which our common education is so defective in that I need not expose it. They should be brought to read books, and especially history, and so to read as to make them understand the world, and be able to know and judge of things when they hear of them.

To such whose genius would lead them to it I would deny no sort of learning; but the chief thing in general is to cultivate the understanding of the sex, that they may be capable of all sorts of conversation; that, their parts and judgments being improved, they may be as profitable in their conversation as they are pleasant.

Women, in my observation, have little or no difference in them but as they are or are not distinguished by education. Tempers, indeed, may in some degree influence them, but the main distinguishing part is their breeding.

The whole sex are generally quick and sharp: I believe I may be allowed to say generally so; for you rarely see them lumpish and heavy when they are children, as boys will often be. If a woman be well bred, and taught the proper management of her natural wit, she proves generally very sensible and retentive; and, without partiality, a woman of sense and manners is the finest and most delicate part of God's creation, the glory of her Maker, and the great instance of His singular regard to man, His darling creature, to whom He gave the best gift either God could bestow or man receive; and 'tis the sordid'st piece of folly and ingratitude in the world to withhold from the sex the due lustre which the advantages of education gives to the natural beauty of their minds.

A woman well bred and well taught, furnished with the additional accomplishments of knowledge and behavior, *is a creature without comparison:* her society is the emblem of sublimer enjoyments; her person is angelic, and her conversation heavenly; she is all softness and sweetness, peace, love, wit, and delight; she is every way suitable to the sublimest wish; and the man that has such a one to his portion has nothing to do but to rejoice in her and be thankful.

On the other hand, suppose her to be the *very same* woman and rob her of the benefit of education, and it follows thus:

If her temper be good, want of education makes her soft and easy.

Her wit, for want of teaching, makes her impertinent and talkative.

Her knowledge, for want of judgment and experience, makes her fanciful and whimsical.

If her temper be bad, want of breeding makes her worse, and she grows haughty, insolent, and loud.

If she be passionate, want of manners makes her termagant and a scold, *which is much at one with lunatic.*

If she be proud, want of discretion (which still is breeding) makes her conceited, fantastic, and ridiculous.

And from these she degenerates to be turbulent, clamorous, noisy, nasty, *and the devil.*

Methinks mankind for their own sakes, since, say what we will of the women, we all think fit, one time or other, to be concerned with 'em, should take some care to breed them up to be suitable and serviceable, if they expected no such thing as delight from 'em. Bless us! What care do we take to breed up a good horse, and to break him well! and what a value do we put upon him when it is done!—and all because he should be fit for our use. And why not a woman?—since all her ornaments and beauty, without suitable behavior, is a cheat in nature, like the false tradesman who puts the best of his goods uppermost that the buyer may think the rest are of the same goodness.

ROBERT LOUIS STEVENSON

An Apology for Idlers

FROM *Virginibus Pueresque*

Robert Louis Stevenson makes a persuasive case for idling—but of a particular sort—in this beguiling essay. This is idling of a very demanding variety, with eyes and ears and mind open and receptive "to the warm and palpitating facts of life."

Stevenson was an indifferent scholar in the formal sense. He "attended" the University of Edinburgh—one could hardly say he studied there. He was much more taken with the velvet-coated bohemianism of the period than with classroom or study, he helped to found a university magazine of short-lived but intensely active memory, and was a member of the "Speculative Society," an undergraduate debating club. These activities seem to have left him little time for the college curriculum.

THE greatest difficulty with most subjects is to do them well; therefore, please to remember this is an apology. It is certain that much may be judiciously argued in favour of diligence; only there is something to be said against it, and that is what, on the present occasion, I have to say. To state one argument is not necessarily to be deaf to all others, and that a man has written a book of travels in Montenegro, is no reason why he should never have been to Richmond.

It is surely beyond a doubt that people should be a good deal idle in youth. For though here and there a Lord Macaulay may escape from school honours with all his wits about him, most boys pay so dear for their medals that they never afterwards have a shot in their locker, and begin the world bankrupt. And the same holds true during all the time a lad is educating himself, or suffering others to educate him. It must have been a very foolish old gentleman who addressed Johnson at Oxford in these words: "Young man, ply your book diligently now, and acquire a stock of knowledge; for when years come upon you, you will find that poring upon books will be but an irksome task." The old gentleman seems to have been unaware that many other things besides reading grow irksome, and not a few become impossible, by the time a man has to use spectacles and cannot walk without a stick. Books are good enough in their own way, but they are a mighty bloodless substitute for life. It seems a pity to sit, like the Lady of Shalott, peering into a mirror, with your back turned on all the bustle and glamour of reality. And if a man reads very hard, as the old anecdote reminds us, he will have little time for thoughts.

If you look back on your own education, I am sure it will not be the full, vivid, instructive hours of truantry that you regret; you would rather cancel some lack-lustre periods between sleep and waking in the class. For my own part, I have attended a good many lectures in my time. I still remember that the spinning of a top is a case of Kinetic Stability. I still remember that Emphyteusis is not a disease, nor Stillicide a crime. But though I would not willingly part with such scraps of science, I do not set the same store by them as by certain other odds and ends that I came by in the open street while I was playing truant. This is not the moment to dilate on that mighty place of education, which was the favourite school of Dickens and Balzac, and turns out yearly many inglorious masters in the Science of the Aspects of Life. Suffice it to say this: if a lad does not learn in the streets, it is because he has no faculty of learning. Nor is the truant always in the streets, for if he prefers, he may go out by the gardened suburbs into the country. He may pitch on some tuft of lilacs over a burn, and some innumerable pipes to the tune of the water on the stones. A bird will sing in the thicket. And there he may fall into a vein of kindly thought, and see things in a new perspective. Why, if this be not education, what is? We may conceive Mr. Worldly Wiseman accosting such an one, and the conversation that should thereupon ensue:—

"How now, young fellow, what dost thou here?"

"Truly, sir, I take mine ease."

"Is not this the hour of the class? and should'st thou not be plying thy Book with diligence, to the end thou mayest obtain knowledge?"

"Nay, but thus also I follow after Learning, by your leave."

"Learning, quotha! After what fashion, I pray thee? Is it mathematics?"

"No, to be sure."

"Is it metaphysics?"

"Nor that."

"Is it some language?"

"Nay, it is no language."

"Is it a trade?"

"Nor a trade neither."

"Why, then, what is't?"

"Indeed, sir, as a time may soon come for me to go upon Pilgrimage, I am desirous to note what is commonly done by persons in my case, and where are the ugliest Sloughs and Thickets on the Road; as also, what manner of Staff is of the best service. Moreover, I lie here, by this water, to learn by root-of-heart a lesson which my master teaches me to call Peace, or Contentment."

Hereupon Mr. Wordly Wiseman was much commoved with passion, and shaking his cane with a very threatful countenance, broke forth upon this wise: "Learning, quotha!" said he; "I would have all such rogues scourged by the Hangman!"

And so he would go his way, ruffling out his cravat with a crackle of starch, like a turkey when it spread its feathers.

Now this, of Mr. Wiseman's, is the common opinion. A fact is not called a fact, but a piece of gossip, if it does not fall into one of your scholastic categories. An inquiry must be in some acknowledged direction, with a name to go by; or else you are not inquiring at all, only lounging; and the work-house is too good for you. It is supposed that all knowledge is at the bottom of a well, or the far end of a telescope. Sainte-Beuve, as he grew older, came to regard all experience as a single great book, in which to study for a few years ere we go hence; and it seemed all one to him whether you should read in Chapter xx., which is the differential calculus, or in Chapter xxxix., which is hearing the band play in the gardens. As a matter of fact, an intelligent person, looking out of his eyes and hearkening in his ears, with a smile on his face all the time, will get more true education than many another in a life of heroic vigils. There is certainly some chill and arid knowledge to be found upon the summits of formal and laborious science; but it is all round about you, and for the trouble of looking, that you will acquire the warm and palpitating facts of life. While others are filling their memory with a lumber of words, one-half of which they will forget before the week be out, your truant may learn some really useful art: to play the fiddle, to know a good cigar, or to speak with ease and opportunity to all varieties of men. Many who have "plied their book diligently," and know all about some one branch or another of accepted lore, come out of the study with an ancient and owl-like demeanour, and prove dry, stockish, and dyspeptic in all the better and brighter parts of life. Many make a large fortune, who remain underbred and pathetically stupid to the last. And meantime there goes the idler, who began life along with them—by your leave, a different picture. He has had time to take care of his health and his spirits; he has been a good deal in the open air, which is the most salutary of all things for both body and mind; and if he has never read the great Book in very recondite places, he has dipped into it and skimmed it over to excellent purpose. Might not the student afford some Hebrew roots, and the business man some of his half-crowns, for a share of the idler's knowledge of life at large, and Art of Living? Nay, and the idler has another and more important quality than these. I mean his wisdom. He who has much looked on at the childish satisfaction of other people in their hobbies, will regard his own with only a very ironical indulgence. He will not be heard among the dogmatists. He will have a great and cool allowance for all sorts of people and opinions. If he finds no out-of-the-way truths, he will identify himself with no very burning falsehood. His way takes him along a by-road, not much frequented, but very even and pleasant, which is called Commonplace Lane, and leads to the Belvedere of Commonsense. Thence he shall command an agreeable, if no very noble prospect; and while others behold the East and West, the Devil and the Sunrise, he will be contentedly aware of a sort of morning hour upon all sublunary things, with an army of shadows running speedily and in many different directions into the great daylight of Eternity. The shadows and the generations, the shrill doctors and the plangent wars, go by into ultimate silence and emptiness; but underneath all this, a man may see, out of the Belvedere windows, much green and peaceful landscape; many firelit parlours; good people laughing, drinking, and making love as they did before the Flood or the French Revolution; and the old shepherd telling his tale under the hawthorn.

The Harvard Stamp

FROM *The Education of Henry Adams*

Henry Adams—of the famous Adams family—was a man in search of an education. At the end of his long and creative life, when he had achieved stature as perhaps the finest historian of his generation, he acknowledged himself defeated—he had "learned little," he said, "and that little ill."

Adams was a student at Harvard in the turbulent years just preceding the Civil War. Even then he was out of tune with his world, an America that was beginning to move rapidly away from the traditional values he lived by, toward an industrial capitalism which he felt had no place for the "sensitive mind and scrupulous conscience."

For generation after generation, Adamses and Brookses and Boylstons and Gorhams had gone to Harvard College, and although none of them, as far as known, had ever done any good there, or thought himself the better for it, custom, social ties, convenience, and, above all, economy, kept each generation in the track. Any other education would have required a serious effort, but no one took Harvard College seriously. All went there because their friends went there, and the College was their ideal of social self-respect.

Harvard College, as far as it educated at all, was a mild and liberal school, which sent young men into the world with all they needed to make respectable citizens, and something of what they wanted to make useful ones. Leaders of men it never tried to make. Its ideals were altogether different. The Unitarian clergy had given to the College a character of moderation, balance, judgment, restraint, what the French called *mesure;* excellent traits, which the College attained with singular success, so that its graduates could commonly be recognized by the stamp, but such a type of character rarely lent itself to autobiography. In effect, the school created a type but not a will. Four years of Harvard College, if successful, resulted in an autobiographical blank, a mind on which only a water-mark had been stamped.

The stamp, as such things went, was a good one. The chief wonder of education is that it does not ruin everybody concerned in it, teachers and taught. Sometimes in after life, Adams debated whether in fact it had not ruined him and most of his companions, but, disappointment apart, Harvard College was probably less hurtful than any other university then in existence. It taught little, and that little ill, but it left the mind open, free from bias, ignorant of facts, but docile. The graduate had few strong prejudices. He knew little, but his mind remained supple, ready to receive knowledge.

What caused the boy most disappointment was the little he got from his mates. Speaking exactly, he got less than nothing, a result common enough in education. Yet the College Catalogue for the years 1854 to 1861 shows a list of names rather distinguished in their time. Alexander Agassiz and Phillips Brooks led it; H. H. Richardson and O. W. Holmes helped to close it. As a rule the most promising of all die early, and never get their names into a Dictionary of Contemporaries, which seems to be the only popular standard of success. Many died in the war. Adams knew them all, more or less; he felt as much regard, and quite as much respect for them then, as he did after they won great names and were objects of a vastly wider respect; but, as help towards education, he got nothing whatever from them or they from him until long after they had left college. Possibly the fault was his, but one would like to know how many others shared it. Accident counts for much in companionship as in marriage. Life offers perhaps only a score of possible companions, and it is mere chance whether they meet as early as school or college, but it is more than a chance that boys brought up together under like conditions have nothing to give each other. The Class of 1858, to which Henry Adams belonged, was a typical collection of young New Englanders, quietly penetrating and aggressively commonplace; free from meannesses, jealousies, intrigues, enthusiasms, and passions; not exceptionally quick; not consciously sceptical; singularly indifferent to display, artifice, florid expression, but not hostile to it when it amused them; distrustful of themselves, but little disposed to trust any one else; with not much humor of their own, but full of readiness to enjoy the humor of others; negative to a degree that in the long run became positive and triumphant. Not harsh in manners or judgment, rather liberal and open-minded, they were still as a body the most formidable critics one would care to meet, in a long life exposed to criticism. They never flattered, seldom praised; free from vanity, they were not intolerant of it; but they were objectiveness itself; their attitude was a law of nature; their judgment beyond appeal, not an act either of intellect or emotion or of will, but a sort of gravitation.

This was Harvard College incarnate, but even for Harvard College, the Class of 1858 was somewhat extreme. Of unity this band of nearly one hundred young men had no keen sense, but they had equally little energy of repulsion. They were pleasant to live with, and above the average of students—German, French, English, or what not—but chiefly because each individual appeared satisfied to stand alone. It seemed a sign of force; yet to stand alone is quite natural when one has no passions; still easier when one has no pains.

Into this unusually dissolvent medium, chance insisted on enlarging Henry Adams's education by tossing a trio of Virginians as little fitted for it as Sioux Indians to a treadmill. By some further affinity, these three outsiders fell into relation with the Bostonians among whom Adams as a schoolboy belonged, and in the end with Adams himself, although they and he knew well how thin an edge of friendship separated them in 1856 from mortal enmity. One of the Virginians was the son of Colonel Robert E. Lee, of the Second United States Cavalry; the two others who seemed instinctively to form a staff for Lee, were town-Virginians from Petersburg. A fourth outsider came from Cincinnati and was half Kentuckian, N. L. Anderson, Longworth on the mother's side. For the first time Adams's education brought him in contact with new types and taught him their values. He saw the New England type measure itself with another, and he was part of the process.

Lee, known through life as "Roony," was a Virginian of the eighteenth century, much as Henry Adams was a Bostonian of the same age. Roony Lee had changed little from the type of his grandfather, Light Horse Harry. Tall, largely built, handsome, genial, with liberal Virginian openness towards all he liked, he had also the Virginian habit of command and took leadership as his natural habit. No one cared to contest it. None of the New Englanders wanted command. For a year, at least, Lee was the most popular and prominent young man in his class, but then seemed slowly to drop into the background. The habit of command was not enough, and the Virginian had little else. He was simple beyond analysis; so simple that even the simple New England student could not realize him. No one knew enough to know how ignorant he was; how childlike; how helpless before the relative complexity of a school. As an animal, the Southerner seemed to have every advantage, but even as an animal he steadily lost ground.

The lesson in education was vital to these young men, who, within ten years, killed each other by scores in the act of testing their college conclusions. Strictly, the Southerner had no mind; he had temperament. He was not a scholar; he had no intellectual training; he could not analyze an idea, and he could not even conceive of admitting two; but in life one

could get along very well without ideas, if one had only the social instinct.
Dozens of eminent statesmen were men of Lee's type, and maintained
themselves well enough in the legislature, but college was a sharper test.
The Virginian was weak in vice itself, though the Bostonian was hardly a
master of crime. The habits of neither were good; both were apt to drink
hard and live low lives; but the Bostonian suffered less than the Virginian.
Commonly the Bostonian would take some care of himself even in his worst
stages, while the Virginian became quarrelsome and dangerous. When a
Virginian had brooded a few days over an imaginary grief and substantial
whiskey, none of his Northern friends could be sure that he might not be
waiting, round the corner, with a knife or pistol, to revenge insult by the
dry light of *delirium tremens;* and when things reached this condition, Lee
had to exhaust his authority over his own staff. Lee was a gentleman of the
old school, and, as every one knows, gentlemen of the old school drank
almost as much as gentlemen of the new school; but this was not his trouble.
He was sober even in the excessive violence of political feeling in those
years; he kept his temper and his friends under control.

Adams liked the Virginians. No one was more obnoxious to them, by
name and prejudice; yet their friendship was unbroken and even warm.
At a moment when the immediate future posed no problem in education so
vital as the relative energy and endurance of North and South, this momentary contact with Southern character was a sort of education for its own
sake; but this was not all. No doubt the self-esteem of the Yankee, which
tended naturally to self-distrust, was flattered by gaining the slow conviction
that the Southerner, with his slave-owning limitations, was as little fit to
succeed in the struggle of modern life as though he was still a maker of
stone axes, living in caves, and hunting the *bos primigenius,* and that
every quality in which he was strong, made him weaker; but Adams had
begun to fear that even in this respect one eighteenth-century type might
not differ deeply from another. Roony Lee had changed little from the
Virginian of a century before; but Adams was himself a good deal nearer
the type of his great-grandfather than to that of a railway superintendent.
He was little more fit than the Virginians to deal with a future America
which showed no fancy for the past. Already Northern society betrayed a
preference for economists over diplomats or soldiers—one might even call it
a jealousy—against which two eighteenth-century types had little chance
to live, and which they had in common to fear.

Nothing short of this curious sympathy could have brought into close
relations two young men so hostile as Roony Lee and Henry Adams, but
the chief difference between them as collegians consisted only in their
difference of scholarship: Lee was a total failure; Adams a partial one.
Both failed, but Lee felt his failure more sensibly, so that he gladly seized

the chance of escape by accepting a commission offered him by General Winfield Scott in the force then being organized against the Mormons. He asked Adams to write his letter of acceptance, which flattered Adams's vanity more than any Northern compliment could do, because, in days of violent political bitterness, it showed a certain amount of good temper. The diplomat felt his profession.

If the student got little from his mates, he got little more from his masters. The four years passed at college were, for his purposes, wasted. Harvard College was a good school, but at bottom what the boy disliked most was any school at all. He did not want to be one in a hundred—one per cent of an education. He regarded himself as the only person for whom his education had value, and he wanted the whole of it. He got barely half of an average. Long afterwards, when the devious path of life led him back to teach in his turn what no student naturally cared or needed to know, he diverted some dreary hours of faculty-meetings by looking up his record in the class-lists, and found himself graded precisely in the middle. In the one branch he most needed—mathematics—barring the few first scholars, failure was so nearly universal that no attempt at grading could have had value, and whether he stood fortieth or ninetieth must have been an accident or the personal favor of the professor. Here his education failed lamentably. At best he could never have been a mathematician; at worst he would never have cared to be one; but he needed to read mathematics, like any other universal language, and he never reached the alphabet.

Beyond two or three Greek plays, the student got nothing from the ancient languages. Beyond some incoherent theories of free-trade and protection, he got little from Political Economy. He could not afterwards remember to have heard the name of Karl Marx mentioned, or the title of "Capital." He was equally ignorant of Auguste Comte. These were the two writers of his time who most influenced its thought. The bit of practical teaching he afterwards reviewed with most curiosity was the course in Chemistry, which taught him a number of theories that befogged his mind for a lifetime. The only teaching that appealed to his imagination was a course of lectures by Louis Agassiz on the Glacial Period and Palæontology, which had more influence on his curiosity than the rest of the college instruction altogether. The entire work of the four years could have been easily put into the work of any four months in after life.

Harvard College was a negative force, and negative forces have value. Slowly it weakened the violent political bias of childhood, not by putting interests in its place, but by mental habits which had no bias at all. It would also have weakened the literary bias, if Adams had been capable of finding other amusement, but the climate kept him steady to desultory and useless

reading, till he had run through libraries of volumes which he forgot, even
to their title-pages. Rather by instinct than by guidance, he turned to
writing, and his professors or tutors occasionally gave his English composition a hesitating approval; but in that branch, as in all the rest, even when
he made a long struggle for recognition, he never convinced his teachers
that his abilities, at their best, warranted placing him on the rank-list,
among the first third of his class. Instructors generally reach a fairly accurate
gauge of their scholars' powers. Henry Adams himself held the opinion
that his instructors were very nearly right, and when he became a professor
in his turn, and made mortifying mistakes in ranking his scholars, he still
obstinately insisted that on the whole, he was not far wrong. Student or
professor, he accepted the negative standard because it was the standard of
the school.

He never knew what other students thought of it, or what they thought
they gained from it; nor would their opinion have much affected his. From
the first, he wanted to be done with it, and stood watching vaguely for a
path and a direction. The world outside seemed large, but the paths that
led into it were not many and lay mostly through Boston, where he did
not want to go. As it happened, by pure chance, the first door of escape that
seemed to offer a hope led into Germany, and James Russell Lowell opened it.

Lowell, on succeeding Longfellow as Professor of Belles-Lettres, had
duly gone to Germany, and had brought back whatever he found to bring.
The literary world then agreed that truth survived in Germany alone, and
Carlyle, Matthew Arnold, Renan, Emerson, with scores of popular followers, taught the German faith. The literary world had revolted against
the yoke of coming capitalism—its money-lenders, its bank directors, and its
railway magnates. Thackeray and Dickens followed Balzac in scratching and
biting the unfortunate middle class with savage ill-temper, much as the
middle class had scratched and bitten the Church and Court for a hundred
years before. The middle class had the power and held its coal and iron
well in hand, but the satirists and idealists seized the press, and as they
were agreed that the Second Empire was a disgrace to France and a danger
to England, they turned to Germany because at that moment Germany was
neither economical or military, and a hundred years behind western Europe
in the simplicity of its standard. German thought, method, honesty, and
even taste, became the standards of scholarship. Goethe was raised to the
rank of Shakespeare—Kant ranked as a law-giver above Plato. All serious
scholars were obliged to become German, for German thought was revolu-
tionizing criticism. Lowell had followed the rest, not very enthusiastically,
but with sufficient conviction, and invited his scholars to join him. Adams
was glad to accept the invitation, rather for the sake of cultivating Lowell
than Germany, but still in perfect good faith. It was the first serious

attempt he had made to direct his own education, and he was sure of getting some education out of it; not perhaps anything that he expected, but at least a path.

Singularly circuitous and excessively wasteful of energy the path proved to be, but the student could never see what other was open to him. He could have done no better had he foreseen every stage of his coming life, and he would probably have done worse. The preliminary step was pure gain. James Russell Lowell had brought back from Germany the only new and valuable part of its universities, the habit of allowing students to read with him privately in his study. Adams asked the privilege, and used it to read a little, and talk a great deal, for the personal contact pleased and flattered him, as that of older men ought to flatter and please the young even when they altogether exaggerate its value. Lowell was a new element in the boy's life. As practical a New Englander as any, he leaned towards the Concord faith rather than towards Boston where he properly belonged; for Concord, in the dark days of 1856, glowed with pure light. Adams approached it in much the same spirit as he would have entered a Gothic Cathedral, for he well knew that the priests regarded him as only a worm. To the Concord Church all Adamses were minds of dust and emptiness, devoid of feeling, poetry or imagination; little higher than the common scourings of State Street; politicians of doubtful honesty; natures of narrow scope; and already, at eighteen years old, Henry had begun to feel uncertainty about so many matters more important than Adamses that his mind rebelled against no discipline merely personal, and he was ready to admit his unworthiness if only he might penetrate the shrine. The influence of Harvard College was beginning to have its effect. He was slipping away from fixed principles; from Mount Vernon Street; from Quincy; from the eighteenth century; and his first steps led toward Concord.

He never reached Concord, and to Concord Church he, like the rest of mankind who accepted a material universe, remained always an insect, or something much lower—a man. It was surely no fault of his that the universe seemed to him real; perhaps—as Mr. Emerson justly said—it was so; in spite of the long-continued effort of a lifetime, he perpetually fell back into the heresy that if anything universal was unreal, it was himself and not the appearances; it was the poet and not the banker; it was his own thought, not the thing that moved it. He did not lack the wish to be transcendental. Concord seemed to him, at one time, more real than Quincy; yet in truth Russell Lowell was as little transcendental as Beacon Street. From him the boy got no revolutionary thought whatever—objective or subjective as they used to call it—but he got good-humored encouragement to do what amused him, which consisted in passing two years in Europe after finishing the four years of Cambridge.

The result seemed small in proportion to the effort, but it was the only positive result he could ever trace to the influence of Harvard College, and he had grave doubts whether Harvard College influenced even that. Negative results in plenty he could trace, but he tended towards negation on his own account, as one side of the New England mind had always done, and even there he could never feel sure that Harvard College had more than reflected a weakness. In his opinion the education was not serious, but in truth hardly any Boston student took it seriously, and none of them seemed sure that President Walker himself, or President Felton after him, took it more seriously than the students. For them all, the college offered chiefly advantages vulgarly called social, rather than mental.

Unluckily for this particular boy, social advantages were his only capital in life. Of money he had not much, of mind not more, but he could be quite certain that, barring his own faults, his social position would never be questioned. What he needed was a career in which social position had value. Never in his life would he have to explain who he was; never would he have need of acquaintance to strengthen his social standing; but he needed greatly some one to show him how to use the acquaintance he cared to make. He made no acquaintance in college which proved to have the smallest use in after life. All his Boston friends he knew before, or would have known in any case, and contact of Bostonian with Bostonian was the last education these young men needed. Cordial and intimate as their college relations were, they all flew off in different directions the moment they took their degrees. Harvard College remained a tie, indeed, but a tie little stronger than Beacon Street and not so strong as State Street. Strangers might perhaps gain something from the college if they were hard pressed for social connections. A student like H. H. Richardson, who came from far away New Orleans, and had his career before him to chase rather than to guide, might make valuable friendships at college. Certainly Adams made no acquaintance there that he valued in after life so much as Richardson, but still more certainly the college relation had little to do with the later friendship. Life is a narrow valley, and the roads run close together. Adams would have attached himself to Richardson in any case, as he attached himself to John LaFarge or Augustus St. Gaudens or Clarence King or John Hay, none of whom were at Harvard College. The valley of life grew more and more narrow with years, and certain men with common tastes were bound to come together. Adams knew only that he would have felt himself on a more equal footing with them had he been less ignorant, and had he not thrown away ten years of early life in acquiring what he might have acquired in one.

Socially or intellectually, the college was for him negative and in some ways mischievous. The most tolerant man of the world could not see good in the lower habits of the students, but the vices were less harmful than the virtues. The habit of drinking—though the mere recollection of it made him doubt his own veracity, so fantastic it seemed in later life—may have done no great or permanent harm; but the habit of looking at life as a social relation—an affair of society—did no good. It cultivated a weakness which needed no cultivation. If it had helped to make men of the world, or give the manners and instincts of any profession—such as temper, patience, courtesy, or a faculty of profiting by the social defects of opponents—it would have been education better worth having than mathematics or languages; but so far as it helped to make anything, it helped only to make the college standard permanent through life. The Bostonian educated at Harvard College remained a collegian, if he stuck only to what the college gave him. If parents went on, generation after generation, sending their children to Harvard College for the sake of its social advantages, they perpetuated an inferior social type, quite as ill-fitted as the Oxford type for success in the next generation.

Luckily the old social standard of the college, as President Walker or James Russell Lowell still showed it, was admirable, and if it had little practical value or personal influence on the mass of students, at least it preserved the tradition for those who liked it. The Harvard graduate was neither American nor European, nor even wholly Yankee; his admirers were few, and his critics many; perhaps his worst weakness was his self-criticism and self-consciousness; but his ambitions, social or intellectual, were not necessarily cheap even though they might be negative. Afraid of serious risks, and still more afraid of personal ridicule, he seldom made a great failure of life, and nearly always led a life more or less worth living. So Henry Adams, well aware that he could not succeed as a scholar, and finding his social position beyond improvement or need of effort, betook himself to the single ambition which otherwise would scarcely have seemed a true outcome of the college, though it was the last remnant of the old Unitarian supremacy. He took to the pen. He wrote.

The College Magazine printed his work, and the College Societies listened to his addresses. Lavish of praise the readers were not; the audiences, too, listened in silence; but this was all the encouragement any Harvard collegian had a reasonable hope to receive; grave silence was a form of patience that meant possible future acceptance; and Henry Adams went on writing. No one cared enough to criticise, except himself who soon began to suffer from reaching his own limits. He found that he could not be this —or that—or the other; always precisely the things he wanted to be. He had not wit or scope or force. Judges always ranked him beneath a rival, if he had any; and he believed the judges were right. His work seemed to him thin, commonplace, feeble. At times he felt his own weakness so fatally that he could not go on; when he had nothing to say, he could not say it, and he found that he had very little to say at best. Much that he then wrote must be still in existence in print or manuscript, though he never cared to see it again, for he felt no doubt that it was in reality just what he thought it. At best it showed only a feeling for form; an instinct of exclusion. Nothing shocked—not even its weakness.

Inevitably an effort leads to an ambition—creates it—and at that time the ambition of the literary student, which almost took the place of the regular prizes of scholarship, was that of being chosen as the representative of his class—the Class Orator—at the close of their course. This was political as well as literary success, and precisely the sort of eighteenth-century combination that fascinated an eighteenth-century boy. The idea lurked in his mind, at first as a dream, in no way serious or even possible, for he stood outside the number of what were know as popular men. Year by year, his position seemed to improve, or perhaps his rivals disappeared, until at last, to his own great astonishment, he found himself a candidate. The habits of the college permitted no active candidacy; he and his rivals had not a word to say for or against themselves, and he was never even consulted on the subject; he was not present at any of the proceedings, and how it happened he never could quite divine, but it did happen, that one evening on returning from Boston he received notice of his election, after a very close contest, as Class Orator over the head of the first scholar, who was undoubtedly a better orator and a more popular man. In politics the success of the poorer candidate is common enough, and Henry Adams was a fairly trained politician, but he never understood how he managed to defeat not only a more capable but a more popular rival.

To him the election seemed a miracle. This was no mock-modesty; his head was as clear as ever it was in an indifferent canvass, and he knew his rivals and their following as well as he knew himself. What he did not know, even after four years of education, was Harvard College. What he could never measure was the bewildering impersonality of the men, who, at twenty years old, seemed to set no value either on official or personal standards. Here were nearly a hundred young men who had lived together intimately during four of the most impressionable years of life, and who, not only once but again and again, in different ways, deliberately, seriously, dispassionately, chose as their representatives precisely those of their companions who seemed least to represent them. As far as these Orators and Marshals had any position at all in a collegiate sense, it was that of indifference to the college. Henry Adams never professed the smallest faith in universities of any kind, either as boy or man, nor had he the faintest admiration for the university graduate, either in Europe or in America; as a collegian he was only known apart from his fellows by his habit of standing outside the college; and yet the singular fact remained that this commonplace body of young men chose him repeatedly to express his and their commonplaces. Secretly, of course, the successful candidate flattered himself—and them—with the hope that they might perhaps not be so commonplace as they thought themselves; but this was only another proof that all were identical. They saw in him a representative—the kind of representative they wanted—and he saw in them the most formidable array of judges he could ever meet, like so many mirrors of himself, an infinite reflection of his own shortcomings.

All the same, the choice was flattering; so flattering that it actually shocked his vanity; and would have shocked it more, if possible, had he known that it was to be the only flattery of the sort he was ever to receive. The function of Class Day was, in the eyes of nine-tenths of the students, altogether the most important of the college, and the figure of the Orator was the most conspicuous in the function. Unlike the Orators at regular Commencements, the Class Day Orator stood alone, or had only the Poet for rival. Crowded into the large church, the students, their families, friends, aunts, uncles, and chaperones, attended all the girls of sixteen or twenty who wanted to show their summer dresses or fresh complexions, and there, for an hour or two, in a heat that might have melted bronze, they listened to an Orator and a Poet in clergyman's gowns, reciting such platitudes as their own experience and their mild censors permitted them to utter. What Henry Adams said in his Class Oration of 1858 he soon forgot to the last word, nor had it the least value for education; but he naturally remembered what was said of it. He remembered especially one of his eminent uncles or relations remarking that, as the work of so young a man, the oration was singularly wanting in enthusiasm. The young man—always in search of education—asked himself whether, setting rhetoric aside, this absence of enthusiasm was a defect or a merit, since, in either case, it was all that Harvard College taught, and all that the hundred young men, whom he was trying to represent, expressed. Another comment threw more light on the effect of the college education. One of the elderly gentlemen noticed the orator's "perfect self-possession." Self-possession indeed! If Harvard College gave nothing else, it gave calm. For four years each student had been obliged to figure daily before dozens of young men who knew each other to the last fibre. One had done little but read papers to Societies, or act comedy in the Hasty Pudding, not to speak of all sorts of regular exercises, and no audience in future life would ever be so intimately and terribly intelligent as these. Three-fourths of the graduates would rather have addressed the Council of Trent or the British Parliament than have acted Sir Anthony Absolute or Dr. Ollapod before a gala audience of the Hasty Pudding. Self-possession was the strongest part of Harvard College, which certainly taught men to stand alone, so that nothing seemed stranger to its graduates than the paroxysms of terror before the public which often overcame the graduates of European universities. Whether this was, or was not, education, Henry Adams never knew. He was ready to stand up before any audience in America or Europe, with nerves rather steadier for the excitement, but whether he should ever have anything to say, remained to be proved. As yet he new nothing. Education had not begun.

A Liberal Education;
and Where to Find It

FROM *Collected Essays*

This selection is from a lecture that T. H. Huxley, eminent Victorian scientist, scholar and teacher, gave in 1868 at the South London Working Men's College—an eloquent argument for life-long self-education.

Huxley himself was largely self taught. His formal education ended at ten, when his father, a schoolmaster, lost his post. Thereafter the young Huxley read widely and omnivorously. He was apprenticed to a doctor in the East End of London and from that apprenticeship, in a setting of poverty and ignorance, developed his intense interest in education for workers.

WHAT is education? Above all things, what is our ideal of a thoroughly liberal education?—of that education which, if we could begin life again, we would give ourselves—of that education which, if we could mould the fates to our own will, we would give our children? Well, I know not what may be your conceptions upon this matter, but I will tell you mine, and I hope I shall find that our views are not very discrepant.

Suppose it were perfectly certain that the life and fortune of every one of us would, one day or other, depend upon his winning or losing a game of chess. Don't you think that we should all consider it to be a primary duty to learn at least the names and the moves of the pieces; to have a notion of a gambit, and a keen eye for all the means of giving and getting out of check? Do you not think that we should look with a disapprobation amounting to scorn, upon the father who allowed his son, or the state which allowed its members, to grow up without knowing a pawn from a knight?

Yet it is a very plain and elementary truth, that the life, the fortune, and the happiness of every one of us, and, more or less, of those who are connected with us, do depend upon our knowing something of the rules of a game infinitely more difficult and complicated than chess. It is a game which has been played for untold ages, every man and woman of us being one of the two players in a game of his or her own. The chess-board is the world, the pieces are the phænomena of the universe, the rules of the game are what we call the laws of Nature. The player on the other side is hidden from us. We know that his play is always fair, just and patient. But also we know, to our cost, that he never overlooks a mistake, or makes the smallest allowance for ignorance. To the man who plays well, the highest stakes are paid, with that sort of overflowing generosity with which the strong shows delight in strength. And one who plays ill is checkmated—without haste, but without remorse.

My metaphor will remind some of you of the famous picture in which Retzsch has depicted Satan playing at chess with man for his soul. Substitute for the mocking fiend in that picture a calm, strong angel who is playing for love, as we say, and would rather lose than win—and I should accept it as an image of human life.

Well, what I mean by Education is learning the rules of this mighty game. In other words, education is the instruction of the intellect in the laws of Nature, under which name I include not merely things and their forces, but men and their ways; and the fashioning of the affections and of the will into an earnest and loving desire to move in harmony with those laws. For me, education means neither more nor less than this. Anything which professes to call itself education must be tried by this standard, and if it fails to stand the test, I will not call it education, whatever may be the force of authority, or of numbers, upon the other side.

It is important to remember that, in strictness, there is no such thing as an uneducated man. Take an extreme case. Suppose that an adult man, in the full vigour of his faculties, could be suddenly placed in the world, as Adam is said to have been, and then left to do as he best might. How long would he be left uneducated? Not five minutes. Nature would begin to teach him, through the eye, the ear, the touch, the properties of objects. Pain and pleasure would be at his elbow telling him to do this and avoid that; and by slow degrees the man would receive an education which, if narrow, would be thorough, real, and adequate to his circumstances though there would be no extras and very few accomplishments.

And if to this solitary man entered a second Adam, or, better still, an Eve, a new and greater world, that of social and moral phænomena, would be revealed. Joys and woes, compared with which all others might seem but faint shadows, would spring from the new relations. Happiness and sorrow would take the place of the coarser monitors, pleasure and pain; but conduct would still be shaped by the observation of the natural consequences of actions; or, in other words, by the laws of the nature of man.

To every one of us the world was once as fresh and new as to Adam. And then, long before we were susceptible of any other modes of instruction, Nature took us in hand, and every minute of waking life brought its educational influence, shaping our actions into rough accordance with Nature's laws, so that we might not be ended untimely by too gross disobedience. Nor should I speak of this process of education as past for any one, be he as old as he may. For every man the world is as fresh as it was at the first day, and as full of untold novelties for him who has the eyes to see them. And Nature is still continuing her patient education of us in that great university, the universe, of which we are all members—Nature having no Test-Acts.[1]

Those who take honours in Nature's university, who learn the laws which govern men and things and obey them, are the really great and successful men in this world. The great mass of mankind are the 'Poll,'[2] who pick up just enough to get through without much discredit. Those who won't learn at all are plucked; and then you can't come up again. Nature's pluck means extermination.

Thus the question of compulsory education is settled so far as Nature is concerned. Her bill on that question was framed and passed long ago. But, like all compulsory legislation, that of Nature is harsh and wasteful in its operation. Ignorance is visited as sharply as wilful disobedience— incapacity meets with the same punishment as crime. Nature's discipline is not even a word and a blow, and the blow first; but the blow without the word. It is left to you to find out why your ears are boxed.

The object of what we commonly call education—that education in which man intervenes and which I shall distinguish as artificial education— is to make good these defects in Nature's methods; to prepare the child to receive Nature's education, neither incapably nor ignorantly, nor with wilful disobedience; and to understand the preliminary symptoms of her pleasure, without waiting for the box on the ear. In short, all artificial education ought to be an anticipation of natural education. And a liberal education is an artificial education which has not only prepared a man to escape the great evils of disobedience to natural laws, but has trained him to appreciate and to seize upon the rewards, which Nature scatters with as free a hand as her penalties.

---

[1] Up to the nineteenth century all people who would not take the Communion according to the rite of the Church of England were excluded from the political life of the nation. The sacramental test for civil office was established in 1828, but it was not until 1868 that Oxford and Cambridge opened their doors to Dissenters.

[2] Students who pass without taking honors.

That man, I think, has had a liberal education who has been so trained in youth that his body is the ready servant of his will, and does with ease and pleasure all the work that, as a mechanism, it is capable of; whose intellect is a clear, cold, logic engine, with all its parts of equal strength, and in smooth working order; ready, like a steam engine, to be turned to any kind of work, and spin the gossamers as well as forge the anchors of the mind; whose mind is stored with a knowledge of the great and fundamental truths of Nature and of the laws of her operations; one who, no stunted ascetic, is full of life and fire, but whose passions are trained to come to heel by a vigorous will, the servant of a tender conscience; who has learned to love all beauty, whether of Nature or of art, to hate all vileness, and to respect others as himself.

Such an one and no other, I conceive, has had a liberal education; for he is, as completely as a man can be, in harmony with Nature. He will make the best of her, and she of him. They will get on together rarely; she as his ever beneficent mother; he as her mouthpiece, her conscious self, her minister and interpreter. . . .

What Is a University?

FROM *Historical Sketches*

Today, a hundred years later, we argue much the same question John Henry Newman poses in this selection—what constitutes the educated citizen in a changing world?

Newman was educated at Trinity College, Oxford, where he founded the Oxford Movement in 1833, to carry into the Church of England the feeling and character of the church of the Middle Ages. He found reconciliation of Anglican and Catholic doctrine impossible, and subsequently joined the Roman Church. He was made a cardinal in 1879.

Newman's lectures on education, delivered when he was a rector of the Catholic University of Dublin, have long been considered models of persuasiveness and eloquence.

I PROTEST to you, Gentlemen, that if I had to choose between a so-called University, which dispensed with residence and tutorial superintendence, and gave its degrees to any person who passed an examination in a wide range of subjects, and a University which had no professors or examinations at all, but merely brought a number of young men together for three or four years, and then sent them away as the University of Oxford is said to have done some sixty years since, if I were asked which of these two methods was the better discipline of the intellect,—mind, I do not say which is *morally* the better, for it is plain that compulsory study must be a good and idleness an intolerable mischief,—but if I must determine which of the two courses was the more successful in training, moulding, enlarging the mind, which sent out men the more fitted for their secular duties, which produced better public men, men of the world, men whose names would descend to posterity, I have no hesitation in giving the preference to that University which did nothing, over that which exacted of its members an acquaintance with every science under the sun. And, paradox as this may seem, still if results be the test of systems, the influence of the public schools and colleges of England, in the course of the last century, at least will bear out one side of the contrast as I have drawn it. What would come, on the other hand, of the ideal systems of education which have fascinated the imagination of this age, could they ever take effect, and whether they would not produce a generation frivolous, narrow-minded, and resourceless, intellectually considered, is a fair subject for debate; but so far is certain, that the Universities and scholastic establishments, to which I refer, and which did little more than bring together first boys and then youths in large numbers, these institutions, with miserable deformities on the side of morals, with a hollow profession of Christianity, and a heathen code of ethics,—I say, at least they can boast of a succession of heroes and statesmen, of literary men and philosophers, of men conspicuous for great natural virtues, for habits of business, for knowledge of life, for practical judgment, for cultivated tastes, for accomplishments, who have made England what it is,—able to subdue the earth, able to domineer over Catholics.

How is this to be explained? I suppose as follows: When a multitude of young men, keen, open-hearted, sympathetic, and observant, as young men are, come together and freely mix with each other, they are sure to learn one from another, even if there be no one to teach them; the conversation of all is a series of lectures to each, and they gain for themselves new ideas and views, fresh matter of thought, and distinct principles for judging and acting, day by day. An infant has to learn the meaning of the information which its senses convey to it, and this seems to be its employment. It fancies all that the eye presents to it to be close to it, till it actually learns the contrary, and thus by practice does it ascertain the relations and uses of those first elements of knowledge which are necessary for its animal existence. A parallel teaching is necessary for our social being, and it is secured by a large school or a college; and this effect may be fairly called in its own department an enlargement of mind. It is seeing the world on a small field with little trouble; for the pupils or students come from very different places, and with widely different notions, and there is much to generalize, much to adjust, much to eliminate, there are inter-relations to be defined, and conventional rules to be established, in the process, by which the whole assemblage is moulded together, and gains one tone and one character.

Let it be clearly understood, I repeat it, that I am not taking into account moral or religious considerations; I am but saying that that youthful community will constitute a whole, it will embody a specific idea, it will represent a doctrine, it will administer a code of conduct, and it will furnish principles of thought and action. It will give birth to a living teaching, which in course of time will take the shape of a self-perpetuating tradition, or a *genius loci,* as it is sometimes called; which haunts the home where it has been born, and which imbues and forms, more or less, and one by one, every individual who is successively brought under its shadow. Thus it is that, independent of direct instruction on the part of Superiors, there is a sort of self-education in the academic institutions of Protestant England; a characteristic tone of thought, a recognized standard of judgment is found in them, which, as developed in the individual who is submitted to it, becomes a twofold source of strength to him, both from the distinct stamp it impresses on his mind, and from the bond of union which it creates between him and others,—effects which are shared by the authorities of the place, for they themselves have been educated in it, and at times are exposed to the influence of its ethical atmosphere. Here then is a real teaching, whatever be its standards and principles, true or false; and it at least tends towards cultivation of the intellect; it at least recognizes that knowledge is something more than a sort of passive reception of scraps and details; it is a something, and it does a something, which never will issue from the most strenuous efforts of a set of teachers, with no mutual sympathies and no intercommunion, of a set of examiners with no opinions which they dare profess, and with no common principles, who are teaching or questioning a set of youths who do not know them, and do not know each other, on a large number of subjects, different in kind, and connected by no wide philosophy, three times a week, or three times a year, or once in three years, in chill lecture-rooms or on a pompous anniversary.

*   *   *

Nay, self-education in any shape, in the most restricted sense, is preferable to a system of teaching which, professing so much, really does so little for the mind. Shut your College gates against the votary of knowledge, throw him back upon the searchings and the efforts of his own mind; he will gain by being spared an entrance into your Babel. Few indeed there are who can dispense with the stimulus and support of instructors, or will do anything at all, if left to themselves. And fewer still (though such great minds are to be found), who will not, from such unassisted attempts, contract a self-reliance and a self-esteem, which are not only moral evils, but serious hindrances to the attainment of truth. And next to none, perhaps, or none, who will not be reminded from time to time of the disadvantage under which they lie, by their imperfect grounding, by the breaks, deficiencies, and irregularities of their knowledge, by the eccentricity of opinion and the confusion of principle which they exhibit. They will be too often ignorant of what every one knows and takes for granted, of that multitude of small truths which fall upon the mind like dust, impalpable and ever accumulating; they may be unable to converse, they may argue perversely, they may pride themselves on their worst paradoxes or their grossest truisms, they may be full of their own mode of viewing things, unwilling to be put out of their way, slow to enter into the minds of others;—but, with these and whatever other liabilities upon their heads, they are likely to have more thought, more mind, more philosophy, more true enlargement, than those earnest but ill-used persons, who are forced to load their minds with a score of subjects against an examination, who have too much on their hands to indulge themselves in thinking or investigation, who devour premiss and conclusion together with indiscriminate greediness, who hold whole sciences on faith, and commit demonstrations to memory, and who too often, as might be expected, when their period of education is passed, throw up all they have learned in disgust, having gained nothing really by their anxious labours, except perhaps the habit of application.

Yet such is the better specimen of the fruit of that ambitious system which has of late years been making way among us; for its result on ordinary minds, and on the common run of students, is less satisfactory still; they leave their place of education simply dissipated and relaxed by the multiplicity of subjects, which they have never really mastered, and so shallow as not even to know their shallowness. How much better, I say, is it for the active and thoughtful intellect, where such is to be found, to eschew the College and the University altogether, than to submit to a drudgery so ignoble, a mockery so contumelious! How much more profitable for the independent mind, after the mere rudiments of education, to range through a library at random, taking down books as they meet him, and pursuing the trains of thought which his mother wit suggests! How much healthier to wander into the fields, and there with the exiled Prince to find "tongues in the trees, books in the running brooks!" How much more genuine an education is that of the poor boy in the Poem—a Poem, whether in conception or in execution, one of the most touching in our language—who, not in the wide world, but ranging day by day around his widowed mother's home, "a dexterous gleaner" in a narrow field, and with only such slender outfit

"as the village school and books a few Supplied,"

contrived from the beach, and the quay, and the fisher's boat, and the inn's fireside, and the tradesman's shop, and the shepherd's walk, and the smuggler's hut, and the mossy moor, and the screaming gulls, and the restless waves, to fashion for himself a philosophy and a poetry of his own!

Education
Gets Longer and Longer

FROM *Too Much College*

Stephen Leacock, Canadian humorist and pedagogue, blends a highly personal mixture of the comic and the earnest in his query: Is Education Eating Up Life?

As an educator, Leacock spoke with the authority of a long and distinguished career. He was head of the department of Economics and Political Science at McGill, and held many honorary degrees. But it is as one of the top humorists of the past few decades that he is best and most lovingly remembered by aficionados of gay and wonderful nonsense.

IN THIS discussion of education, I am addressing myself to plain people. By this I mean people who shudder at mathematics, go no further in Latin than *E Pluribus Unum* and take electricity as they find it. As opposed to these are the academic class who live in colleges, or in the shadow of them, and claim education as their province. But the plain people are of necessity interested in education because their sons and daughters go to college, or, more important, can't go to college.

Now the plain people have noticed that education is getting longer and longer. Fifty years ago people learned to read out of a spelling-book at six years old, went to high school at twelve, and taught school (for money) on a third-class certificate at sixteen. After that, two years in a saw-mill and two at a medical school made them doctors, or one year in a saw-mill and one in divinity fitted them for the church. For law they needed no college at all, just three summers on a farm and three winters in an office.

All our great men in North America got this education. Pragmatically, it worked. They began their real life still young. With the money they didn't spend they bought a wife. By the age of thirty they had got somewhere, or nowhere. It is true that for five years of married life, they carried, instead of a higher degree, bills for groceries, coal, doctors and babies' medicine. Then they broke out of the woods, into the sunlight, established men—at an age when their successors are still demonstrating, interning, or writing an advanced thesis on social impetus.

Now it is all changed. Children in school at six years old cut up paper dolls and make patterns. They are still in high school till eighteen, learning civics and social statistics—studies for old men. They enter college at about nineteen or twenty, take prerequisites and post-requisites in various faculties for nearly ten years, then become demonstrators, invigilators, researchers, or cling to a graduate scholarship like a man on a raft.

At thirty they are just beginning, ten years too late. They can't marry till it's ten years too late; they have children ten years too late, and die ten years too early. They know nothing of the early life of the man who worked in saw-mills, practiced medicine at twenty and married six months later, with no other property than a stethoscope and a horse and buggy; or of the young lawyer who married in debt, and lived happy in it ever after.

"Safety first" has put its stamp on life. Population begins to die at the top. And, all the time, education grows longer and longer. This does not deny that the average human life is now longer. It means that paternity is shorter. People do not see enough of their grandchildren—the sweetest prospect in the world. Life has all too little evening. It has all run in arrears and never catches up.

All this, you will say, is exaggerated, is overcolored, is not truth. Very likely. But a half truth in argument, like a half brick, carries better. High colors show up where neutral tints blend to nothing. Yet the main truth gets over. Education is eating up life.

In the above paragraphs I have formulated the plain man's accusations against the continued lengthening of education; or, rather, I must not say his accusation. The poor fellow hasn't the spirit to accuse. It is not an accusation that he formulates or a grievance that he voices. It is just a burden that he carries.

He carries it because of the prestige of education. Round the idea of education, as effort and opportunity, there have clustered centuries in tradition and association. These are stamped in such words and phrases as "the little red schoolhouse," "the midnight oil," "the eager student," "the kindly dominie," "the absent-minded professor." With this has grown up the notion—no doubt partly true—that the harder the path of learning the higher the achievement. "There is no royal road to learning" still cheers those who are unaware that the public road itself has become overgrown with a jungle of underbrush.

In other words, people don't complain. On the contrary, they are often proud of the burden that they carry. Parents have no regrets for the fifteen years of sacrifice that they made to give their children the education they should have had in half the time.

It is a tradition with us that education opens opportunity. To send a boy to college is an ambition that wakes to life beside a cradle. "How is your son doing at school, Mr. McGregor?" I once asked of a Scotsman of the traditional type. "Fine!" he answered. "If he keeps on as he is, we'll have to put the college to him."

Even in the clutter and failure of youth's career among the blocked avenues of our misfit world the college comes into its own as a sort of refuge. "My son," said another parent, "doesn't seem to have any particular ability, so we think we'll have to send him to college. He seems no good for anything else." The one anxiety of such parents is, "Can he get in?" Beyond that no need to look. It's like being dipped in the Jordan.

But even if the plain man were to raise his complaint against the lengthening road and the increasing burden, he would be laughed out of court by the academic class. He would be told that our education is all too short. The teachers in the high schools would say that the children come to them hopelessly unprepared and ought to stay a year longer in public school.

Every professor will tell them that the first-year students at college are simply hopeless and ought to have stayed at least a year, or call it two, at high school. The students in the second year ought never to have left the first; the third-year men haven't the proper grounding for their work; and the fourth-year are so rotten that they have to be given degrees to get rid of them. As for the graduate school, the students in it should never have been admitted; they are not yet fit for advanced work. Their minds are immature. And even when they do get out of the graduate school, by sheer lapse of time, it seems ridiculous to think of them as fit to teach, or do anything. Oh, no; they have to go to Germany for a year—anyway, to somewhere for a year—and come back with whiskers and look like something.

I once put the question of shortening the college curriculum to my old friend Dean Elderberry Foible, dean of the Faculty of Arts. You didn't know him, but there was a dean at your college just like him. "Preposterous," he said, "preposterous!" And that settled it.

If we turn from the general view to the particular subjects, the case against any attempt to shorten the curriculum becomes simply overwhelming—so much so that we are crushed and humbled in presenting it. Imagine trying to leave out mathematics—the queen of sciences; or history—the very basis for understanding our modern life; or English literature—our legacy common to England and America, dear as the very hearthstones of our homes—who dares touch that?

Or who will dare disturb Latin, the bedrock of our culture; or foreign languages, the amenity of polite life; or geology, deep as the caverns of thought; biology, life's interpretation; or the social sciences, the key to the padlock of happiness still closed. Help! Nothing but pretentious ignorance could suggest leaving out anything. As to any shortening, ask again my friend Dean Elderberry Foible and he will tell you that you can't. "My dear sir, you may wish to, but you simply can't"—with that academic finality with which professors dismiss the ideas of students.

So it appears even to ourselves on a first survey. Take mathematics. How can you shorten the subject? That stern struggle with the multiplication table, for many people not yet ended in victory, how can you make it less? Square root, as obdurate as a hardwood stump in a pasture—nothing but years of effort can extract it. You can't hurry the process.

Or pass from arithmetic to algebra: you can't shoulder your way past quadratic equations or ripple through the binomial theorem. Indeed, the other way; your feet are impeded in the tangled growth, your pace slackens, you sink and fall somewhere near the binomial theorem with the calculus in sight on the horizon. So died, for each of us, still bravely fighting, our mathematical training; except only for a set of people called "mathematicans"—born so, like crooks. Yet would we leave mathematics out? No, we hold our cross.

Latin too: do you want your son to grow up not knowing what a *sine qua non* is, and who wrote Virgil's *Aeneid?* Then he not only needs the whole present curriculum but more! At present the student learns just enough Latin not to be able to read it; he stops short of the saturation point—just gets wet with it and no more.

But why recite the entire list? The same truth holds, for the academic profession, of every one of the subjects of the school and college course. The student is not saturated, when he ought really to be soaked.

A parallel resistance blocks the pathway leading to the professions. The idea of any immediate entry into them, for a young man just out of college is ridiculous. A hundred years ago a man just out of college looked as good as a coin fresh from the mint, a sickle from the whetstone. At twenty-seven he was a Member of Congress, had four or five children, owned three or four thousand dollars' worth of property in his own right—and owed five thousand dollars. But nowadays! Imagine trusting a serious case of illness to a young fellow of twenty-seven barely out of college, and till yesterday an interne in a hospital. Out of the question!

And, later, when at last his turn comes, it is but a brief acme of success, and then, all of a sudden, it seems people are saying, "He's too old for the job, losing his grip—in fact, he's nearly fifty." He's an "old doctor"—once a term of esteem and confidence but now equivalent to an "old horse."

Thus in our ill-fit world youth and age jostle and hurry one another together—too young and then too old. Those who follow gardening know that green peas are first too young to pick and then, overnight as it seems, too old to eat. So with our educated people. Homer long ago said, "As is the race of leaves, so is the race of men." Make it college graduates and garden peas and it still holds good.

How did all this come about? Our system of education arose out of the mediaeval Latin schools of the church. It still carries, like a fossil snake in a stone, the mark of its original structure. Not that this was the earliest kind of education. But the others were different. Greek education included music and dancing and what we call the arts. It was supposed to fit people to live. Mediaeval education was supposed to fit people to die. Any school-boy of today can still feel the effect of it.

Greek education was free from the problems that have beset our own. It didn't include the teaching of languages, the Greeks despising all foreigners as barbarians. It avoided everything "practical" like the plague, and would have regarded a professor of Engineering as a child of the devil, misusing truth. Mathematics, crippled by the want of symbols, became a sort of dream—intense, difficult and proudly without purpose. Greek education carried with it no "exams" and "tests" for entry to the professions. A Greek dentist didn't have to pass in Latin. He used a hammer.

Thus philosophy, "the love of knowledge," came into its own, in talk as endless as on the porch of a Kentucky country store.

"Scholars" would deny the truth of this summary and talk of Archimedes, the world's first engineer, and Hippocrates, its earliest physician. But the proof of what I say is that Archimedes found no followers and Hippocrates waited five hundred years for Galen. Scholars always see exceptions where a plain man sees an even surface. But even a billiard ball, if you look close enough, is all covered with bumps.

Our education, then, comes down to us from the schools of the Middle Ages. These were organized by the church and the first aim was piety, not competence; the goal was the reading of the Scriptures and by that the salvation of the soul. On this basis, Alfred the Great planned schools for Saxon England. So, too, in France did Charlemagne, who couldn't read or write and felt a religious admiration for those who could—the same as an oil magnate of today feels toward a university.

So presently the monastic schools arose, and from their oriel windows came forth among the elm trees the sound of Latin chants intoned by choristers; and in the silent scriptorium the light from a stained window fell on the quiet "copyist" rewriting, letter by letter, in pigment upon parchment, "In the beginning was the Word." Thus passed monastic life in its quiet transition to Eternity.

These were the earliest schools—secluded, scholarly—born ancient like the "old-fashioned" children of aging parents. For the date, place them anywhere in the four hundred years from Alfred and Charlemagne to the days of Oxford and Paris.

These later schools—Oxford, Paris, and such—came when study no longer taught people how to die and keep out of hell, but how to live, as lawyers—two ambitions with an obvious relationship. Law hatched out under the wings of the church, as a duck hatches under a hen, later to horrify its parent.

Here again the vertebrate structure is still seen in the rock. Lincoln's Inn and Grey's Inn were originally, in a sense, works of God, the defunct Doctors Commons till its end a spirituality. Law, in England at least, struggled long before it shook off the hand of ghostly guidance. Even now the connection between law and religion remains in the quantity of oaths by which the business of the law secures its righteousness.

So there came, then, such schools as Oxford and Paris, which seem to have been at first huge random gatherings of students—mediaeval exaggeration puts 30,000 at Oxford in pre-record days. They had, before printing, hardly any books, and no examinations. The curriculum ran to endless discussion—more Kentucky. These "disputations" begot "tests" and awards (degrees) and brought into the world that child of sin, the written examination. A few odd people like Roger Bacon began digging into black knowledge about gunpowder, and so forth, and got put into jail for it. The lamp of learning still fell only on the Kingdom of Light, with lawyers dancing in the shadow.

The curriculum of these schools, the bedrock on which ours still rest, was the famous trinity of study, the Trivium, which meant grammar, rhetoric and logic; to this was supplemented the four further studies called the Quadrivium—music, arithmetic, geometry and astronomy. All were based on the use of Latin; they comprehended the whole circuit of human knowledge, and the supreme purpose of it all was salvation. The monk Alcuin, who was Charlemagne's "specialist" in education, has described for us how he taught his students:

To some I administer the honey of the sacred writings; others I try to inebriate with the wine of the ancient classics. I begin the nourishment of some with the apples of grammatical subtlety. I strive to illuminate many by the arrangement of the stars, as from the painted roof of a lofty palace.

The whole extent of human knowledge was still within human comprehension. In our own day we meet men who think they "know it all." In the Middle Ages there were men who were sure they did. Of course, where knowledge ended superstition began, and that was infinite.

It was this curriculum which in the course of centuries has been expanded beyond recognition like the toad in Aesop that would be an ox. And still it has not burst. It drags along its huge amorphous outline, flabby as a dinosaur, over fifteen years of life.

Here is what happened to expand it. The revival of learning resuscitated Greek, a study forgotten by all but the Arabs. The rising kingdoms that replaced feudalism brought national States and set people to learning one another's languages. The English, having forgotten French, had to learn it again. Italian became "polite." Milton suggested that one ought to learn it, "in an odd hour." Modern languages were still not a part of education, but a sort of annex; so they remained till yesterday in England where all Englishmen were supposed to "know French" from a governess and a copy of Ollendorff's *Grammar* and a trip to Boulogne. But, till yesterday, Eton, Rugby and Oxford never heard of it.

Printing, once in real use, expanded both opportunity and obligation. Students henceforth had books. Contacts with the Arabs revealed a system of decimal notation that made arithmetic a reality and algebra a power. Mathematics in the time of the Stuarts, with logarithms and the calculus, ceased to be a dream. Physics converted Alcuin's wonder of the sky into classroom formulae.

But even though mathematics in the sixteen hundreds, in the days of Newton and Descartes, had become a real and intensive study—far transcending in reach and in difficulty anything within the range of the ordinary college man of today—it was still regarded rather as an annex to learning than as learning itself. The place of priority still lay with classical study, with the literature of Greece and Rome. In this America was a faithful child of England. Our earliest college education was stamped with Roman letters, and its passion for the Bible in the wilderness made it even revert somewhat to the mediaeval type. The rules that were promulgated in 1642 for admission to Harvard College lay down the qualification thus:—

When any scholar is able to understand Tully or such like classical Latin author extempore, and to make and speak true Latin in verse and prose, suo ut aiunt Marte: *and to decline perfectly the paradigms of nouns and verbs in the Greek tongue: let him then and not before be capable of admission into the college.*

For readers whose Latinity has slipped away from them, let it be explained that Tully is not Irish, but means Cicero. Earlier generations properly called Romans by their names, and not, as we have come to do, with many of them, by their nicknames. Tully was called "Cicero" (or bean-head) as one of us might be called "Shorty." Harvard Latin in 1642 was still undefiled.

On the terms indicated few of us now would get into Harvard. Fewer still would get out, since, for that, every scholar had to be

"found able to read the originals of the Old and New Testaments into the Latin tongue and to resolve them logically: withal being of godly life and conversation."

On the outside edge or fringe of the classical studies, of which mathe-matics and logic formed an adjunct, were such things as natural philosophy, destined to vast and rapid expansion, but of which the classical doctors of divinity remained ignorant.

By the time of Queen Anne, some scholars already admitted that they didn't know everything—not many, though, or at least they qualified it by saying that what they didn't know wasn't worth knowing.

What they referred to by this last phrase was this natural philosophy, the new range of knowledge that the eighteenth century was gathering, item by item, fact by fact. These grew into the sciences of life—botany and zoology, later to get their true name of biology. Reverend classical scholars, full to the throat with declensions, set them aside as a disturbance of the Book of Genesis. But they wouldn't down.

Beside them grew, equally despised by the classicists, the electric science drawn by Franklin from the clouds, the oxygen distilled by Priestley from water, the geology of Lyell, dug up from what was once called Hades. All the world knows the story. Within another hundred years a vast series of studies known as the natural sciences—at first opposed, derided and left to mechanics and steam-engine drivers—broke at last the barriers of the schools and flooded wide over the curriculum.

But the barriers, in England at least, did not break until the waters had risen high and the pressure had become overwhelming. In the middle nine-teenth century, as Professor Huxley complained, the so-called public schools had still a curriculum of the Middle Ages.

Until a few years back [he wrote in 1893], a boy might have passed through any one of the great public schools with the greatest distinction and credit and might never so much as heard of modern geography, modern history and modern literature, of the English language as a language, or of the whole circle of the sciences, physical, moral and social; might never have heard that the earth goes round the sun; that England underwent a great

*revolution in 1688 and France another in 1789; that there once lived certain
notable men called Chaucer, Shakespeare, Milton, Voltaire, Goethe, Schiller.*

With this protest of common sense went a certain protest of spite—as
against aristocratic culture by those unable to share it. Witness Herbert
Spencer's diatribe against "The Education of a Gentleman."

*Men dress their children's minds as they do their bodies in the prevailing
fashion. As the Orinoco Indian puts on his paint before he leaves his hut
. . . so a boy's drilling in Latin and Greek is insisted on, not because of their
intrinsic value, but that he may not be disgraced by being found ignorant
of them—that he may have the education of a gentleman.*

But when at last the barriers broke, the new science came in a flood,
till every high school student, in America more even than in England,
turned alchemist, and every class-room sputtered with electricity. And with
this, in the colleges first and spreading downwards to the schools, came a
still newer set of studies—the social studies, economics and politics, the
mingled brood of happiness and despair, of progress and poverty that Mill
and Spencer and such people let loose upon the world. So deeply have they
spread that little children learn "civics" first and find out what it means
after; and so widely that the Japanese have studied it from Europe and
teach it to the Chinese.

And as if civics and social welfare were not enough for the already
overburdened curriculum, a chariot creaking up the rough slope of
Parnassus, "Business," in the form of schools of commerce, must needs leap
on top of the load. It handed so heavy a tip to the driver that it could not
be put off, and more than that it began to demand that the oldest and most
respectable of the passengers be thrown out to make room for it.

So there we stand, or rather move slowly onward, the ascent of Parnassus
turned into a ten years' journey during which the passengers must amuse
themselves as best they may with the cards and dice of college activities.

Meantime it is only to be expected that the conditions of the journey
react upon the minds of the passengers. In other words it is only natural
that this vast burden of an increasing curriculum sets up a reaction in the
minds of the pupil and the student. From their earliest years they become
accustomed to reckon up the things that they have done and finished with.
"We've finished Scripture," says a little girl in a child's school; "we had it
last year." For her the mould of religious thought is all set. Don't ask her
the names of the twelve Apostles. She's had them—last year. She is not

responsible for the Apostles any more. So does the high school student count up his years still needed for matriculation as eagerly as a mariner measures his distance to the shore. The college student opens his career by classing himself not according to the year in which he enters but according to the year in which he hopes to get out. The class matriculating in 1940 call out in their infant breath, "Rah! Rah! Forty-four."

How strange it is, our little procession of life! The child says, "When I am a big boy." But what is that? The big boy says, "When I grow up." And then, grown up, he says, "When I get married." But to be married, what is that after all? The thought changes to, "When I'm able to retire." And then, when retirement comes, he looks back over the landscape traversed; a cold wind seems to sweep over it; somehow he has missed it all, and it is gone. Life, we learn too late, is in the living, in the tissue of every day and hour. So it should be with education.

But so it is not; a false view discolours it all. For the vastly great part of it the student's one aim is to get done with it. There comes a glad time in his life when he has "finished" mathematics, a happy day when he has done philosophy, an exhilarating hour when he realizes that he is finished with "compulsory English." Then at last his four years are out, his sentence expired, and he steps out of college a free man, without a stain on his character—and not much on his mind. . . . Later on, he looks back wistfully and realizes how different it might have been.

The Student Life

FROM *Aequanimitas*

This selection is part of a farewell address delivered by Sir William Osler, one of the great men of medicine, when he left America to go to England.

Sir William had a long and distinguished career as physician and teacher. He taught at the medical schools of McGill, the University of Pennsylvania, Johns Hopkins, Oxford and elsewhere, and left a strong impression on medical education. His farewell addresses have been read and pondered by generations of pre-medics and doctors, and are likely to be so for many generations. This is partially due to the fact that portions of one of them were exaggeratedly interpreted as suggesting that men over forty make few contributions to human progress.

EXCEPT it be a lover, no one is more interesting as an object of study than a student. Shakespeare might have made him a fourth in his immortal group. The lunatic with his fixed idea, the poet with his fine frenzy, the lover with his frantic idolatry, and the student aflame with the desire for knowledge are of "imagination all compact." To an absorbing passion, a whole-souled devotion, must be joined an enduring energy, if the student is to become a devotee of the grey-eyed goddess to whose law his services are bound. Like the quest of the Holy Grail, the quest of Minerva is not for all. For the one, the pure life; for the other, what Milton calls "a strong propensity of nature." Here again the student often resembles the poet—he is born, not made. While the resultant of two moulding forces, the accidental, external conditions, and the hidden germinal energies, which produce in each one of us national, family, and individual traits, the true student possesses in some measure a divine spark which sets at naught their laws. Like the Snark, he defies definition, but there are three unmistakable signs by which you may recognize the genuine article from a Boojum—an absorbing

378

desire to know the truth, an unswerving steadfastness in its pursuit, and an open, honest heart, free from suspicion, guile, and jealousy.

At the outset do not be worried about this big question—Truth. It is a very simple matter if each one of you starts with the desire to get as much as possible. No human being is constituted to know the truth, the whole truth, and nothing but the truth; and even the best of men must be content with fragments, with partial glimpses, never the full fruition. In this unsatisfied quest the attitude of mind, the desire, the thirst—a thirst that from the soul must rise!—the fervent longing, are the be-all and the end-all. What is the student but a lover courting a fickle mistress who ever eludes his grasp? In this very elusiveness is brought out his second great characteristic —steadfastness of purpose. Unless from the start the limitations incident to our frail human faculties are frankly accepted, nothing but disappointment awaits you. The truth is the best you can get with your best endeavour, the best that the best men accept—with this you must learn to be satisfied, retaining at the same time with due humility an earnest desire for an ever larger portion. Only by keeping the mind plastic and receptive does the student escape perdition. It is not, as Charles Lamb remarks, that some people do not know what to do with truth when it is offered to them, but the tragic fate is to reach, after years of patient search, a condition of mind-blindness in which the truth is not recognized, though it stares you in the face. This can never happen to a man who has followed step by step the growth of a truth, and who knows the painful phases of its evolution. It is one of the great tragedies of life that every truth has to struggle to acceptance against honest but mind-blind students. Harvey knew his contemporaries well, and for twelve successive years demonstrated the circulation of the blood before daring to publish the facts on which the truth was based. Only steadfastness of purpose and humility enable the student to shift his position to meet the new conditions in which new truths are born, or old ones modified beyond recognition. And, thirdly, the honest heart will keep him in touch with his fellow students, and furnish that sense of comradeship without which he travels an arid waste alone. I say advisedly an honest *heart*—the honest head is prone to be cold and stern, given to judgment, not mercy, and not always able to entertain that true charity which, while it thinketh no evil, is anxious to put the best possible interpretation upon the motives of a fellow worker. It will foster, too, an attitude of generous, friendly rivalry untinged by the green peril, jealousy, that is the best preventive of the growth of a bastard scientific spirit, loving seclusion and working in a lock-and-key laboratory, as timorous of light as is a thief.

You have all become brothers in a great society, not apprentices, since that implies a master, and nothing should be further from the attitude of the teacher than much that is meant in that word, used though it be in another sense, particularly by our French brethren in a most delightful way, signifying a bond of intellectual filiation. A fraternal attitude is not easy to cultivate—the chasm between the chair and the bench is difficult to bridge. Two things have helped to put up a cantilever across the gulf. The successful teacher is no longer on a height, pumping knowledge at high pressure into passive receptacles. The new methods have changed all this. He is no longer *Sir Oracle,* perhaps unconsciously by his very manner antagonizing minds to whose level he cannot possibly descend, but he is a senior student anxious to help his juniors. When a simple, earnest spirit animates a college, there is no appreciable interval between the teacher and the taught—both are in the same class, the one a little more advanced than the other. So animated, the student feels that he has joined a family whose honour is his honour, whose welfare is his own, and whose interests should be his first consideration.

The hardest conviction to get into the mind of a beginner is that the education upon which he is engaged is not a college course, not a medical course, but a life course, for which the work of a few years under teachers is but a preparation. Whether you will falter and fail in the race or whether you will be faithful to the end depends on the training before the start, and on your staying powers, points upon which I need not enlarge. You can all become good students, a few may become great students, and now and again one of you will be found who does easily and well what others cannot do at all, or very badly, which is John Ferriar's excellent definition of a genius.

In the hurry and bustle of a business world, which is the life of this continent, it is not easy to train first-class students. Under present conditions it is hard to get the needful seclusion, on which account it is that our educational market is so full of wayside fruit. I have always been much impressed by the advice of St. Chrysostom: "Depart from the highway and transplant thyself in some enclosed ground, for it is hard for a tree which stands by the wayside to keep her fruit till it be ripe." The dilettante is abroad in the land, the man who is always venturing on tasks for which he is imperfectly equipped, a habit of mind fostered by the multiplicity of subjects in the curriculum; and while many things are studied, few are studied thoroughly. Men will not take time to get to the heart of a matter. After all, concentration is the price the modern student pays for success. Thoroughness is the most difficult habit to acquire, but it is the pearl of great price, worth all the worry and trouble of the search. The dilettante lives an easy, butterfly life, knowing nothing of the toil and labour with which the treasures of knowledge are dug out of the past, or wrung by patient research in the laboratories. Take, for example, the early history of this country— how easy for the student of the one type to get a smattering, even a fairly full acquaintance with the events of the French and Spanish settlements. Put an original document before him, and it might as well be Arabic. What we need is the other type, the man who knows the records, who, with a broad outlook and drilled in what may be called the embryology of history, has yet a powerful vision for the minutiae of life. It is these kitchen and backstair men who are to be encouraged, the men who know the subject in hand in all possible relationships. Concentration has its drawbacks. It is possible to become so absorbed in the problem of the "enclitic $\delta\epsilon$," or the structure of the flagella of the Trichomonas, or of the toes of the prehistoric horse, that the student loses the sense of proportion in his work, and even wastes a lifetime in researches which are valueless because not in touch with current knowledge. You remember poor Casaubon, in *Middlemarch,* whose painful scholarship was lost on this account. The best preventive to this is to get denationalized early. The true student is a citizen of the world, the allegiance of whose soul, at any rate, is too precious to be restricted to a single country. The great minds, the great works transcend all limitations of time, of language, and of race, and the scholar can never feel initiated into the company of the elect until he can approach all of life's problems from the cosmopolitan standpoint. I care not in what subject he may work, the full knowledge cannot be reached without drawing on supplies from lands other than his own—French, English, German, American, Japanese, Russian, Italian—there must be no discrimination by the loyal student, who should willingly draw from any and every source with an open mind and a stern resolve to render unto all their dues. I care not on what stream of knowledge he may embark, follow up its course, and the rivulets that feed it flow from many lands. If the work is to be effective he must keep in touch with scholars in other countries. How often has it happened that years of precious time have been given to a problem already solved or shown to be insoluble, because of the ignorance of what had been done elsewhere. And it is not only book knowledge and journal knowledge, but a knowledge of men that is needed. The student will, if possible, see the men in other lands. Travel not only widens the vision and gives certainties in place of vague surmises, but the personal contact with foreign workers enables him to appreciate better the failings or successes in his own line of work, perhaps to look with more charitable eyes on the work of some brother whose limitations and opportunities have been more restricted than his own. Or, in contact with a mastermind, he may take fire, and the glow of the enthusiasm may be the inspiration of his life. Concentration must then be associated with large views on the relation of the problem, and a knowledge of its status elsewhere; otherwise it may land him in the slough of a special-ism so narrow that it has depth and no breadth, or he may be led to make what he believes to be important discoveries, but which have long been current coin in other lands. It is sad to think that the day of the great polymathic student is at an end; that we may, perhaps, never again see a Scaliger, a Haller, or a Humboldt—men who took the whole field of knowledge for their domain and viewed it as from a pinnacle. And yet a great specializing generalist may arise, who can tell? Some twentieth-century Aristotle may be now tugging at his bottle, as little dreaming as are his parents or his friends of a conquest of the mind, beside which the wonderful victories of the Stagirite will look pale. The value of a really great student to the country is equal to half a dozen grain elevators or a new transcontinental railway. He is a commodity singularly fickle and variable, and not to be grown to order. So far as his advent is concerned there is no telling when or where he may arise. The conditions seem to be present even under the most unlikely externals. Some of the greatest students this country has produced have come from small villages and country places. It is impossible to predict from a study of the environment, which a "strong propensity of nature," to quote Milton's phrase again, will easily bend or break.

The student must be allowed full freedom in his work, undisturbed by the utilitarian spirit of the Philistine, who cries, *Cui bono?* and distrusts pure science. The present remarkable position in applied science and in industrial trades of all sorts has been made possible by men who did pioneer work in chemistry, in physics, in biology, and in physiology, without a thought in their researches of any practical application. The members of this higher group of productive students are rarely understood by the common spirits, who appreciate as little their unselfish devotion as their unworldly neglect of the practical side of the problems. . . .

Divide your attentions equally between books and men. The strength of the student of books is to sit still—two or three hours at a stretch—eating the heart out of a subject with pencil and notebook in hand, determined to master the details and intricacies, focussing all your energies on its difficulties. Get accustomed to test all sorts of book problems and statements for yourself, and take as little as possible on trust. The Hunterian "Do not think, but try" attitude of mind is the important one to cultivate. The question came up one day, when discussing the grooves left on the nails after fever, how long it took for the nail to grow out, from root to edge. A majority of the class had no further interest; a few looked it up in books; two men marked their nails at the root with nitrate of silver, and a few months later had positive knowledge on the subject. They showed the proper spirit. The little points that come up in your reading try to test for yourselves. With one fundamental difficulty many of you will have to contend from the outset—a lack of proper preparation for really hard study. No one can have watched successive groups of young men pass through the special schools without profoundly regretting the haphazard, fragmentary character of their preliminary education. It does seem too bad that we cannot have a student in his eighteenth year sufficiently grounded in the humanities and in the sciences preliminary to medicine—but this is an educational problem upon which only a Milton or a Locke could discourse with profit. With pertinacity you can overcome the preliminary defects and once thoroughly interested, the work in books becomes a pastime. A serious drawback in the student life is the selfconsciousness, bred of too close devotion to books. A man gets shy, "dysopic," as old Timothy Bright calls it, and shuns the looks of men, and blushes like a girl.

The strength of a student of men is to travel—to study men, their habits, character, mode of life, their behaviour under varied conditions, their vices, virtues, and peculiarities. Begin with a careful observation of your fellow students and of your teachers; then, every patient you see is a lesson in much more than the malady from which he suffers. Mix as much as you possibly can with the outside world, and learn its ways. Cultivated systematically, the student societies, the students' union, the gymnasium, and the outside social circle will enable you to conquer the diffidence so apt to go with bookishness and which may prove a very serious drawback in after-life. I cannot too strongly impress upon the earnest and attentive men among you the necessity of overcoming this unfortunate failing in your student days. It is not easy for every one to reach a happy medium, and the distinction between a proper self-confidence and "cheek," particularly in junior students, is not always to be made. The latter is met with chiefly among the student pilgrims who, in travelling down the Delectable Mountains, have gone astray and have passed to the left hand, where lieth the country of Conceit, the country in which you remember the brisk lad Ignorance met Christian.

I wish we could encourage on this continent among our best students the habit of wandering. I do not know that we are quite prepared for it, as there is still great diversity in the curricula, even among the leading schools, but it is undoubtedly a great advantage to study under different teachers, as the mental horizon is widened and the sympathies enlarged. The practice would do much to lessen that narrow "I am of Paul and I am of Apollos" spirit which is hostile to the best interests of the profession.

There is much that I would like to say on the question of work, but I can spare only a few moments for a word or two. Who will venture to settle upon so simple a matter as the best time for work? One will tell us there is no best time; all are equally good; and truly, all times are the same to a man whose soul is absorbed in some great problem. The other day I asked Edward Martin, the well-known story-writer, what time he found best for work. "Not in the evening, and never between meals!" was his answer, which may appeal to some of my hearers. One works best at night;

another, in the morning; a majority of the students of the past favour the latter. Erasmus, the great exemplar, says, "Never work at night; it dulls the brain and hurts the health." One day, going with George Ross through Bedlam, Dr. Savage, at that time the physician in charge, remarked upon two great groups of patients—those who were depressed in the morning and those who were cheerful, and he suggested that the spirits rose and fell with the bodily temperature—those with very low morning temperatures were depressed, and vice versa. This, I believe, expresses a truth which may explain the extraordinary difference in the habits of students in this matter of the time at which the best work can be done. Outside of the asylum there are also the two great types, the student-lark who loves to see the sun rise, who comes to breakfast with a cheerful morning face, never so "fit" as at 6 a.m. We all know the type. What a contrast to the student-owl with his saturnine morning face, thoroughly unhappy, cheated by the wretched breakfast bell of the two best hours of the day for sleep, no appetite, and permeated with an unspeakable hostility to his *vis-à-vis*, whose morning garrulity and good humour are equally offensive. Only gradually, as the day wears on and his temperature rises, does he become endurable to himself and to others. But see him really awake at 10 p.m. while our blithe lark is in hopeless coma over his books, from which it is hard to rouse him sufficiently to get his boots off for bed, our lean owl-friend, Saturn no longer in the ascendant, with bright eyes and cheery face, is ready for four hours of anything you wish—deep study, or

Heart affluence in discoursive talk,

and by 2 a.m. he will undertake to unsphere the spirit of Plato.

FINLEY PETER DUNNE

What I Larned in Colledge

FROM *Mr. Dooley's Philosophy*

Some of Frankenstein's feelings—though none of his misgivings—must have animated Finley Peter Dunne, creator of Mr. Dooley. Mr. Dooley was a national figure at the turn of the century—quite possibly the most widely quoted man in America at that time and certainly the most famous fictitious philosopher of the homely, homespun school. He had his witty and pointed say about anything and everything—education and colleges not excepted— in Dunne's circulation-boosting newspaper column which appeared in Chicago and New York papers.

IF ye had a boy wud ye sind him to colledge?" asked Mr. Hennessy.

"Well," said Mr. Dooley, "at th' age whin a boy is fit to be in colledge I wudden't have him around th' house."

The troubled Mr. Hennessy had been telling Mr. Dooley about the difficulty of making a choice of schools for Packy Hennessy, who at the age of six was at the point where the family must decide his career.

" 'Tis a big question," said Mr. Dooley, "an' wan that seems to be worryin' th' people more thin it used to whin ivry boy was designed f'r th' priesthood, with a full undherstandin' be his parents that th' chances was in favor iv a brick yard. Nowadays they talk about th' edycation iv th' child befure they choose th' name. 'Tis: 'Th' kid talks in his sleep. 'Tis th' fine lawyer he'll make.' Or, 'Did ye notice him admirin' that photygraph? He'll be a gr-reat journalist.' Or, 'Look at him fishin' in Uncle Tim's watch pocket. We must thrain him f'r a banker.' Or, 'I'm afraid he'll niver be sthrong enough to wurruk. He must go into th' church.' Befure he's baptized too, d'ye mind. 'Twill not be long befure th' time comes whin th' soggarth'll christen th' infant: 'Judge Pathrick Aloysius Hinnissy, iv th' Northern District iv Illinye,' or 'Profissor P. Aloysius

Hinnissy, LL.D., S.T.D., P.G.N., iv th' faculty iv Nothre Dame.' Th' innocent child in his cradle, wondherin' what ails th' mist iv him an' where he
got such funny lookin' parents fr'm, has thim to blame that brought him
into th' wurruld if he dayvilops into a sicond story man befure he's twinty-
wan an' is took up be th' polis. Why don't you lade Packy down to th'
occylist an' have him fitted with a pair iv eye-glasses? Why don't ye put
goloshes on him, give him a blue umbrelly an' call him a doctor at wanst
an' be done with it?

"To my mind, Hinnissy, we're wastin' too much time thinkin' iv th'
future iv our young, an' thryin' to larn thim early what they oughtn't to
know till they've growed up. We sind th' childher to school as if 'twas a
summer garden where they go to be amused instead iv a pinitinchry where
they're sint f'r th' original sin. Whin I was a la-ad I was put at me ah-bee
abs, th' first day I set fut in th' school behind th' hedge an' me head was sore
inside an' out befure I wint home. Now th' first thing we larn th' future
Mark Hannas an' Jawn D. Gateses iv our naytion is waltzin', singin', an'
cuttin' pitchers out iv a book. We'd be much betther teachin' thim th'
sthrangle hold, f'r that's what they need in life.

"I know what'll happen. Ye'll sind Packy to what th' Germans call a
Kindygartin, an' 'tis a good thing f'r Germany, because all a German knows
is what some wan tells him, an' his grajation papers is a certy-ficate that he
don't need to think annymore. But we've inthrajooced it into this counthry,
an' whin I was down seein' if I cud injooce Rafferty, th' Janitor iv th' Isaac
Muggs Grammar School, f'r to vote f'r Riordan—an' he's goin' to—I
dhropped in on Cassidy's daughter, Mary Ellen, an' see her kindygartnin.'
Th' childher was settin' ar-round on th' flure an' some was moldin' dachs-
hunds out iv mud an' wipin' their hands on their hair, an' some was carvin'
figures iv a goat out iv paste-board an' some was singin' an' some was sleepin'
an' a few was dancin' an' wan la-ad was pullin' another la-ad's hair. 'Why
don't ye take th' coal shovel to that little barbaryan, Mary Ellen?' says I.
'We don't believe in corporeal punishment,' says she. 'School shud be made
pleasant f'r th' childher," she says. 'Th' child who's hair is bein' pulled is
larnin' patience,' she says, 'an' th' child that's pullin' th' hair is discoverin'
th' footility iv human indeavor,' says she. 'Well, oh, well,' says I, 'times has
changed since I was a boy,' I says. 'Put thim through their exercises,' says I.
'Tommy,' says I, 'spell cat,' I says. 'Go to th' divvle,' says th' cheerub. 'Very
smartly answered,' says Mary Ellen. 'Ye shud not ask thim to spell,' she
says. 'They don't larn that till they get to colledge,' she says, 'an',' she says,
'sometimes not even thin,' she says. 'An' what do they larn?' says I.
'Rompin',' she says, 'an' dancin',' she says, 'an' indepindance iv speech, an'
beauty songs, an' sweet thoughts, an' how to make home home-like,' she
says. 'Well,' says I, 'I didn't take anny iv thim things at colledge, so ye needn't

unblanket thim,' I says. 'I won't put thim through anny exercise to-day,' I says. 'But whisper, Mary Ellen,' says I, 'Don't ye niver feel like bastin' th' seeraphims?' 'Th' teachin's iv Freebull and Pitzotly is conthrary to that,' she says. 'But I'm goin' to be marrid an' lave th' school on Choosdah, th' twinty-sicond iv Janooary,' she says, 'an' on Mondah, th' twinty-first, I'm goin' to ask a few iv th' little darlin's to th' house an',' she says, 'stew thim over a slow fire,' she says. Mary Ellen is not a German, Hinnissy.

"Well, afther they have larned in school what they ar-re licked f'r larnin' in th' back yard—that is squashin' mud with their hands—they're conducted up through a channel iv free an' beautiful thought till they're r-ready f'r colledge. Mamma packs a few doylies an' tidies into son's bag, an' some silver to be used in case iv throuble with th' landlord, an' th' la-ad throts off to th' siminary. If he's not sthrong enough to look f'r high honors as a middleweight pugilist he goes into th' thought departmint. Th' prisidint takes him into a Turkish room, gives him a cigareet an' says: 'Me dear boy, what special branch iv larnin' wud ye like to have studied f'r ye be our compitint profissors? We have a chair iv Beauty an' wan iv Puns an' wan iv Pothry on th' Changin' Hues iv th' Settin' Sun, an' wan on Platonic Love, an' wan on Nonsense Rhymes, an' wan on Sweet Thoughts, an' wan on How Green Grows th' Grass, an' wan on th' Relation iv Ice to th' Greek Idee iv God,' he says. 'This is all ye'll need to equip ye f'r th' perfect life, onless," he says, 'ye intind bein' a dintist, in which case,' he says, 'we won't think much iv ye, but we have a good school where ye can larn that disgraceful thrade,' he says. An' th' la-ad makes his choice, an' ivry mornin' whin he's up in time he takes a whiff iv hasheesh an' goes off to hear Profissor Maryanna tell him that 'if th' dates iv human knowledge must be rejicted as subjictive, how much more must they be subjicted as rejictive if, as I think, we keep our thoughts fixed upon th' inanity iv th' finite in comparison with th' onthinkable truth with th' ondivided an' onimaginable reality. Boys, ar-re ye with me?' . . ."

"I don't undherstand a wurrud iv what ye're sayin'," said Mr. Hennessy.

"No more do I," said Mr. Dooley. "But I believe 'tis as Father Kelly says: 'Childher shuddn't be sint to school to larn, but to larn how to larn. I don't care what ye larn thim so long as 'tis onpleasant to thim.' 'Tis thrainin' they need, Hinnissy. That's all. I niver cud make use iv what I larned in colledge about thrigojoomethry an'—an'—grammar an' th' welts I got on th' skull fr'm th' schoolmasther's cane I have niver been able to turn to anny account in th' business, but 'twas th' bein' there an' havin' to get things to heart without askin' th' meanin' iv thim an' goin' to school cold an' comin' home hungry, that made th' man iv me ye see befure ye."

"That's why th' good woman's throubled about Packy," said Hennessy.

"Go home," said Mr. Dooley.

The Boon of Culture

FROM *A Mencken Chrestomathy*

Few writers have had such a profound influence on the more liberal intellectual collegians of a generation than did Henry Louis Mencken in the '20s. His formidable, sometimes crudely guffawing attacks on sham, pretense and stuffy tradition won for him and for his American Mercury *a following whose devotion remained intact until his New Deal-baiting phase. Even then his spotty but wide-ranging erudition (abetted by intuitive and shrewd guesses) and his outrageously opinionated employment of it in writing on any subject that struck his fancy or abraded his nerves, earned him the continued loyalty of a hard-core coterie—and garnered him new devotees.*

Here he has some astringent comments to make about the state of American higher education.

EVERY American college president, it appears, is in duty bound to write and utter at least one book upon the nature, aims and usufructs of the Higher Education. That responsibility lies upon him as heavily as the obligation to edit at least one edition of "The Deserted Village" lies upon every professor of English. As a rule, he puts it off to his later Autumn days, when the hemlock of senility has begun to dull the edge of his troubles, but he seldom dodges it altogether. I have on my shelves a long row of such books, and I have read all of them in a respectful and hopeful spirit, for I may call myself, without vanity, a fan of learned men. But I must add in all honesty that I have yet to find, in any such tome, anything properly describable as wisdom.

What afflicts all of them—or, at all events, all of them that I have collected and read—is the assumption that the chief if not the only end of education is education. This, in the United States, is very far from true. Only a small minority of boys and girls go to college for the purpose of stuffing their heads with knowledge, whether real or false; the majority go there simply because it has come to be the prudent thing to do. What they get out of it is mainly what they will get, later on, out of joining country clubs, Rotary, the Nobles of the Mystic Shrine, and other such fraternities—a feeling that they have somehow plunged into the main current of correct American thought, that they have emerged from the undifferentiated mass and gained admittance into an organized and privileged class, that they have ceased to be nobodies and come to be somebodies.

The impulse to make this grade is not to be confused with mere social pushing, which may go on (and usually does) on much lower levels. Nor is it to be confused, on the other hand, with genuine intellectual aspiration. The basic motive is probably a desire for security rather than a yearning for superiority. The virtue of a college degree is that it shuts off the asking of certain kinds of questions, some of them embarrassing. It is a certificate of safety, both to the holder and to the nation in general. A graduate is one who has been trained to act according to a pattern that is publicly considered to be normal and trustworthy. When he gets his diploma he makes a change, not in mere station, but in status. It lifts him over a definite fence, and maketh him to lie down in greener pastures.

Perhaps all of this should have been put into the past tense instead of the present. The general confidence in "education" has greatly multiplied the candidates for it, and this multiplication has encouraged the proliferation of colleges. They spring up, in fact, in every third country town, and operating them becomes a kind of racket, carried on by all sorts of dubious persons, lay and clerical. They are even spattered over such barbaric States as Mississippi and North Dakota, where it would be dangerous to be educated in any real sense. The result is somewhat unhappy. The public belief that four years in college make a boy measurably more reliable, socially speaking, than he was before is still entertained, but it begins to be suspected that one college is not precisely like another. Thus there is a noticeable movement among the lesser ones to imitate, as closely as possible, the greater ones—first, by throwing off their theological obsessions (the real moving springs, in many cases, of their being), and secondly, by going in for gaudy Gothic buildings, and other such prodigalities.

But these gestures fool only the most naïve. Everyone who knows anything at all knows that a boy who has been through Harvard or Yale is apt to run far nearer to the American ideal than a boy who has been through, say, the Hardshell Baptist "University" of Smithville, Okla. He has been broken to an older, and hence to a better esteemed tradition, he has encountered more ornaments of it, and he has seen more impressive evidences of its value. No one knows this better than the graduate of the Hardshell seminary. It doesn't take him long to discover that what he sweated to attain was not quite attained, after all—that if he has escaped from the scullery he is not yet admitted to the first table in the hall. He is somewhat in the position of a conscript who went through all the pains of training, and then missed service at the front. Such a conscript is, of course, a war hero, but he is plainly a war hero of a lesser sort.

I suspect that a growing realization of all this is gradually filling the United States with inferiority complexes of a peculiarly malignant type. We are turning out thousands of college graduates who will have to go through life explaining and apologizing, which is precisely what college training among us is mainly designed to prevent. They have got the appearance without the essence. In fact, such one-legged collegians are already innumerable, for there have been bad colleges in the country since the earliest days. One cannot fail to observe their discomfort in the presence of graduates of the more tasty and reliable seminaries. They have, in many cases, far more actual education than the latter, but they lack the inner assurance; they are not so confident that sound American opinion respects and trusts them. Nor does it. It is a sad state of mind to be in.

If I had a son I should send him to Harvard, for more is to be had for the money there than anywhere else — more that is real, and will last. I don't think he'd learn more at Cambridge than he could learn at Siwash (given any desire to learn at all), but I believe a Harvard diploma would help him a great deal more in his later life, American ideas being what they are, whether God cast him for the rôle of metaphysician or for that of investment securities broker.

GERALD W. JOHNSON

Should Our Colleges Educate?

Gerald Johnson presents a somewhat unorthodox definition of what constitutes the educated man, suggesting that a student be required to prove he is fit to live among civilized people before he is awarded a degree.

Johnson, a biographer, historian and novelist, is professor of journalism at the University of North Carolina

MEMORIES of my own college days, observation from the outside of students in half a dozen other institutions, and direct contact with them as a faculty member in a representative American university lead me to the conviction that what the American college student needs—and what he gets—is not primarily education, but civilization.

Perhaps this should come to him in the classroom; but does it? Where are the excitement, the stress and strain, the triumphs and defeats, the thrills, joys, bitterness, and lingering memories—in short, the kick—in a man's college career? In the classroom? Sometimes, perhaps, but not in mine, my lords and gentlemen—as student and as teacher, assuredly not in mine. All the kick lay in what are well and unfavorably known as "student activities." For some it was found on the athletic field, for some in the debating halls, for others in the Glee Club, or the Debating Society, or the frat house, or the student publications, or the fascinating area of campus politics. The coach, not the professor, was the tyrannous but unchallenged master; and all the sad young men on the faculty observed with pain and agitation that students were coached so much and so incessantly that they hadn't time to acquire an education while in college.

But who created this condition? Why, the students, the lads who are putting up the time, the money, and the energy expended in going to college, aided and abetted by alumni, that is, men who have themselves been to college and ever since have been slowly and painfully acquiring an education.

Now, having been a college professor, I agree fervently with the dictum that a student has no sense. But neither has a bee, yet the hive is a marvel of organized efficiency. The fact that an individual student subordinates classroom work to other things means precisely nothing, but when half a million students do so it means a great deal. If American students as a class are going in for things not prescribed in the catalogue, the chances are that there is a flaw in the catalogue. The condition indicates that the things they need most are not in the catalogue.

And what, indeed, are these prescriptions? They are adaptations of the courses of study originated in European, especially English, universities. Basically, they represent the sort of thing required to educate the son of an English gentleman, that is to say, an Englishman who has inherited money. What it takes to make a scholar of an English gentleman's son, that the catalogue has. But it is applied to the education of the sons of American farmers, store-keepers, plumbers, policemen, and street-car conductors, who have not inherited money and have made enough to send their boys to college only by years of intense concentration on their jobs, to the exclusion of purely intellectual interests. Secondary education in every other country in the world—Revolutionary Russia perhaps excepted—has always been and is yet highly selective, restricted to an extremely small class. Only America has undertaken anything resembling mass education in the higher branches.

If America is making something of a mess of it, that need occasion no surprise. The first experiment along any line is likely to be messy. But for my part, I decline to believe that anything of the sort is happening, because I believe that the students are rescuing the colleges in the teeth of the deans, professors, pedagogical associations, and committees on academic standards. I think that the average American youth who goes to college gets something that he needs badly, in spite of the frantic efforts of the faculty to make him take something that he needs less.

There comes to mind the case of a boy who drifted into conversation with me one day after class. Theoretically, we were discussing some point in the day's work, but the talk shuffled around until the point was lost and the chap began to talk of what really interested him, namely the Glee Club. Then it developed that two years in the University had resulted in one complete alteration in his point of view. To that extent the University had functioned in this man's case, but it did not function in the classroom.

He had come to the campus with the desire to make the Glee Club; for in his native village he had been a member of a notable street-corner quartet and loved to sing. But when he attended the first rehearsal he was appalled, for the Glee Club was working on a program of old German chorales and medieval Latin hymns. He would have walked out in disgust but for the fact that the Glee Club was, after all, an organization of considerable social prestige. So he continued to hang around at rehearsals and at his seventeenth hearing of *Plorate, filii Israel* it struck him with the force of a sensational discovery that the tune had a kick in it! Then and there he was hooked, and into his subsequent successful effort to make the Glee Club he threw a passion, a fervor, a single-minded devotion that would have been good for an A-plus in the most difficult course open to freshmen.

As it was, he ended the term with more conditions than A's, and at the end of the year he squeezed into the sophomore class by a sickeningly narrow margin. He made the Glee Club easily, almost brilliantly, but deans shook their heads over his case, and instructors lamented the folly of a young man with an excellent mind who frittered away his time on outside interests, spending a year and a thousand of his father's dollars only to be left hanging on, so to speak, by his eyebrows.

But as he talked to me that afternoon my sympathy with the faculty point of view began to waver. I had hammered at him all the year, and the dint I had made in his consciousness could, perhaps, be detected with a micrometer but certainly not with the unaided eye. But he had been hammered into a new shape, all the same. Johann Sebastian Bach and Georg Friedrich Handel had been working on him, and he had paid attention to them, if not to me; and I decline to admit in public that I think him a fool for doing so. He had learned little Latin and less Greek. But he had learned that Palestrina is not the name of the Holy Land, and he had lost completely his former partiality for "The Red, Red Robin Comes a-Bob, Bob, Bob-bin'." He had learned that music is an expression of civilization which affords to the intelligent listener a dozen kinds of pleasure apart from the tickling of his ears with concord of sweet sounds. Hence life will hereafter be to him interesting and amusing in a dozen new ways. As he talked to me that afternoon, with all his conditions lowering over his head, he was years farther along the road to becoming a civilized man than he was when he had heard *Plorate, filii Israel* only sixteen times.

*   *   *

We may say he should have had all this before he came to college. A boy raised in a highly civilized home, the son of parents with leisure, money, and intelligence, does not have to learn appreciation of music in the Glee Club, or sportsmanship on the football field, or readiness in the debating society, or manners in the frat house. He may lack familiarity with the worlds of sports, art, politics and good society, but he is aware of their existence. He is in a position to appreciate and to begin assimilating the essence of civilization presented in the works of men of genius which are the material of classroom study.

But masses of college students come to-day from homes in which the arts and graces of civilization are at most matters of hearsay; and they are not educable until they have had some experience of the matters of which the masters treat in their books. Student activities, for all their inanity, are to a certain extent a simulacrum of the world of the intellect, and participation in the affairs of this small world prepares the student for assimilation of information touching the great one.

It is unfortunately true that this preparation is not absolutely essential to the reception and retention of information, but only to its assimilation. The colleges are so perniciously efficient that they not infrequently graduate men without first civilizing them. These fill the world and, what is worse, college faculties with doctors of philosophy who are no more educated men than are so many Tennessee legislators, although they are stuffed with fantastic and perfectly useless knowledge.

There is probably nothing that can be done about this, or, rather, nothing that will be done about it. In view of our present mania for education mere advocacy of the abolition of a degree is something less than respectable. But to advocate the raising of standards is another thing. Why not raise the requirements of the Ph.D. by adding to the present examinations one or two designed to prove that the candidate is fit to live among civilized people? It should be simple enough. All that is necessary to clear him of the suspicion of monomania is to make sure that he knows something and can do something not related to his major, and unlikely in any conceivable circumstances to assist him in his career as a teacher.

As touching knowledge, he might be required, for example, to identify the finale of the César Franck sonata for piano and violin played on a talking machine, or name the winners of the Kentucky derby for the last five years, or translate the cryptogram ABRHPOAE, or tell what three up and two to go means, or distinguish between the Widow Clicquot and the Widow of Windsor. As a test of virtuosity he might be given his choice among dancing the Black Bottom acceptably, driving not less than one hundred and twenty-five yards, walking a six-inch plank with five cocktails aboard, putting three place-kicks out of seven across the bar, or supporting a busted flush so impressively as to cause someone to throw down a pair of tens.

If some such procedure were adopted, the total acreage of Ph.D.'s would be reduced, to be sure, but the value of the remaining crop would rise so sharply that the result would be a net gain. It would make it impossible for a man to be called educated until he had first been at least partially civilized.

The American undergraduate has not known this, but he has felt it, dimly and vaguely. Somehow he is aware that when he comes to college he is not educable, and he casts around desperately for something to make him so.

In student activities he discovers a makeshift. It is unfortunately true that by the time he becomes mentally adult, and, therefore, fit to receive an education, his college days are so nearly over that he has not time to be educated before a diploma is thrust upon him and he is thrust out.

But does it follow that he has thrown away four years and anything from four to ten thousand dollars? I presume to doubt it. It is true that he is likely to spend from fifteen to fifty subsequent years snatching up odds and ends of knowledge that he would have received in school had he been able to assimilate it. But what of that? It amuses him and keeps him mentally fit; and the college did civilize him to the point at which he could assimilate information.

The man who thinks that American undergraduates are as a whole wasting a considerable proportion of their time and money simply has not lately come into intimate contact with college men. By chance I have had opportunity to compare collegians with young Americans selectively drafted into the Army. The best infantry regiment in the service might have the physical advantage over two thousand undergraduates taken at random, but beyond that the soldiers would have no show. And the physical superiority would not be great.

And so, in spite of the clamor of deans and committees on academic standards, I am at ease in Zion. The boys are all right. They are frivolous and light-minded. They are indolent in the classroom. They make perfect idiots of themselves over football and other imbecile contests. They pay the head coach twice as much money and ten times as much honor as they pay the college president because, being realists, they know the coach is worth the difference. They come out of college woefully ignorant of books. But they get their money's worth, because they come out much more apt than they were when they went in to live like civilized men, and much less apt to join the Ku Klux Klan.

I wish, indeed, that I were quite sure that my days are as profitably employed as theirs.

WESTON LaBARRE

Totemistic Celebrations

FROM *The New York Times Magazine*

After studying the Usans (United States of Americans to those unfamiliar with anthropological abbreviations) in their native habitat, Professor Widjojo of Nyabonga University returns to lecture on such totemistic ceremonies as "futbol," the "koktel" ritual, and other such customs of this primitive people.

Weston LaBarre, who reports on the proceedings, is something of an authority on Usan customs himself. He is associate professor of anthropology at Duke University and author of The Human Animal, *in which category he includes the Usans among others.*

O F COURSE," mused Professor Widjojo, the eminent anthropologist of the University of Nyabonga, "the natives of the U. S. A. have many strange and outlandish customs; but I must say the drinking rituals of the Usans impressed me most. These rituals occur yearly during an extended period in the calendrical round, beginning at the time of the harvest rites of Thanks-for-Blessings and ending largely at the drinking bouts at the New Year. This is called The Season, after which those who can afford it usually leave their homes entirely and flee southward into retirement for recuperation."

"Rather like our Nyabongan puberty ordeals?" asked a brilliantly dark matron dressed in a handsome apron of tiki feathers and little else.

"Well, no, not exactly," said Professor Widjojo, fingering his nose-stick politely before replying. "Perhaps I could describe it best by telling you of the Usan *koktel parti*, as they call it. You know, of course, that the Usan women, despite their rigid tribal clothing taboos, in general take off more clothes at their gatherings, depending upon the time of day. The neckline drops more and more, both in front and in back, as the *parti* is held later and later in the evening. They are entirely covered in the daytime, but this

night-time disrobing is considered to be more formal. At the same time the
length of the skirt increases, until it reaches the ground or even drags on it.

"On the other hand, men put on more and more clothes as the formality
of the occasion increases. The interesting point, however, is that the men,
at *koktel partis,* do not ordinarily wear the beetle coats and white cloth
neck-chokers of their most formal rituals, but dress rather more moderately,
as for church; furthermore, the women keep their hats on at *koktel partis,*
thus clearly establishing the ritual significance of these *koktel partis.* . . .

"But I am getting ahead of my chronology. Really, the drinking season
of the Usans begins in the fall of the year, after a wholesome summer vacation, at the time of the *futbol* games. The purpose of the Usan colleges is
to collect young men by competitive subsidies to engage in these mock
battles, during which they rush ferociously at one another wearing padded
armor and ritually kill one another. It seems to be some sort of contest over
a sacred pigskin, and everyone gets up alive after each act in the ceremony.
Rarely is a young man killed. However, the warriors are often 'punch-
drunk' (an odd phrase because they are not allowed to drink, in contrast
with spectators) and they may suffer broken legs, or faces mutilated by the
nailed shoes of their opponents.

"Colleges seem once to have been trade schools where tribal lore was
taught, but this was long ago and is now hardly remembered. The importance of a college nowadays is rated by the number of *futbol* games its team
wins, and this in turn attracts further desirable young warriors to that
college. The watchers urge on the warriors with blood-curdling chants, and
between acts there are military maneuvers of a more rigorous form than in
the battle itself. Afterward, they either celebrate their victory or 'drown
their sorrows' in mourning if their warriors have sustained too many broken
bones to win.

"These *futbol* ceremonies seem to be totemistic celebrations mainly, for
each side has an animal totem—such as a bulldog, a tiger or a goat—
which symbolizes the mystical unity of each side in their oddly named *alma
mater,* or 'protective mother,' probably so called because she is the patron
mother goddess of the young warriors frequently invoked in the battle
hymns at these war games. Strangely, however, these totems do not govern
marriage rules either inside or outside the *alma mater* group. I collected
figures on this critical matter and found it is about as common to marry
outside one's totem as within. In fact, *futbol* games are a recognized way
to meet young people belonging to another totem."

"Are there totems governing marriage in the *koktel* gatherings you
mentioned earlier?" asked a young girl just past her puberty ceremonial.

"No, I would think not," replied Professor Widjojo, thoughtfully. "On
the contrary, the *koktel parti* more resembles a primitive orgy, with no

reference to marriage bonds whatever. You see, as a point of etiquette husbands and wives do not remain near one another at *koktel partis,* but circulate around making conquests." . . .

"Are these *koktel partis* always orgies?" inquired a plump, middle-aged Nyabongan man.

"Not entirely, perhaps," replied Professor Widjojo. "There is one which is called a *literari koktel,* the ostensible reason for which is to celebrate the birth of a new book. Naturally, no one ever discusses the book being celebrated, since no one has read it, although everybody expresses a readiness to analyze it critically." . . .

"Strange people, these Usan natives," said the fat, middle-aged Nyabongan.

"That they are, that they are!" echoed Professor Widjojo, touching his nose-stick thoughtfully.

Ivy Superiority

FROM *Holiday Magazine*

Henry Morton Robinson, in this selection, gives us the lowdown on the Ivy League system and what made it that way—together with some interesting and pertinent observations regarding tradition as it relates to the defense of academic freedom. Mr. Robinson is an Ivy League product himself: Columbia '23. His writings range from a key to James Joyce's Finnegan's Wake, *to the best-selling novel,* The Cardinal.

GOLD and precious stones couldn't induce me to speak slightingly of Amherst, Bowdoin, Colgate or a whole alphabet of liberal-arts colleges that turn out splendid facsimiles of the Ivy League product. I stand in awe and ignorance before the standards and accomplishments of the great technical schools like M.I.T. and California Tech. Nor can I bring myself to say truly uncharitable things about those educational rabbit warrens known as State Universities, whose inmates, I hear from reliable sources, gradually learn the use of commas and can be trained to perform simple feats of logic connected with chain-store management, ethical embalming and other disciplines much revered by the American demos. All of which—in a society that exalts the drum majorette above Minerva—should be regarded, I suppose, as sheer gain, "a triumph of mind over smatter" as Irwin Edman used to say.

Regrettably, however, these folkish activities have nothing to do with education as conceived by the eight eastern colleges that make up what is known as the Ivy League. Despite leveling influences that would "democratize" the B. A. degree—that is, bring it down to the level of a vaccination certificate—the Ivy colleges cling to the somewhat mystical notion that a candidate for the 800-year-old degree of *Baccalaurei in Artibus* shall be, among other thing, a person of marked intellectual promise. They hold further that he shall be capable of achieving a rigorous kind of excellence, not limited to the mind, manners—or even muscles—but penetrating into the very marrow and matrix of life itself. Dean McGeorge Bundy of Harvard states the case for all the Ivy League colleges when he says: "Harvard exists for the student who wants to become a liberally educated man. It is not the place for a person who is interested only in preparing as fast as possible for business or a specialized occupation such as agriculture, journalism, or accounting. It is a college for those who feel the need for a broad development of their powers, for a greater understanding of their world, and for an enriched cultural life."

These patrician ideas sometimes baffle, irk, and infuriate the denizens of Outer Mediocrity. But that's the Ivy League system, men, and if you want a glimpse of the system in action, read on.

Gossip, that malicious crone who gets about on the Canard Line, tells her listeners that the Ivy League is a self-esteeming coterie of eight eastern colleges bound together by secret covenants inscribed on tablets of bronze. The arithmetic here is fine. There are indeed eight colleges in the Ivy group: Harvard, Yale, Columbia, Princeton, Dartmouth, Brown, the University of Pennsylvania and—in Cornell man Morris Bishop's plaintive phrase—"perhaps Cornell." Intensive digging has failed to turn up any bronze tablets; and the only existing covenant, secret or otherwise, is an athletic code designed to keep football players simon pure on the gridiron and wide awake in the classroom.

Despite basic similarities (which I'll describe later) it would be a mistake to suppose that Ivy League colleges or the men they produce are cut from the same bolt of cloth. There's a woof of difference between Hanover flannel and Nassau tweed. The tailoring differs too: Columbia's metropolitan drape is distinguishable at a glance from Brown's more parochial cut. Before this *Sartor Resartus* metaphor gets out of control, let me wind it up with the moral tale of the necktie maker who tried to popularize an Ivy League tie. His basic premises were sound enough: there is always a brisk demand for old-school ties, and the Ivy colleges are certainly old. Therefore (reasoned the necktie maker) a terrific market awaited the four-in-hand item he had in mind. But here he fell flat on his Ascot, and deservedly went broke. Like a lot of other people, he failed to realize that it would be easier to design a single plaid for all the kilts in Scotland than unite Ivy League clans under the aegis of a standardized cravat.

What then, *is* the tie that binds these colleges in common cause against the barbarian? Personal observation leads me to believe that they all suffer from an identical form of paranoia. They imagine, each and severally, that they are the special custodians of a sweet, sharp, salty, priceless and quite generally neglected tradition of humane learning that antedates the pneumatic tire by many years. History supports this stewardly illusion, which began to take shape shortly after the incident at Plymouth Rock. When Chicago was "a place of wild onions" (that's what it means in Ojibway), the Harvard elm had been sheltering scholarship for more than two hundred years. While the natives of Detroit were trading bearskins with the aborigines, sheepskins embossed with classical Latin were being handed out at Yale (1702), Columbia (1754), Pennsylvania (1755), and Dartmouth (1759). In these tiny colonial seedbeds a few scholars starved and struggled to keep alive a corpus of learning that might otherwise have perished. Whole centuries had to pass before this culture could be transplanted to regions west of Harvard Square. Exactly what happened to it after crossing the Alleghenies is still a matter of conjecture. All we know for certain is that when a young man wants a superlative education, he usually comes East to get it.

Personally I wouldn't enjoy serving on any admissions board that screens Ivy League candidates. This task of selection becomes, as Dean Chamberlain of Columbia says, "increasingly formidable every year." The statistics alone are frightening: of the 400,000 male students who will besiege the nation's academic gates this fall, Ivy League colleges have room for only 7,500—or less than two per cent. There's no difficulty in choosing the obviously superior applicant, the standout who would make a welcome addition to any freshman class. The real agony occurs when a director of admissions must make a decision involving four or five candidates of nearly equal merit. Let's suppose that they have all passed their aptitude and achievement tests with excellent marks. Their geographic, racial and religious distribution (all very important) follow the prescribed graph, and searching personal interviews disclose in each case a youngster of high potential promise. Glowing letters of recommendation from secondary-school headmasters testify to their character, qualities of leadership and past performance. It's an agonizing business, but when the ordeal of sifting, weighing and comparing is over, three or four boys must be turned down in favor of the lucky candidate who is accepted.

This heartbreaking process, accepted in the past as part and parcel of Ivy practice, is now undergoing severe scrutiny by its own people. President Dodds of Princeton admits, with his customary candor, that he is finding it harder each year to justify "the exclusion of many qualified students who seek the kind of educational experience we offer." A possible remedy, he suggests, lies in a program of expansion that will accommodate "a more sizable number of students." But Dodds and other Ivy League educators fear that such expansion will entail the "real risk of a deteriorating scholastic performance." It's this frank insistence on academic *quality*—as opposed to assembly-line production—that exposes Ivy League deans, dons, and directors of admissions to charges of snobbery and elitism.

If there's one thing that Americans won't tolerate, it's an intellectual aristocracy. Why this intolerance should be so widespread and virulent is beyond my comprehension. Judging from Army intelligence tests and the entrance requirements in effect at most State universities, I see no immediate danger of a sudden cultural uprising in this country. But the unanointed majority seems to think otherwise. Hence the popular demand that a college education should be made "more democratic"—i.e., reduced to the level of a television quiz program. Some months ago Professor Douglas Bush of Harvard caused quite a flurry by taking issue with this shoddy concept of higher education. In a *New York Times* article entitled *Education for All Is Education for None*, Professor Bush made the delicate point that higher learning for masses—however fine as a political theory—was a shocking failure in actual practice. Herd culture, said Bush, was threatening the existence of whatever intellectual enlightenment we possess.

Dozens of professorlings west of the Monongahela took pen in hand to defend *lower* educational standards as the main prop of democracy. "Equal opportunity for all" they cried, then proceeded to belabor Professor Bush as a "Piltdown pedagogue," "a champion of elitism" and, naturally, an "intellectual snob."

Come now, gentlemen, can such abuse be justified? No one accuses Casey Stengel of being snobbish when he refuses to clutter up his Yankee infield with stumblebums. And would anyone dream of calling Terry Brennan "undemocratic" because he selects an elite of brawn for his Notre Dame squad? I suggest that the exponents of cut-rate college standards are holding the wrong end of the stick. Keen competition and emphasis on proficiency are, and always have been, the only guarantees of superiority in Big League baseball, Big Ten football, or Ivy League education. Candidates for admission to Harvard, Yale, Princeton, Columbia and the others are strictly out of bounds if they claim exemption from the competitive struggle that goes relentlessly forward in every other phase of our national life.

Nor do the men who guide these institutions of higher learning need any tutoring in the subject of democracy. They know from experience that the best cider is made from a mixed crush of apples, and they rejoice accordingly when they discover a pippin from Hayfork High School, North Padlock Prep, or anyplace else that will add a regional flavor to the Groton-Lawrenceville-Andover mixture. Nor do these orchard keepers wait for the product to drop in their laps; they assist its discovery and growth with scores of regional scholarships and quick encouragement to *all* prospective students of real quality.

One week after a freshman enters an Ivy League college he wishes that he had enrolled at Abilene Christian, Muhlenberg, Yankton, or some other place where the going isn't so rough. For the first few months he feels like a man standing under an avalanche. The required reading ranges from 300 to 400 pages a day—every day—and not random gulpings or dilettante pap, either. Although Ivy League curricula differ widely, both in emphasis and subject matter, the basic materials are as carefully selected and integrated as the works of an expensive watch. Take, for example, the famous Contemporary Civilization courses at Columbia—a "must" for every underclassman. The CC course is a two-year survey of man's ascent from anthropoid simplicity to his present state of H-bomb dismay. The better to understand this triumphal progress, CC students are required to march at the rate of twenty parasangs a day (Xenophon did it) across a mountainous terrain of history, literature, science and philosophy. When I first took the course in 1920 it seemed inconceivable that any freshman should ever survive its rigors. Yet when my son took the same course in 1950 it had become, after a dozen revisions, immeasurably more difficult and comprehensive.

As one of the oldest living survivors of the CC wars, I can assure you this course alone will forever guard a man against the short view and the terror of dark places. Having seen twenty-two previous civilizations rise and fall, the CC veteran is able to set day-to-day events in a fairly sound frame of reference. The world doesn't fall apart when his football team takes a 59-6 trouncing from Army. *"Vive le sport!"* he exclaims, and goes about the business of living.

Whether in CC or the General Studies program at Harvard, the classes are small (usually fifteen students to one instructor), the tempo of the discussion is brisk, and there is no infallible side of the desk. On the other hand, there's no escape from the instructor's probing questions, and damned little leniency anywhere. But now an amazing thing happens;— *only two per cent of students are flunked out!* Quite a contrast to the forty per cent of first-year failures in State colleges. Here is where the Ivy League policy of careful selection pays dividends to the students. Ninety per cent of the entering class will go on—with the aid of alert and sympathetic faculty advisors—to take the cherished degree of B.A. No, "take" isn't the word. They'll *earn* it, and not all the frustrations and compromises of later life will have any power to tarnish the prize they've won.

At this point I must pause to consider the possible effect of my remarks upon the loyal sons of Turpentine Tech and Moline Subnormal. Experience warns me that these gentlemen will spray some mean letters in my direction. Here's how a couple of them will run: "Your article was mighty saddening to one like me who missed schooling in the Ivy League. I almost cried out loud while driving my Cadillac to the bank." And: "Happened to read your article while waiting for a shave at our local tonsoreal parlor. You make a lot of fancy statements about the supierority of the Ivy Leage but you don't back them up with concrete proofs."

I had hoped to avoid this embarrassing matter of "concrete proofs" because it may suggest a purse-proud emphasis on handsome architecture and huge endowments. It would be absurd, of course, to speak of any college as wealthy; the Augustan era of great benefactors—Harkness, Flagler and Baker—is forever fled, and all privately endowed colleges are relatively poor. But in the matter of material resources the Ivy League colleges have been comparatively fortunate. Harvard has an endowment of $213,000,000; Yale $147,000,000; and Columbia $113,000,000. Princeton struggles along with $59,000,000; while Dartmouth and Brown must make ends meet with $32,000,000 and $17,000,000 respectively. By contrast, consider the financial plight of Guilford (N.C.) with an endowment of slightly over $1,000,000. But even Guilford is relatively affluent; of the two thousand senior colleges in the United States, eighteen hundred are obliged to count their blessings in nickels and dimes.

The Ivy colleges, with resources totaling $700,000,000, attract the best teachers and maintain huge libraries and superb physical plants. Viewed merely as pieces of real estate, Harvard, Yale, Columbia and Princeton are, each in its own way, eye-satisfying developments—handsome academic landscapes fitted with accessories that don't come cheaply. Small wonder that the visitor from Turpentine Tech hugs the illusion (shared by many uninformed persons) that the Ivy League colleges are tenanted solely by sons of millionaires.

The actual facts reveal that nearly half of all Ivy League undergraduates either hold part-time jobs or receive financial aid through loans and scholarships. With such assistance to offer young men who can meet the rugged entrance requirements, the Ivy group exercises a virtual monopoly over the top ten per cent of secondary-school graduates. How could it be otherwise? Would any brilliant young man voluntarily exile himself to a four-year term at Wofford or Idaho State, if he could win a scholarship at Dartmouth or Cornell? Anyone seeking a reason for Ivy League superiority will find part of his answer in the quality of scholarship students recruited from the nation's most promising material.

Among the special advantages of an Ivy League education is the unpurchasable element of academic freedom. This freedom has two major aspects: it protects the institution itself against outside interference or control, and defends in fiercely militant fashion the scholar's traditional right to free inquiry and independent expression. The first of these freedoms is based in this country on the famous Dartmouth College case argued by Daniel Webster before the Supreme Court in 1818. Two years previously, the New Hampshire State legislature had voted to change the name of the college, seize its physical plant and appoint a new board of trustees. Webster, a loyal Dartmouth alumnus as well as the greatest constitutional lawyer of his time, fought these intrusions all the way up to the Supreme Court. In his summation before that august body, Webster pointed out that if state legislatures, or any other pressure group, could tinker with a college charter, higher learning in the United States would be at the mercy of cranks and meddlers of every description.

The Supreme Court agreed and handed down the historic decision that guarantees the inviolability of charters of private colleges. Today, no outside group or individual—however powerful or well-meaning—can dictate policy to an Ivy League president or board of trustees. It would be easier, I think, to blast the hinges off Fort Knox than to bully Grayson Kirk of Columbia, Henry Wriston of Brown or their opposite numbers at Yale, Princeton, Dartmouth and the other Ivy League colleges. These men believe that their contract with society obliges them to resist—on moral, intellectual and constitutional grounds—any invasion of the university's right to manage its internal affairs.

This position was grimly tested during the recent showdown between Harvard's President Pusey and Sen. Joseph McCarthy. Late in 1953, McCarthy discovered that a former Communist, Associate Professor Wendell H. Furry, was teaching physics at Harvard. At one point in his testimony before the McCarthy Committee, Furry pleaded the Fifth Amendment, although he had long since broken with communism and had made his position clear both to his colleagues and the Harvard Corporation. But this intramural settlement of the affair didn't satisfy McCarthy. Various interpretations were read into his subsequent actions. Possibly the senator —an alumnus of Marquette University—simply wanted to make certain that a sister university was not being gulled by the two-talk tactics so often used by Communists. Perhaps he was being solicitous about Harvard's apparent refusal to abolish the Fifth Amendment. And perhaps he had forgotten or never heard of the Dartmouth College case. In any event, on November 6, 1953, he sent a telegram to President Pusey. At one point in the telegram, he said:

I WOULD LIKE TO KNOW WHAT IF ANY ACTION THE UNIVERSITY INTENDS TO TAKE IN FURRY'S CASE AND WHAT YOUR ATTITUDE GENERALLY IS TOWARD RETAINING TEACHERS AT HARVARD WHO REFUSE TO STATE WHETHER THEY ARE COMMUNISTS ON THE GROUNDS THAT THE TRUTH WOULD TEND TO INCRIMINATE THEM. . . . I AM SURE (your answer) WILL INTEREST THE MOTHERS AND FATHERS WHOSE SONS AND DAUGHTERS ARE BEING TAUGHT BY FURRY. . . .

Catching the old-grad spirit of the thing, Pusey wired back that everything was under control at Cambridge, that Harvard had conducted its own research into Furry's background and was content that Furry was not a spy nor presently a Communist and that he had not attempted to indoctrinate his students. His telegram contained some simple sentences indicating Harvard's awareness that academic and personal freedom are rather more difficult and important matters than the senator seemed to think them:

> HARVARD IS UNALTERABLY OPPOSED TO COMMUNISM. IT IS DEDICATED TO FREE INQUIRY BY FREE MEN . . . WE DEPLORE THE USE OF THE FIFTH AMENDMENT (Note: Shortly after this, Furry waived reliance on the Fifth Amendment) . . . BUT DO NOT REGARD THE USE OF THIS CONSTITUTIONAL SAFEGUARD AS A CONFESSION OF GUILT.

Now deeply hurt by Harvard's lack of concern about her own safety and its fusty old attitude toward the Constitution, McCarthy trumpeted *all* American parents to alertness:

> YOU AND THE HARVARD CORPORATION CAN OF COURSE CONTINUE TO KEEP FIFTH AMENDMENT COMMUNISTS TEACHING THE SONS AND DAUGHTERS OF AMERICA. HOWEVER HARVARD WILL LEARN HOW REPREHENSIBLE AND UN-AMERICAN THE MOTHERS AND FATHERS OF AMERICA CONSIDER THIS ATTITUDE . . .

Something, at this point, had to give way—and it wasn't Pusey. At a time when Pentagon brass was shivering like the tin jingles on a gypsy's tambourine, Pusey neither ducked nor cowered. Quickly he repeated the gist of his first telegram. " . . . I am content," he finished coolly, "to stand on Harvard's record . . ."

At this writing, Harvard's record still stands intact. Wendell H. Furry still holds his billet in the Physics Department. The mothers and fathers of America confidently continue to pack their sons off to Cambridge, and everyone—including Marquette's distinguished alumnus—seems to have caught Pusey's point, i.e.: that a teacher's freedom is his own, and that Harvard is quite able to run its own show and, in fact, insists upon doing so.

It would be fatuous to claim that academic freedom was invented—or is now monopolized—by Ivy League colleges. It is as old as Salamanca or Göttingen; theoretically it is the animating principle of colleges everywhere. Yet one of the tragedies of our time is the reluctance of many scholars to assert their hereditary independence of thought and speech. This timidity is understandable, perhaps most of all in those "denominational" schools whose faculty members are expected to sneeze in unison whenever the prebendary takes snuff. And one can almost sympathize with the plight of teachers in state universities where county politicians "vote the school money." Caution is the watchword in such places; any departure from orthodoxy—in curriculum, teaching methods, published findings, even in personal reading matter—may cost a man his job.

The Ivy League scholar is happily exempt from these frightening pressures. He speaks out and fears no one. He knows, moreover, that his president and board of trustees will back him up—even though they may not agree with his opinions. Such was the case when the late Prof. Charles A. Beard of Columbia published his epochal paper *The Economic Interpretation of the U. S. Constitution*. Screams of anguish arose from a press and public shocked by Beard's thesis that motives of personal profit (rather than twenty-four-carat idealism) had swayed our Founding Fathers. For a time, Beard's name was anathema; jingo patriots demanded his head on a platter. And what happened? President Butler of Columbia (a very staid gentleman who didn't particularly like Beard or his teachings) yielded not one sixteenth of an inch in defending the historian's right to state the facts as he saw them. Butler knew, as every college president knows, that a scholar's findings may be challenged or refuted—but if they are suppressed, the spirit of free inquiry dies, and the university becomes a darkened temple, the haunt of stuffed owls. So Beard kept his job, and lived to see his "economic interpretation" accepted by scholars everywhere.

The atmosphere of intellectual courage that prevails at Ivy colleges is the breath of life to the student body. Socially and politically, Ivy League men can be fairly described as liberals. Unlike their brethren at European universities, they aren't given to rioting in the public squares (except in celebration of springtime and youth) and I can't conceive of a Hasty Pudding man hurling cobblestones, or even loud epithets, at the existing government. Their independence takes the subtler form of making intelligent decisions as to what they shall think, say and do as responsible individuals. Naturally a great deal of whey has to be squeezed out of them in the process, but the final result is fairly close to the ideal that Andrew White, co-founder of Cornell, had in mind when he said: "I propose to raise up a generation of students who will disagree with me, and I propose further to give them very poor marks if they don't."

Ivy League students sometimes find it hard to disagree with their teachers—not because the students lack courage, but because (and this is difficult for authoritarian minds to grasp) Ivy League teachers seldom take a dogmatic stand. Columbia's Mark Van Doren, for instance, probably knows as much about Shakespeare as any man living, but he declines to pontificate on the subject. Students who expect to hear ultimate certainties in his classes had better take themselves off to another shop. Van Doren would probably admit that his philosophy of suspended judgment stems from Montaigne's *"Que sais-je?"*— a question that underlies all Ivy

League thinking. Teachers and students alike realize that the door must be kept open for further evidence and that this constant search for fresh evidence is the true goal of education.

It has always seemed strange to me that this quest for the ever evolving, many-faceted thing called truth should be regarded in some quarters as an undesirable activity. I was particularly disturbed by an incident that occurred last year at West Point. The U. S. Military Academy debating team was preparing to meet all comers on the question—then being mooted in Ivy League circles as elsewhere—*Resolved: that Red China shall be recognized by the U.N.* On the eve of battle, so to speak, the West Point debaters received orders from G.H.Q. to suspend "Operation Think." Evidently the high command feared that it was unwise—*unsafe* perhaps— for future generations to delve into the pros and cons of a problem that must eventually be faced and decided by everyone. No such fears faced the debaters from Brown. A naughty humor inspired them to send the following telegram to the West Pointers:

> SINCE YOU'RE NOT ALLOWED TO DEBATE THE QUESTION OF RED CHINA'S RECOG-
> NITION, WE CHALLENGE YOU TO DEBATE THE REASONS WHY YOU'RE NOT AL-
> LOWED TO DEBATE IT.

Now do you understand why I bless the liberal breeze that blow through Ivy League halls?

Contrast this refreshing atmosphere with the smog that hangs over many state universities, where legislative committees are forever prying into textbooks in search of an unorthodox paragraph. In these shadow zones of culture, luckless chancellors can be twitched onto the carpet by veterans' groups of self-appointed censors and inquisitors.

More terrifying yet are the laws that require many state universities to accept all comers who have completed high school with a C average. A secret form of revenge is practiced by outraged teachers. Forty per cent of the entering class is flunked out during the freshman year to make room for the galloping herd of new arrivals. Meanwhile the democratic illusion has been preserved. Everyone can say that he or she has gone to State U. The heart of the country is sound, though the brain may be as hollow as the bass drum at a Cotton Bowl game.

There remain to be considered a few small, privately endowed colleges of good fame and modest resources—I think of Hamilton, Haverford, Beloit, DePauw and the members of the "Little Ivy League"—which play an important role in the scheme of higher education. I readily admit the advantages enjoyed by members of these provincial academies. But, in my opinion, these advantages are outweighed by definite limitations, perhaps not noticeable during the first two years. Many small college ade-

"Elizabeth Conner McMeekin, '15?"   *Drawing by Helen E. Hokinson*

"Present. After graduation, I started to take an M.A. at Teachers College, but gave it up to marry Roy McMeekin, Cornell, '12. My husband was only a plant engineer with the telephone company at the time and had not yet become an executive. We lived in Columbus, Ohio, until 1927, when Mr. McMeekin was called to New York, and we built a home in Westchester. I have two children, a girl, Elsie, aged nineteen, and a boy, Donald, aged seventeen. I want to say that I think this Alpha Delta Alpha alumnae picnic is a wonderful idea and that Penny Trowbridge should be congratulated on getting it up. I hope we can get together next summer and repeat it with all the same people."   © *1943 The New Yorker Magazine, Inc.*

"The student body's counting on you, the alumni's counting on you, I'm counting on you, and tomorrow I want you to go into that examination room and *pass!*"

Drawing by Richard Decker

© 1951 The New Yorker Magazine, Inc.

"I must show you the room I had when I was in college."

From Vassar: A Second Glance © 1942 Anne Cleveland and Jean Anderson. Published by Vassar Cooperative Bookshop

"Let's go up to Union Square and hear somebody who has something to say."

Drawing by Garrett Price © 1932 The New Yorker Magazine, Inc.

Going to the Race

Intercollegiate Football—"Down!"

West Point Cadet made prisoner and "despoiled" on "Flirtation Walk" by a group of girls who wanted "trophies."

Party at Yale

Match between Harvard Sophomores

Freshmen

Sophomores

and Freshmen (1857)

Juniors

Seniors

WINSLOW HOMER   *Culver*

New York City Medical College for Women (1870)

Bettman

Chem lab at M.I.T. (1860)

Culver

quately satisfy the intellectual hunger of freshmen and sophomores. But all too often, symptoms of scholastic malnutrition begin to appear among the upperclassmen. The undeniable fact is that the superior student at a small college eventually becomes bored by the monotony and limitations of his environment.

This slow starvation can't possibly happen to an Ivy League upperclassman. These colleges are part of a university, which by definition is a seat of advanced study and learning. The resources of graduate faculties, tremendous libraries and distinguished scholars are at the undergraduate's command. He may, at will, wade into the unplumbed area of learning that surrounds him. Ivy League educators seem uniquely aware of the upperclassman's need to venture forth on his own, and have made special provisions for his benefit. Columbia, for example, has instituted a whole new Upper College program designed to challenge the maturing energy of students who might otherwise drift lazily through the junior and senior years.

The second advantage is one often overlooked: the proximity of most Ivy colleges to large cities. Old Ben Franklin observed that large cities were the natural habitat of inquiring minds. As Ivy League men can testify, Poor Richard never said a wiser thing in his life. If bored in Cambridge, Harvard students can ferry themselves across the placid Charles River to the Parker House, Locke-Obers or Scollay Square. Jaded brain cells can be recharged at the Sheraton-Plaza, the Old Howard or Vincent Club affairs, or even at a Beacon Hill dinner table. The only drawback from the Harvard point of view is the danger of running into husky skiers down from Dartmouth, or quick Brown foxes just up from Providence. Weekends, in the Ivy League, can be as educational (in the largest sense) as any weekday lectures.

Southbound trains from New Haven debouch hourly into Grand Central, carrying the spiritual descendants of Dink Stover, Frank Merriwell and Lucius Beebe. Merely by crossing Vanderbilt Avenue they reach the Yale club, take a quick shower, and after consulting little black books, disperse in quest of the finer things that New York offers in abundance. It begins to appear, however, that these junkets are due for serious curtailment. Yale's Committee on General Education, headed by Pres. A. Whitney Griswold, now proposes to stiffen undergraduate courses of study at the expense of athletics, extracurricular activities, and the three-day weekend—which according to the committee, "involve serious conflicts with important educational goals."

Of all the Ivy League colleges, perhaps the least understood are Pennsylvania and Cornell. The University of Pennsylvania got its start when old Ben Franklin penned a memo entitled *Proposals Relating to the Ed-*

ucation of Youth in Pensilvania. The proposals led to the founding of
the Charity School at Fourth and Arch Streets, in the heart of old Philadelphia—an institution that later became the University of Pennsylvania. In spite of its name, the U. of P. is *not* a state school, but a privately
endowed seat of higher learning, now located along the banks of the
Schuylkill in West Philadelphia. By far the largest of the Ivy League
colleges, it has full-time enrollment of 8,000 students and a truly awe-
some campus. To put it plainly, both the University and the College,
under the leadership of Dr. Gaylord P. Harnwell, are a magnificent asset
to American cultural life.

And now—"perhaps Cornell." There is no earthly reason why I should
be especially fond of this place; indeed my undergraduate years were
spent in fear and trembling at its name. Hopefully I helped string "Beat
Cornell" streamers across 116th Street, then dejectedly helped take them
down after the annual autumn butchery. But mingled with my physical
fear was a kind of intellectual disdain for the Cornell bruisers. I tabbed
them as agricultural students—hay-kickers, apple-knockers—and on one
occasion flung my contempt in their faces by wearing brown shoes at a
black-tie affair held in the Cornell Phi Psi house—just to show them. Pitiful!

Contrition, envy and respect are today my principal emotions about
the youngest and in some ways most progressive of the Ivy League group.
I'm contrite because I underestimated (or was ignorant of) the traditions
and achievements of this great school. I envy the scenic grandeur and
spaciousness of the campus perched above Cayuga's waters. And belatedly
I have come to recognize the unique contributions that Ezra Cornell and
Andrew D. White made to higher education when they founded their
college in 1865. It was a time of stagnation, of adherence to outworn
philosophies of education. White broke all the academic bric-a-brac in
sight, threw away the book and produced a system combining the best
features of classic and democratic culture, including girls.

I propose to let one of Cornell's distinguished sons describe the place
in his own language. E. B. White (no relation to Andrew) in his charming essay *I'd Send My Son to Cornell,* affirms his faith as follows:

"Cornell is not only big and high, it is cosmopolitan and friendly; and
it is an infinitely various place. Its students do not run to type. On the
Campus are found both sexes, all colors, all beliefs—from the most conservative fraternity sophomore with Republican tendencies and a contempt for the irregular, to the bloody-eyed anarchist who wants to tear
the vines right off the buildings. My son will probably be a Christian, five
feet nine; but he will make a great many friends in Ithaca who do not
conform to that amazing standard. When I was there I knew two men
from Hawaii, a girl from Johannesburg, a Cuban, a Turk, an English-

man from India, a Negro from New York, two farmers, three Swedes, a Quaker, five Southerners, a reindeer butcher, a second lieutenant, a Christian Scientist, a retired dancer, a motorcyclist, a man who had known Theda Bara, three gnomes, and a lutist. That's not counting the general run of broad-jumpers, second tenors, and veterinarians who make up the great body of the undergraduates, the same as in any school."

To which I can only add; *stet*, and thanks, E. B. W., for permission to quote. I never knew any gnomes or reindeer butchers at Columbia, but during my senior years on Morningside I holed up in an 8x12 cell on the top floor of Livingston—a region dedicated to simple living and high thinking. The adjoining cell was occupied by James Warner Bellah, who could fence like D'Artagnan and write (for my money) better than Scott Fitzgerald. We were both racing for the Alfred Knopf Prize—the publication of a first novel; Bellah won by a bodkin's breadth, but made a characteristic *beau geste* by financing my poetry magazine *Contemporary Verse* with his advance royalties. Across the corridor was a double suite that housed a concert grand Steinway and its owner, Al Fried, who could simultaneously play Bach and four games of chess and tutor me in trigonometry —a notably weak line in my chain of Universal Knowledge. Among the chess players was a fellow named Mortimer Adler, best known at the time for his psychological experiments involving a mouse, a Barnard girl and a galvanometer (details on request). In the late 20s Adler skipped west, taking with him the Hundred Great Books program, originated by John Erskine but now the official property of the University of Chicago. Other comers-and-goers on the tenth floor of Livingston were Clifton Fadiman and Corey Ford—then green in reputation but ripening fast. Lionel Trilling, later to gain fame as "the perfect don," would drop in with a copy of Sainte-Beuve under his arm. And am I likely to forget Marcus Goodrich, whose novel *Delilah* ranks beside that other Columbia-sprung sea tale, *The Caine Mutiny?*

The rubbing together of these highly-charged personalities generated a special kind of intellectual helium that threatened at times to blast the cornices off Livingston. I recall one particular gaseous session that was interrupted by a mustached intruder who opened the door and asked if anyone had a copy of *Wigmore on Evidence*. The intruder was a law student, name of Tom Dewey, who later did a long stretch in a state institution at Albany.

Every Ivy Leaguer is entitled to at least one perfect recollection. Mine came while I was holding the Proudfit Fellowship in Letters (that's really the name). It seems that a bunch of non-Proudfit chaps—including Lou Gehrig and our All-American halfback, Wally Koppisch—had neglected to spend enough time in reading *Beowulf, The Canterbury Tales,* Spenser's *Faerie Queene* and Malory's fanciful account of life at the court of King

Arthur. On the night before final exams I admitted fifteen selected laggards (at a dollar a head) into my Proudfit diggings, and after gazing into my crystal ball, prophesied the questions that would be asked on the morrow. I then provided suitable answers—suitable enough that is, to pull fourteen of my customers through with a creditable C. Paunchy strangers still stop me on the street, wring my hand in gratitude, and say that I gave them the best dollar's worth of education they ever got, and I still glow at the thought that I helped save the Columbia backfield and the New York Yankees' infield from dark outer reaches of ignorance.

Well, that just about winds up my remarks on the superiority of Ivy League men. I'm not sure that I've convinced the jury of my cool detachment and utter lack of special pleading. Quite possibly the trustees of Macalester (Minn.) will change their minds about offering me that honorary LL.D.; and perhaps Baylor won't invite me to deliver its baccalaureate address next year. These are risks that I'm quite willing to take. For if even a few readers have detected some seriousness here in my plea for higher standards of college education, I shall be content.

Make no mistake about it, my friends. The Levelers are gathering in great strength, and the Day of Rabblement is nearer than you think. In the intellectual Armageddon now looming over America, the enemies of higher education will attempt to destroy all cultural standards but their own; and if they succeed our final state of mediocrity will be infinitely worse than anything yet seen. The outright collapse of Ivy League ideals is not likely to happen overnight; and I am enough of an optimist to hope that it may never happen at all. But it will be a sad day for our democracy when and if some prancing drum majorette leads a commencement procession of gowned Harvard, Columbia or Cornell scholars toward that final indignity, the conferring of meaningless B.A. degrees on students who couldn't possibly have earned them under the present great standards and high demands of the Ivy League.

5

And Fond Recall

THEY have a glow, these captured memories of older men on younger days, brightened somehow by time and distance as though in defiance of physical law. For with Oliver Wendell Holmes, they pay no heed to the clock. "Old time is a liar," they say, "we're twenty tonight." There are skeptics and critics among them, who peer through doubting eyes at their college years and speak with scoffing phrase, but these are not many.

The college years were years of magic, a time and a kind of life set apart, physically, emotionally, spiritually, intellectually. They were years which profoundly affected the total being. In a sense they were "years between," between child and adult, between the world of one's parental home and one's own. And coming from the parental hearth to the university and a novel degree of independence and privacy, there was also a new kind of non-privacy, a sharing of one's life without the closeness of supervision encountered, perhaps, at boarding or prep school, or summer camp.

It is hard for an adult to recall with any accuracy the years of childhood: it is done, often with considerable success, but always at one remove, because the mind and the outlook of the child and of the adult are so widely different. The child's sense of self and of others and the world in which he so restrictedly moves can be recreated in the imagination, but cannot be revisited in recall. Not so with the world of youth. In the college years the personality, the brain, the body and the psyche of the fully mature adult are prefigured. They will be modified—perhaps more radically and more rapidly than ever again—but they are there, quickened, fresh, responsive. For most, remembering, those years were full and happy and only too soon over.

Possibly, this explains why some of the finest writing about university days—as seen in the ensuing selections—takes the form of vivid recall.

STEPHEN VINCENT BENÉT

Class Reunion

FROM *Selected Works of Stephen Vincent Benét*

In this poignant story Stephen Vincent Benét has caught the nostalgia and the groping for disembodied friendships of a class reunion. And with it the doubt with which every man asks himself, ten or twenty years after leaving college, "What have I done with the bright and shining promise of my life?"

Benét was a graduate of Yale. He did graduate work at the Sorbonne, and received an honorary degree from his university in 1937. He died a few years ago at the height of his creative work as poet and short story writer.

W HEN he said good night to his son and Tom Drury and the rest of them, Lane Parrington walked down the steps of the Leaf Club and stood, for a moment, breathing in the night air. He had made the speech they'd asked him to make, and taken pains with it, too—but now he was wondering whether it wasn't the same old graduate's speech after all. He hadn't meant it to be so, but you ran into a lingo, once you started putting thoughts on paper—you began to view with alarm and talk about imperiled bulwarks and the American way of life.

And yet he'd been genuinely pleased when the invitation came—and they'd asked him three months ahead. That meant something, even to the Lane Parrington of United Investments—it was curious how old bonds held. He had been decorated by two foreign governments and had declined a ministry—there was the place in Virginia, the place on Long Island, the farm in Vermont and the big apartment on the river. There were the statements issued when sailing for Europe and the photographs and articles in news weeklies and magazines. And yet he had been pleased when they asked him to speak at the annual dinner of an undergraduate club in his own college. Of course, the Leaf was a little different, as all Leaf members

423

knew. When he had been a new member, as his son was now, the speech had been made by a Secretary of State.

Well, he'd done well enough, he supposed—at least Ted had come up, afterward, a little shyly, and said, "Well, Dad, you're quite an orator." But, once or twice, in the course of the speech, he had caught Ted fiddling with his coffee spoon. They were almost always too long—those speeches by graduates—he had tried to remember that. But he couldn't help running a little overtime—not after he'd got up and seen them waiting there. They were only boys, of course, but boys who would soon be men with men's responsibilities—he had even made a point of that.

One of the things about the Leaf—you got a chance of hearing what— well, what really important men thought of the state of the world and the state of the nation. They could get a lot from professors but hardly that. So, when a sensible fellow got up to explain what sensible men really thought about this business at Washington—why, damn it, nobody was going to ring a gong on him! And they'd clapped him well, at the end, and Ted's face had looked relieved. They always clapped well, at the end.

Afterward, he had rather hoped to meet Ted's friends and get in a little closer touch with them than he did at the place in Virginia or the place on Long Island or the apartment in New York. He saw them there, of course—they got in cars and out of cars, they dressed and went to dances, they played on the tennis courts and swam in the pool. They were a good crowd—a typical Leaf crowd, well-exercised and well-mannered. They were polite to Cora and polite to him. He offered them cigars now and then; during the last two years he offered them whisky and soda. They listened to what he had to say and, if he told a good story, they usually laughed at it. They played tennis with him, occasionally, and said, "Good shot, sir!"—afterward, they played harder tennis. One of them was Ted, his son, well-mannered, well-exercised, a member of the Leaf. He could talk to Ted about college athletics, the college curriculum, his allowance, the weather, the virtues of capitalism and whether to get a new beach wagon this summer. Now, to these subjects was added the Leaf and the virtues of the Leaf. He could talk to Ted about any number of things.

Nevertheless, sometimes when the annual dinner was over, there would be a little group at the Leaf around this graduate or that. He remembered one such group his senior year, around a sharp-tongued old man with hooded eyes. The ex-senator was old and broken, but they'd stayed up till two while his caustic voice made hay of accepted catchwords. Well, he had met Ted's friends and remembered most of their names. They had congratulated him on his speech and he had drunk a highball with them. It had all been in accord with the best traditions of the Leaf but it hadn't lasted very long.

For a moment, indeed, he had almost gotten into an argument with one of them—the pink-faced, incredibly youthful one with the glasses who was head of the Student Union—they hadn't had student unions in his time. He had been answering a couple of questions quite informally, using slang, and the pink-faced youth had broken in with, "But, look here, sir— I mean, that was a good speech you made from the conservative point of view and all that—but when you talk about labor's being made responsible, just what do you mean and how far do you go? Do you mean you want to scrap the Wagner Act or amend it or what?"

But then the rest of them had said, "Oh, don't mind Stu—he's our communist. Skip it, Stu—how's dialectic materialism today?" and it had passed off in kidding. Lane Parrington felt a little sorry about that—he would have enjoyed a good argument with an intelligent youngster—he was certainly broad-minded enough for that. But, instead, he'd declined another highball and said, well, he supposed he ought to be getting back to the inn. It had all been very well-mannered and in accord with the best traditions of the Leaf. He wondered how the old ex-senator had got them to talk.

Ted had offered to walk along with him, of course, and, equally, of course, he had declined. Now he stood for a moment on the sidewalk, wondering whether he ought to look in at class headquarters before going back to the inn. He ought to, he supposed—after all, it was his thirtieth reunion. It would be full of cigar smoke and voices and there would be a drunk from another class—there was always, somehow or other, a drunk from another class who insisted on leading cheers. And Schooner Fairchild, the class funny man, would be telling stories—the one about the Kickapoo chief, the one about President Dodge and the telephone. As it was in the beginning, is now and ever shall be. He didn't dislike Schooner Fairchild any more—you couldn't dislike a man who had wasted his life. But Schooner, somehow, had never seemed conscious of that.

Yes, he'd go to class headquarters—he'd go, if for no other reason than to prove that he did not dislike Schooner Fairchild. He started walking down Club Row. There were twelve of the clubhouses now—there had been only eight in his time. They all looked very much alike, even the new ones—it took an initiated eye to detect the slight enormous differences —to know that Wampum, in spite of its pretentious lanterns, was second-rate and would always be second-rate, while Abbey, small and dingy, ranked with Momus and the Leaf. Parrington stood still, reliving the moment of more than thirty years ago when he'd gotten the bid from Wampum and thought he would have to accept it. It hadn't been necessary—the Leaf messenger had knocked on his door at just three minutes to nine. But whenever he passed the Wampum house he remembered.

For, for almost an hour, it had seemed as if the destined career of Lane Parrington wasn't going to turn out right after all.

The small agonies of youth—they were unimportant, of course, but they left a mark. And he'd had to succeed—he'd had to have the Leaf, just as later on, he'd had to have money—he wasn't a Schooner Fairchild, to take things as they came. You were geared like that or you weren't—if you weren't, you might as well stay in Emmetsburg and end up as a harried high school principal with sick headaches and a fine Spencerian handwriting, as his father had. But he had wanted to get out of Emmetsburg the moment he had realized there were other places to go.

He remembered a look through a microscope and a lashing, tailed thing that swam. There were only two classes of people, the wigglers and the ones who stood still—he should have made his speech on that—it would have been a better speech. And the ones who stood still didn't like the wigglers—that, too, he knew, from experience. If they saw a wiggler coming, they closed ranks and opposed their large, well-mannered inertia to the brusque, ill-mannered life. Later on, of course, they gave in gracefully, but without real liking. He had made the Leaf on his record—and a very good record it had had to be. He had even spent three painful seasons with the track squad, just to demonstrate that desirable all-aroundness that was one of the talking points. And even so, they had smelled it—they had known, instinctively, that he wasn't quite their kind. Tom Drury, for instance, had always been pleasant enough—but Tom Drury had always made him feel that he was talking a little too much and a little too loud. Tom Drury, who, even then, had looked like a magnificent sheep. But he had also been class president, and the heir to Drury and Son. And yet, they all liked Schooner Fairchild—they liked him still.

And here was the end of Club Row, and the Momus House. He stopped and took out a cigar. It was silly to fight old battles, especially when they were won. If they asked the Drurys to dinner now, the Drurys came—he'd been offered and declined a partnership in Drury and Son. But he had helped Tom out with some of their affiliates and Tom had needed help—Tom would always be impressive, of course, but it took more than impressiveness to handle certain things. And now Ted was coming along—and Ted was sound as a bell. So sound he might marry one of the Drury daughters, if he wanted—though that was Ted's business. He wondered if he wanted Ted to marry young. He had done so himself—on the whole, it had been a mistake.

Funny, how things mixed in your mind. As always, when he remembered Dorothy, there was the sharp, sweet smell of her perfume; then the stubborn, competent look of her hands on the wheel of a car. They had been too much alike to have married—lucky they'd found it out in time. She had let him keep the child—of course he would have fought for it anyway—but it was considered very modern in those days. Then the war had washed over and obliterated a great deal—afterward, he had married Cora. And that had worked out as it should—Ted was fond of her and she treated him with just the right shade of companionableness. Most things worked out in the end. He wondered if Dorothy had gotten what she wanted at last—he supposed she had, with her Texan. But she'd died in a hospital at Galveston, ten years ago, trying to have the Texan's child, so he couldn't ask her now. They had warned her about having more children—but, as soon as you warned Dorothy about anything, that was what she wanted to do. He could have told them. But the Texan was one of those handsome, chivalrous men.

Strange, that out of their two warring ambitions should have come the sound, reliable, healthy Ted. But, no, it wasn't strange—he had planned it as carefully as one could, and Cora had helped a great deal. Cora never got out of her depth and she had a fine social sense. And the very best nurses and schools from the very first—and there you were! You did it as you ran a business—picked the right people and gave them authority. He had hardly ever had to interfere himself.

There would be a great deal of money—but that could be taken care of—there were ways. There were trust funds and foundations and clever secretaries. And Ted need never realize it. There was no reason he should —no reason in the least. Ted could think he was doing it all.

He pulled hard on his cigar and started to walk away. For the door of the Momus Club had suddenly swung open, emitting a gush of light and a small, chubby, gray-haired figure with a turned-up nose and a jack-o'-lantern grin. It stood on the steps for a moment, saying good night a dozen times and laughing. Lane Parrington walked fast—but it was no use. He heard pattering footsteps behind him—a voice cried, "Ought-Eight!" with conviction, then, "Lane Parrington, b'gosh!" He stopped and turned.

"Oh, hello, Schooner," he said, unenthusiastically. "Your dinner over, too?"

"Oh, the boys'll keep it up till three," said Schooner Fairchild, mopping his pink brow. "But, after an hour and a half, I told them it was time they got some other poor devil at the piano. I'm not as young as I was." He panted, comically, and linked arms with Lane Parrington. "Class headquarters?" he said. "I shouldn't go—Minnie will scalp me. But I will."

"Well," said Lane Parrington uncomfortably—he hated having his arm held, "I suppose we ought to look in."

"Duty, Mr. Easy, always duty," said Schooner Fairchild and chuckled. "Hey, don't walk so fast—an old man can't keep up with you." He stopped and mopped his brow again. "By the way," he said, "that's a fine boy of yours, Lane."

"Oh," said Lane Parrington awkwardly. "Thanks. But I didn't know—"

"Saw something of him last summer," said Schooner Fairchild cheerfully. "Sylvia brought him around to the house. He could have a rather nice baritone, if he wanted."

"Baritone?" said Lane Parrington. "Sylvia?"

"Eldest daughter and pride of the Fairchild château," said Schooner Fairchild, slurring his words by a tiny fraction. "She collects 'em—not always—always with Father's approval. But your boy's a nice boy. Serious, of course." He chuckled again, it seemed to Lane Parrington maddeningly. "Oh, the sailor said to the admiral, and the admiral said he—" he chanted. "Remember that one, Lane?"

"No," said Lane Parrington.

"That's right," said Schooner Fairchild, amiably. "Stupid of me. I thought for a minute, you'd been in the quartet. But that was dear old Pozzy Banks. Poor Pozzy—he never could sing 'The Last Rose of Summer' properly till he was as drunk as an owl. A man of great talents. I hoped he'd be here this time but he couldn't make it. He wanted to come," he hummed, "but he didn't have the fare . . ."

"That's too bad," said Lane Parrington, seriously. "And yet, with business picking up . . ."

Schooner Fairchild looked at him queerly, for an instant. "Oh, bless you!" he said. "Pozzy never had a nickel. But he was fun." He tugged at Lane Parrington's arm, as they turned a corner and saw an electric sign— 1908—above the door. "Well, here we go!" he said.

An hour later, Lane Parrington decided that it was just as he had expected. True, the drunk from the unidentified class had gone home. But others, from other classes, had arrived. And Schooner Fairchild was sitting at the piano.

He himself was wedged uncomfortably at the back of the room between Ed Runner and a man whose name, he thought, was either Ferguson or Whitelaw, but who, in any case, addressed him as "Lane, old boy." This made conversation difficult, for it was hard to call his neighbor either "Fergy" or "Whitey" without being sure of his name. On the other hand, conversation with Ed Runner was equally difficult, for that gentleman had embarked upon an interminable reminiscence whose point turned upon the exact location of Bill Webley's room Sophomore year. As Lane Parrington had never been in any of Bill Webley's rooms, he had very little to add to the discussion. He was also drinking beer, which never agreed with him, and the cigar smoke stung his eyes. And around the singer and the piano boiled and seethed a motley crew of graduates of

all classes—the Roman togas of 1913, the convict stripes of 1935, the shorts
and explorers' helmets of 1928. For the news had somehow gone around,
through the various class headquarters, that Schooner Fairchild was doing
his stuff—and, here and there, among the crowd, were undergraduates, who
had heard from brothers and uncles about Schooner Fairchild, but had
never seen him before in the flesh.

He had told the story of the Kickapoo chief, he had given the imitation
of President Dodge and the telephone. Both these and other efforts, Lane
Parrington noted wonderingly, had been received with tumultuous cheers.
Now he played a few chords and swung around on the piano stool.

"I shall now," he said, with his cherubic face very solemn, "emit my
positively last and final number—an imitation of dear old Pozzy Banks,
attempting to sing 'The Last Rose of Summer' while under the influence
of wine. Not all of you have been privileged to know dear old Pozzy—
a man of the most varied and diverse talents—it is our great regret that
he is not with us tonight. But for those of you who were not privileged
to know Pozzy, may I state as an introduction that dear old Pozzy is built
something on the lines of a truck, and that, when under the influence of
wine, it was his custom to sing directly into his hat, which he held out before him like a card tray. We will now begin." He whirled around, struck
a few lugubrious notes and began to sing.

It was, as even Lane Parrington had to admit, extremely funny. He
heard himself joining in the wild, deep roar of laughter that greeted the
end of the first verse—he was annoyed at himself but he could not help it.
By some magic, by some trick of gesture and voice, the chubby, bald-headed
figure had suddenly become a large and lugubrious young man—a young
man slightly under the influence of wine but still with the very best intentions, singing sentimentally and lugubriously into his hat. It was a trick
and an act and a sleight of hand not worth learning—but it did not fail in
its effect. Lane Parrington found himself laughing till he ached—beside him,
the man named either Ferguson or Whitelaw was whooping and gasping
for breath.

"And now," said Schooner Fairchild, while they were still laughing, "let
somebody play who can play!" And, magically crooking his finger, he
summoned a dark-haired undergraduate from the crowd, pushed him down
on the piano stool, and, somehow or other, slipped through the press and
vanished, while they were still calling his name.

Lane Parrington, a little later, found himself strolling up and down the
dejected back yard of class headquarters. They had put up a tent, some iron
tables and a number of paper lanterns, but, at this hour, the effect was not
particularly gay. It must be very late and he ought to go to bed. But he
did not look at his watch. He was trying to think about certain things in his

life and get them into a proportion. It should be a simple thing to do, as simple as making money, but it was not.

Ted—Dorothy—the Leaf—Emmetsburg—Schooner Fairchild—Tom Drury —the place in Virginia and the mean house at Emmetsburg—United Investments and a sleight-of-hand trick at a tiny piano. He shuffled the factors of the equation about; they should add up to a whole. And, if they did, he would be willing to admit it; he told himself that. Yes, even if the final sum proved him wrong for years—that had always been one of the factors of his own success, his knowing just when to cut a loss.

A shaky voice hummed behind him:

> "Oh, the ship's cat said to the cabin boy,
>   To the cabin boy said she . . ."

He turned—it was Schooner Fairchild and, he thought at first, Schooner Fairchild was very drunk. Then he saw the man's lips were gray, caught him and helped him into one of the iron chairs.

"Sorry," wheezed Schooner Fairchild. "Must have run too fast, getting away from the gang. Damn' silly—left my medicine at the inn."

"Here—wait—" said Lane Parrington, remembering the flask of brandy in his pocket. He uncorked it and held it to the other man's lips. "Can you swallow?" he said solicitously.

An elfish, undefeated smile lit Schooner Fairchild's face. "Always could, from a child," he gasped. "Never ask a Fairchild twice." He drank and said, incredibly, it seemed to Lane Parrington, "Napoleon . . . isn't it? Sir, you spoil me." His color began to come back. "Better," he said.

"Just stay there," said Lane Parrington. He dashed back into club headquarters—deserted now, he noticed, except for the gloomy caretaker and the man called Ferguson or Whitelaw, who was ungracefully asleep on a leather couch. Efficiently, he found glasses, ice, soda, plain water and ginger ale, and returned, his hands full of these trophies, to find Schooner Fairchild sitting up in his chair and attempting to get a cigarette from the pocket of his coat.

His eyes twinkled as he saw Lane Parrington's collection of glassware. "My!" he said. "We *are* going to make a night of it. Great shock to me— never thought it of you, Lane."

"Hadn't I better get a doctor?" said Lane Parrington. "There's a telephone—"

"Not a chance," said Schooner Fairchild. "It would worry Minnie sick. It's just the old pump—misses a little sometimes. But I'll be all right now— right as a trivet, whatever a trivet is. Just give me another shot of Napoleon."

"Of course," said Lane Parrington, "but—"

"Brandy on beer, never fear," said Schooner Fairchild. "Fairchild's Medical Maxims, Number One. And a cigarette . . . thanks." He breathed deeply. "And there we are," he said, with a smile. "Just catches you in the short ribs, now and then. But, when it's over, it's over. You ought to try a little yourself, Lane—damn' silly performance of mine and you look tired."

"Thanks," said Lane Parrington, "I will." He made himself, neatly, an efficient brandy and soda and raised the glass to his lips. "Well—er—here's luck," he said, a little stiffly.

"Luck!" nodded Schooner Fairchild. They both drank. Lane Parrington looked at the pleasant, undefeated face.

"Listen, Schooner," said Lane Parrington, suddenly and harshly, "if you had the whole works to shoot over again—" He stopped.

"That's the hell of a question to ask a man at three o'clock in the morning," said Schooner equably. "Why?"

"Oh, I don't know," said Lane Parrington. "But that stuff at the piano you did—well, how did you do it?" His voice was oddly ingenuous, for Lane Parrington.

"Genius, my boy, sheer, untrammeled genius," said Schooner Fairchild. He chuckled and sobered. "Well, somebody has to," he said reasonably. "And you wouldn't expect Tom Drury to do it, would you?—poor old Tom!"

"No," said Lane Parrington, breathing. "I wouldn't expect Tom Drury to do it."

"Oh, Tom's all right," said Schooner Fairchild. "He was just born with an ingrowing Drury and never had it operated on. But he's a fine guy, all the same. Lord," he said, "it must be a curse—to have to be a Drury, whether you like it or not. I never could have stood it—I never could have played the game. Of course," he added hastily, "I suppose it's different, if you do it all yourself, the way you have. That must be a lot of fun."

"I wouldn't exactly call it fun," said Lane Parrington earnestly. "You see, after all, Schooner, there are quite a good many things that enter into . . ." He paused and laughed hopelessly. "Was I always a stuffed shirt?" he said. "I suppose I was."

"Oh, I wouldn't call you a stuffed shirt," said Schooner, a little quickly. "You just had to succeed—and you've done it. Gosh, we all knew you were going to, right from the first—there couldn't be any mistake about that. It must be a swell feeling." He looked at Lane Parrington and his voice trailed off. He began again. "You see, it was different with me," he said. "I couldn't help it. Why, just take a look at me—I've even got a comedy face. Well, I never wanted anything very much except—oh, to have a good time and know other people were having a good time. Oh, I tried taking the other things seriously—I tried when I was a broker, but I couldn't, it was just no go. I made money enough—everybody was making money—but every now and then, in the middle of a million-share day, I'd just think how damn silly it was for everybody to be watching the board and getting all excited over things called ATT and UGI. And that's no way for a broker to act—you've got to believe those silly initials mean something if you want to be a broker.

"Well, I've tried a good many things since. And now and then I've been lucky, and we've gotten along. And I've spent most of Minnie's money, but she says it was worth it—and we've got the five girls and they're wonders —and I'll probably die playing the piano at some fool party, for you can't keep it up forever, but I only hope it happens before somebody says, 'There goes poor old Schooner. He used to be pretty amusing in his time!' But, you see, I couldn't help it," he ended diffidently. "And, you know, I've tried I've tried hard. But then I'd start laughing, and it always got in the way."

Lane Parrington looked at the man who had spent his wife's money and his own for a sleight-of-hand trick, five daughters, and the sound of friendly laughter. He looked at him without understanding, and yet with a curious longing.

"But, Schooner—" he said, "with all you can do—you ought to—"

"Oh," said Schooner, a trifle wearily, "one has one's dreams. Sure, I'd like to be Victor Boucher—he's a beautiful comedian. Or Bill Fields, for instance. Who wouldn't? But I don't kid myself. It's a parlor talent—it doesn't go over the footlights. But, Lord, what fun I've had with it! And the funny things people keep doing, forever and ever, amen. And the decent— the very decent things they keep doing, too. Well, I always thought it would be a good life, while you had it." He paused, and Lane Parrington saw the fatigue on his face. "Well, it's been a good party," he said. "I wish old Pozzy could have been here. But I guess we ought to go to bed."

"I'll phone for a cab," said Lane Parrington. "Nope—you're riding."

Lane Parrington shut the door of Schooner Fairchild's room behind him and stood, for a moment, with his hand on the knob. He had seen Schooner safely to bed—he had even insisted on the latter's taking his medicine, though Schooner had been a little petulant about it. Now, however, he still wondered about calling a doctor—if Schooner should be worse in the morning, he would have Anstey come up by plane. It was nothing to do, though not everybody could do it, and Anstey was much the best man. In any case, he would insist on Schooner's seeing Anstey this week. Then he wondered just how he was going to insist.

The old elevator just across the corridor came to a wheezing stop. Its door opened and a dark-haired girl in evening dress came out. Lane Parrington dropped his hand from the doorknob and turned away. But the girl took three quick steps after him.

"I'm sorry," she said, a little breathlessly, "but I'm Sylvia Fairchild. Is Father ill? The elevator boy said something—and I saw you coming out of his room."

"He's all right," said Lane Parrington. "It was just the slightest sort of—"

"Oh!" said the girl, "do you mind coming back for a minute? You're Ted's father, aren't you? My room's next door, but I've got a key for his, too—Mother told me to be sure—" She seemed very self-possessed. Lane Parrington waited uncomfortably in the corridor for what seemed to him a long time, while she went into her father's room. When she came out again, she seemed relieved.

"It's all right," she said, in a low voice. "He's asleep, and his color's good. And he's . . ." She paused. "Oh, damn!" she said. "We can't talk out here. Come into my room for a minute—we can leave the door open—after all, you *are* Ted's father. I'll have to tell Mother, you see—and Father will just say it wasn't anything."

She opened the door and led the way into the room. "Here," she said. "Just throw those stockings off the chair—I'll sit on the bed. Well?"

"Well, I asked him if he wanted a doctor . . ." said Lane Parrington humbly.

When he had finished a concise, efficient report, the girl nodded, and he saw for the first time that she was pretty, with her dark, neat head and her clever, stubborn chin.

"Thank you," she said. "I mean, really. Father's a perfect lamb—but he doesn't like to worry Mother, and it worries her a lot more not to know. And sometimes it's rather difficult, getting the truth out of Father's friends. Not you," she was pleased to add. "You've been perfectly truthful. And the brandy was quite all right."

"I'm glad," said Lane Parrington. "I wish your father would see Anstey," he added, a trifle awkwardly. "I could—er—make arrangements."

"He has," said the girl. Her mouth twitched. "Oh," she said. "I shouldn't have gone to the dance. I couldn't help the Momus Club, but he might have come back afterward, if I'd been here. Only, I don't know."

"I wouldn't reproach myself," said Lane Parrington. "After all—"

"Oh, I know," said the girl. "After all! If you don't all manage to kill him, between you! Friends!" she sniffed. Then, suddenly, her face broke into lines of amusement. "I sound just like Aunt Emma," she said. "And that's pretty silly of me. Aunt Emma's almost pure poison. Of course it isn't your fault and I really do thank you. Very much. Do you know, I never expected you'd be a friend of Father's."

"After all," said Lane Parrington stiffly, "we were in the same class."

"Oh, I know," said the girl. "Father's talked about you, of course." Her mouth twitched again, but this time, it seemed to Lane Parrington, with a secret merriment. "And so has Ted, naturally," she added politely.

"I'm glad he happened to mention me," said Lane Parrington, and she grinned, frankly.

"I deserved that," she said, while Lane Parrington averted his eyes from what seemed to be a remarkably flimsy garment hung over the bottom of the bed. "But Ted has, really. He admires you quite a lot, you know, though, of course, you're different generations."

"Tell me—" said Lane Parrington. "No, I won't ask you."

"Oh, you know Ted," said the girl, rather impatiently. "It's awfully hard to get him to say things—and he will spend such a lot of time thinking he ought to be noble, poor lamb. But he's losing just a little of that, thank goodness—when he first came to Widgeon Point, he was trying so hard to be exactly like that terrible Drury boy. You see—" she said, suddenly and gravely, "he could lose quite a lot of it and still have more than most people."

Lane Parrington cleared his throat. There seemed nothing for him to say. Then he thought of something.

"His mother was—er—a remarkable person," he said. "We were not at all happy together. But she had remarkable qualities."

"Yes," said the girl. "Ted's told me. He remembers her." They looked at each other for a moment—he noted the stubborn chin, the swift and admirable hands. Then a clock on the mantel struck and the girl jumped.

"Good heavens!" she said. "It's four o'clock! Well—good night. And I do thank you, Mr. Parrington."

"It wasn't anything," said Lane Parrington. "But remember me to your father. But I'll see you in the morning, of course."

The following afternoon, Lane Parrington found himself waiting for his car in the lobby of the inn. There had been a little trouble with the garage and it was late. But he did not care, particularly, though he felt glad to be going back to New York. He had said good-by to Ted an hour before—Ted was going on to a house party at the Chiltons'—they'd eventually meet on Long Island, he supposed. Meanwhile, he had had a pleasant morning, attended the commencement exercises, and had lunch with Ted and the Fairchilds at the inn. Schooner had been a little subdued and both Ted and the girl frankly sleepy, but he had enjoyed the occasion nevertheless. And somehow the fact that the president's baccalaureate address had also viewed with alarm and talked about imperiled bulwarks and the American way of life—had, in fact, repeated with solemn precision a good many of the points in his own speech—did not irk Lane Parrington as it might have the day before. After all, the boys were young and could stand it. They had stood a good deal of nonsense, even in his own time.

Now he thought once more of the equation he had tried too earnestly to solve, in the back yard of commencement headquarters—and, for a moment, almost grinned. It was, of course, insoluble—life was not as neat as that. You did what you could, as it was given you to do—very often you did the wrong things. And if you did the wrong things, you could hardly remedy them by a sudden repentance—or, at least, he could not. There were still the wigglers and the ones who stood still—and each had his own virtues. And because he was a wiggler, he had thoughtfully and zealously done his best to make his son into the image of one of the magnificent sheep—the image of Tom Drury, who was neither hungry nor gay. He could not remedy that, but he thought he knew somebody who could remedy it, remembering the Fairchild girl's stubborn chin. And, in that case at least, the grandchildren ought to be worth watching.

"Your car, Mr. Parrington," said a bellboy. He moved toward the door. It was hard to keep from being a stuffed shirt, if you had the instinct in you, but one could try. A good deal might be done, with trying.

As he stepped out upon the steps of the inn, he noticed a figure, saluting —old Negro Mose, the campus character who remembered everybody's name.

"Hello, Mose!" said Lane Parrington. "Remember me?"

"Remember you—sho,' Mr. Parrington," said Mose. He regarded Lane Parrington with beady eyes. "Let's see—you was 1906."

"Nineteen hundred and eight," said Lane Parrington, but without rancor.

Mose gave a professional chuckle. "Sho'!" he said. "I was forgettin'! Let's see—you hasn't been back fo' years, Mister Parrington—but you was in Tom Drury's class—an' Schooner Fairchild's class—"

"No," said Lane Parrington and gave the expected dollar, "not Tom Drury's class, Schooner Fairchild's class."

University Days

FROM *The New Yorker*

🏠 *In his own whimsical, bemused and bemusing fashion, James Thurber, creator in words and pictures of a warm-heartedly screwball gallery of men, women and dogs, gives us a few highlights of his college days at Ohio State University. No wonder some college teachers have the pitifully harassed look of driven people!*

Thurber entered Ohio State in 1913, but with a year off "just to read," and another year of war service, he did not graduate until 1919. Since then his stories and drawings have won him a vast audience of bewitched readers. He was one of the founding editors of The New Yorker.

I PASSED all the other courses I took at my university, but I could never pass botany. This was because all botany students had to spend several hours a week in a laboratory looking through a microscope at plant cells, and I could never see through a microscope. I never once saw a cell through a microscope. This used to enrage my instructor. He would wander around the laboratory pleased with the progress all the students were making in drawing the involved and, so I am told, interesting structure of flower cells, until he came to me. I would just be standing there. "I can't see anything," I would say. He would begin patiently enough, explaining how anybody can see through a microscope, but he would always end up in a fury, claiming that I could *too* see through a microscope but just pretended that I couldn't. "It takes away from the beauty of flowers anyway," I used to tell him. "We are not concerned with beauty in this course," he would say. "We are concerned solely with what I may call the *mechanics* of flars." "Well," I'd say, "I can't see anything." "Try it just once again," he'd say, and I would put my eye to the microscope and see nothing at all, except now and again a nebulous milky substance—a phenomenon of maladjustment.

You were supposed to see a vivid, restless clockwork of sharply defined plant cells. "I see what looks like a lot of milk," I would tell him. This, he claimed, was the result of my not having adjusted the microscope properly, so he would readjust it for me, or rather, for himself. And I would look again and see milk.

I finally took a deferred pass, as they called it, and waited a year and tried again. (You had to pass one of the biological sciences or you couldn't graduate.) The professor had come back from vacation brown as a berry, bright-eyed, and eager to explain cell structure again to his classes. "Well," he said to me, cheerily, when we met in the first laboratory hours of the semester, "we're going to see the cells this time, aren't we?" "Yes, sir," I said. Students to right of me and to left of me and in front of me were seeing cells; what's more, they were quietly drawing pictures of them in their notebooks. Of course, I didn't see anything.

"We'll try it," the professor said to me, grimly, "with every adjustment of the microscope known to man. As God is my witness, I'll arrange this glass so that you see cells through it or I'll give up teaching. In twenty-two years of botany, I——" He cut off abruptly for he was beginning to quiver all over, like Lionel Barrymore, and he genuinely wished to hold onto his temper; his scenes with me had taken a great deal out of him.

So we tried it with every adjustment of the microscope known to man. With only one of them did I see anything but blackness or the familiar lacteal opacity, and that time I saw, to my pleasure and amazement, a variegated constellation of flecks, specks, and dots. These I hastily drew. The instructor, noting my activity, came back from an adjoining desk, a smile on his lips and eyebrows high in hope. He looked at my cell drawing. "What's that?" he demanded, with a hint of a squeal in his voice. "That's what I saw," I said. "You didn't, you didn't, you *didn't*!" he screamed, losing control of his temper instantly, and he bent over and squinted into the microscope. His head snapped up. "That's your eye!" he shouted. "You've fixed the lens so that it reflects! You've drawn your eye!"

Another course I didn't like, but somehow managed to pass, was economics. I went to that class straight from the botany class, which didn't help me any in understanding either subject. I used to get them mixed up. But not as mixed up as another student in my economics class who came there directly from a physics laboratory. He was tackle on the football team, named Bolenciecwcz. At that time Ohio State University had one of the best football teams in the country, and Bolenciecwcz was one of its outstanding stars. In order to be eligible to play it was necessary for him to keep up in his studies, a very difficult matter, for while he was not dumber than an ox he was not any smarter. Most of his professors were lenient and helped him along. None gave him more hints, in answering questions, or asked him simpler ones than the economics professor, a thin, timid man named Bassum. One day when we were on the subject of transportation and distribution, it came Bolenciecwcz's turn to answer a question. "Name one means of transportation," the professor said to him. No light came into the big tackle's eyes. "Just any means of transportation," said the professor. Bolenciecwcz sat staring at him. "That is," pursued the professor, "any medium, agency, or method of going from one place to another." Bolenciecwcz had the look of a man who is being led into a trap. "You may choose among steam, horse-drawn, or electrically propelled vehicles," said the instructor. "I might suggest the one which we commonly take in making long journeys across land." There was a profound silence in which everybody stirred uneasily, including Bolenciecwcz and Mr. Bassum. Mr. Bassum abruptly broke this silence in an amazing manner. "Choo-choo-choo," he said, in a low voice, and turned instantly scarlet. He glanced appealingly around the room. All of us, of course, shared Mr. Bassum's desire that Bolenciecwcz should stay abreast of the class in economics, for the Illinois game, one of the hardest and most important of the season, was only a week off. "Toot, toot, too-toooooot!" some student with a deep voice moaned, and we all looked encouragingly at Bolenciecwcz. Somebody else gave a fine imitation of a locomotive letting off steam. Mr. Bassum himself rounded off the little show. "Ding, dong, ding, dong," he said hopefully. Bolenciecwcz was staring at the floor now, trying to think, his great brow furrowed, his huge hands rubbing together, his face red.

"How did you come to college this year, Mr. Bolenciecwcz?" asked the professor. "*Chuffa,* chuffa, *chuffa,* chuffa."

"M' father sent me," said the football player.

"What on?" asked Bassum.

"I git an 'lowance," said the tackle, in a low, husky voice, obviously embarrassed.

"No, no," said Bassum. "Name a means of transportation. What did you *ride* here on?"

"Train," said Bolenciecwcz.

"Quite right," said the professor. "Now, Mr. Nugent, will you tell us——"

If I went through anguish in botany and economics—for different reasons—gymnasium work was even worse. I don't even like to think about it. They wouldn't let you play games or join in the exercises with your glasses on and I couldn't see with mine off. I bumped into professors, horizontal bars, agricultural students, and swinging iron rings. Not being able to see, I could take it but I couldn't dish it out. Also, in order to pass gymnasium (and you had to pass it to graduate) you had to learn to swim if you didn't know how. I didn't like the swimming pool, I didn't like swimming, and I didn't like the swimming instructor, and after all these years I still don't. I never swam but I passed my gym work anyway, by having another student give my gymnasium number (978) and swim across the pool in my place. He was a quiet, amiable blond youth, number 473, and he would have seen through a microscope for me if we could have got away with it, but we couldn't get away with it. Another thing I didn't like about gymnasium work was that they made you strip the day you registered. It is impossible for me to be happy when I am stripped and being asked a lot of questions. Still, I did better than a lanky agricultural student who was cross-examined just before I was. They asked each student what college he was in—that is, whether Arts, Engineering, Commerce, or Agriculture. "What college are you in?" the instructor snapped at the youth in front of me. "Ohio State University," he said promptly.

It wasn't that agricultural student but it was another a whole lot like him who decided to take up journalism, possibly on the ground that when farming went to hell he could fall back on newspaper work. He didn't realize, of course, that that would be very much like falling back full-length on a kit of carpenter's tools. Haskins didn't seem cut out for journalism, being too embarrassed to talk to anybody and unable to use a typewriter, but the editor of the college paper assigned him to the cow barns, the sheep house, the horse pavilion, and the animal-husbandry department generally. This was a genuinely big "beat," for it took up five times as much ground as the College of Liberal Arts. The agricultural student knew animals, but nevertheless his stories were dull and colorlessly written. He took all afternoon on each of them, on account of having to hunt for each letter on the typewriter. Once in a while he had to ask somebody to help him hunt. "C" and "L," in particular, were hard letters for him to find. His editor finally got pretty much annoyed at the farmer-journalist because his pieces were so uninteresting. "See here, Haskins," he snapped at him one day, "why is it we never have anything hot from you on the horse pavilion? Here we have two hundred head of horses on this campus—more than any other university in the Western Conference except Purdue—and yet you never get any real low-down on them. Now shoot over to the horse barns and dig up something lively." Haskins shambled out and came back in about an hour; he said he had something. "Well, start it off snappily," said the editor. "Something people will read." Haskins set to work and in a couple of hours brought a sheet of typewritten paper to the desk; it was a two-hundred-word story about some disease that had broken out among the horses. Its opening sentence was simple but arresting. It read: "Who has noticed the sores on the tops of the horses in the animal-husbandry building?"

Ohio State was a land-grant university and therefore two years of military drill was compulsory. We drilled with old Springfield rifles and studied the tactics of the Civil War even though the World War was going on at the time. At eleven o'clock each morning thousands of freshmen and sophomores used to deploy over the campus, moodily creeping up on the old chemistry building. It was good training for the kind of warfare that was waged at Shiloh but it had no connection with what was going on in Europe. Some people used to think that there was German money behind it, but they didn't dare say so or they would have been thrown in jail as German spies. It was a period of muddy thought and marked, I believe, the decline of higher education in the Middle West.

As a soldier I was never any good at all. Most of the cadets were glumly indifferent soldiers, but I was no good at all. Once General Littlefield, who was commandant of the cadet corps, popped up in front of me during regimental drill and snapped, "You are the main trouble with this university!" I think he meant that my type was the main trouble with the university but he may have meant me individually. I was mediocre at drill, certainly—that is, until my senior year. By that time I had drilled longer than anybody else in the Western Conference, having failed at military at the end of each preceding year so that I had to do it all over again. I was the only senior still in uniform. The uniform which, when new, had made me look like an interurban railway conductor, now that it had become faded and too tight made me look like Bert Williams in his bellboy act. This had a definitely bad effect on my morale. Even so, I had become by sheer practice little short of wonderful at squad maneuvers.

One day General Littlefield picked our company out of the whole regiment and tried to get it mixed up by putting it through one movement after another as fast as we could execute them: squads right, squads left, squads on right into line, squads right about, squads left front into line, etc. In about three minutes one hundred and nine men were marching in one direction and I was marching away from them at an angle of forty degrees, all alone. "Company, halt!" shouted General Littlefield. "That man is the only man who has it right!" I was made a corporal for my achievement.

The next day General Littlefield summoned me to his office. He was swatting flies when I went in. I was silent and he was silent, too, for a long time. I don't think he remembered me or why he had sent for me, but he didn't want to admit it. He swatted some more flies, keeping his eyes on them narrowly before he let go with the swatter. "Button up your coat!" he snapped. Looking back on it now, I can see that he meant me although he was looking at a fly, but I just stood there. Another fly came to rest on a paper in front of the general and began rubbing its hind legs together. The general lifted the swatter cautiously. I moved restlessly and the fly flew away. "You startled him!" barked General Littlefield, looking at me severely. I said I was sorry. "That won't help the situation!" snapped the general, with cold military logic. I didn't see what I could do except offer to chase some more flies toward his desk, but I didn't say anything. He stared out the window at the faraway figures of co-eds crossing the campus toward the library. Finally, he told me I could go. So I went. He either didn't know which cadet I was or else he forgot what he wanted to see me about. It may have been that he wished to apologize for having called me the main trouble with the university; or maybe he had decided to compliment me on my brilliant drilling of the day before and then at the last minute decided not to. I don't know. I don't think about it much any more.

Budding Architect

FROM *An Autobiography*

Frank Lloyd Wright's name is almost synonymous with revolutionary architectural design. His "organic architecture" fuses house and terrain into a functional, harmonious unit and has set the character for much of modern building.

Here we see Wright, the iconoclast, a student at the University of Wisconsin at the turn of the century—as impatient with the tawdry, the meretricious, the "inappropriate" then as he is today, some sixty years after.

ONE day when difficulties between father and mother had grown unbearable the mother, having borne all she could—probably the father had borne all he could bear too—said quietly, "Well, Mr. Wright"—always she spoke of him and to him so—"leave us. I will manage with the children. Go your way. We will never ask you for anything except this home. The savings of my earnings as a teacher have gone into this, and I have put into it so many years of my life.

"No—we will never ask you for help.

"If ever you can send us anything, send it. If you cannot we will do the best we can." . . .

The mother was alone with her son and his two sisters. She found a place for the budding architect with blue-eyed Allen D. Conover, Dean of Engineering at the University of Wisconsin, himself a competent civil engineer. He had an office of his own and a private practice in Madison and probably really needed some boy to work for him. How can one be sure? Professor Conover was a cultivated and kindly man. He allowed the youth to work for him afternoons so that he might have the mornings for classes. He gave him thirty-five dollars a month. This arrangement left the freshman free to study evenings. Architecture, at first his mother's inspiration, then naturally enough his own desire, was the study he wanted. But there was no money to go away to an architectural school. There were classes in engineering at the home university. That was the nearest to architecture within his reach.

So the youth was enrolled at the University of Wisconsin as a prospective civil engineer.

Fortunately, too, by the limitation, he was spared the curse of the "architectural" education of that day as sentimentalized in the United States with its false direction in culture and wrong emphasis on sentiment.

Every morning he walked to the University—a couple of miles away. After recitations there he walked back down to the Conover office at noon to eat the lunch he carried. And, an afternoon's work done at the drawing-board, he walked home again to eat his supper and to study. . . .

The retrospect of university years is mostly dull pain. Thought of poverty and struggle, pathos of a broken home, unsatisfied longings, humiliations—frustration. Mathematics excepted, there seemed little meaning in the studies. At least mathematics "worked." But mathematics was taught by Professor Van Velzer, an academic little man with side-whiskers who had no feeling for romance in his subject. A subject when rightly apprehended most romantic. Music itself but sublimated mathematics.

Consequently the punctilio of the conscientious little professor opened for his pupil the stupendous fact that two plus two equal four. Is it unreasonable to suppose that a professor of mathematics should be a poet? Or a civil engineer be a creative composer of symphonies?

French? Miss Lucy Gay, a charming honest person whom everyone loved and respected, taught him that. He read the "Romance of the Poor Young Man," "Le Cid," etc.

English Composition was taught him by Professor Freeman. A handsome gentleman, deeply afflicted, so it seemed, by a too strong expression of professional dignity.

The youth yearned to read and write his own language—yearned to speak it—supremely well. He had no chance, under the pompous professor. His compositions were all marked "good," "thought excellent," when he already knew both to be dishwater. And barring the correction of gross grammatical errors, which he seldom made anyway, what did he get from that "marking" business? Merely nothing with less subtracted for pleasure or good-measure. English to this day remains more or less a mystery. He was never taught just why English is English—just what it is that makes it English as distinguished from all other languages and what its peculiar and individual resources are. What its limitations are, and how they may be turned to advantages. He was left to find out for himself if he could, and without material.

The hungry student read at this time, at home, Carlyle's *Sartor Resartus,*
Heroes and Hero Worship, Past and Present, the father's calf-bound copy
of Plutarch's *Lives,* Ruskin's *Fors Clavigera, Modern Painters, Stones of*
Venice (gift of Aunt Nell and Jane), Morris's *Sigurd the Volsung,* and
Shelley, Goethe's *Wilhelm Meister,* a little of William Blake, *Les Misé-*
rables, Viollet-le-Duc's *Raisonné de l'architecture.* But he doesn't know in
the least what he read in the school course.

Professors Conover and Storm Bull were the engineers to whom he
reported; they looked over his work in Stereotomy, Graphic Statics, Analytical and Descriptive Geometry. All as painfully spread by him upon his
drawing-board in the drafting room in the old dormitory on the hillside
campus. But it was with Professor Conover, in that practice of his, that
the youth really learned most.

The Freshman Party

Charlie Ware saw May White, his cousin, explained the matter, dif-
fidences, etc., made the engagement after the formality of a call with the
fool who was about to go fearfully in where the angels happily tread.

The morning of the party, a beautiful clear day, the freshman, chesty
as a young cockerel, went for a walk. He ran into Charlie.

"Say, Charlie, I ought to know what I do at this party anyhow, and
how do I, or ought I, to do it."

Said Charles, "Nothing much to know, man. Get May. Take her in.
Dance a few dances with her. Keep off her toes. Then get some of the
fellows to dance with her. There you are! Dance with some of the other
girls yourself. After the last dance—and you dance that with May—mind
you—take May back to 'Ladies' Hall.' "

But the freshman, somehow, thought it good form to kiss the girl when
you left her at the door after the party. It was more of this he had been
thinking than anything else. Charlie laughed. "Oh," he said, "that's
optional." And left the freshman still up in the air.

The class party was to occur in Assembly Hall, next door to Ladies'
Hall. But a carriage was "good form," so carriage it was.

Dressed. White tie. Black suit. Patent-leather pumps. White gloves in
hand. Bouquet for lady. Boutonnière for black coat. So far so good—far
too good. He had an uneasy feeling himself that it was too good.

Got to Ladies' Hall, found May ready. May found her escort too embarrassed to say anything at all. But May had been informed. She got him
safely back to the carriage. No sooner started, May White and Frank Wright
sitting a respectful distance apart, than the carriage stopped at the Hall.
Nothing whatever said. The young couple got out and the amateur led the
way to the entrance.

They got in only to find a crowd of the "fellows" chaffing each other. No ladies in sight.

Blushing painfully, he realized he had brought May to the men's entrance. Helplessly he looked around. Where was the women's dressing room, anyway? May evidently didn't know either.

He went sick with shame.

Charlie Ware, from the other side of the room, took in the situation at a glance and rushed over. "Come with me, May!"

She straightway left the freshman stranded; standing out from the crowd, he felt, like the bull's-eye of a big target. Some boy took pity on him and showed him where to stow his coat and hat. Then he went back to look for his unfortunate lady. He couldn't find her.

Came the promenade. No lady!

Came the first waltz. No lady!

The waltz nearly over and he about to cut it all, when May's voice: "Why here you are! I waited a long time at the dressing-room door. Then I thought you didn't recognize me. You see, you don't know me very well so I came to find you."

He felt he should indignantly deny not knowing her among a thousand like her. But could only murmur—neither ever knew what!

They danced together. Charlie came when the dance was over and got May's programme filled. Got May's partner himself a dance or two for good measure—Charlie was what "Charlies" usually are. All of which went off without resistance or remarks from the green partner. Now he hung around and waited for that last dance with May, wondering if it was going to be expected of him to kiss her when he said "Good night."

He couldn't picture it. But although an amateur, he wanted not to be a duffer and disgrace Charlie. So he made up his mind he would go through with it.

He felt he ought to tell May her dress was pretty and that she danced well. He really admired her dress and white shoes and the way she wore her hair. All he could say was, "We're having a good time, aren't we?"

"Are we?" said May—a bit miffed by now.

The pair got into the carriage after anxious moments when the escort would have given his college education to be well out of the affair forever.

But no more absurdities until—"We had a good time, didn't we?"

"Did we?"

That kiss seemed far away from me! Standing on the steps, time to say good-bye . . . "Well," he stammered—he felt miserably foolish—he felt . . . "Thank you," said he, and ran to the waiting carriage leaving his lady to open the door for herself. He had faith that she got in. But he didn't know.

When home, he lit his lamp, took off the infernal togs he had so miserably betrayed. Threw them aside. Took *Sartor Resartus* to bed for consolation; but was inconsolable. He went over the whole affair and made himself brilliant—irresistible. He staged himself and played the part to perfection—too late! It was next term before he had courage to try again. A nice town girl named Blanche Ryder took pity on him and asked him herself. Tactfully she saw him through.

Tragedy

About this time a vivid tragedy had its life-long effect upon the incipient architect. Passing by the new north-wing of the old State Capitol, he was just in time to hear the indescribable roar of building collapse and see the cloud of white lime dust blown from the windows of the outside walls, the dust cloud rising high into the summer air carrying agonized human-cries with it. The white dust cloud came down to settle white over the trees and grass of the park. Whitened by lime dust as sculpture is white, men with bloody faces came plunging wildly out of the basement entrance blindly striking out about their heads with their arms, still fighting off masonry and falling beams. Some fell dead on the grass under the clear sky. Others fell insensible. One workman, lime-whitened, too, hung head-downward from a fifth-story window, pinned to the sill by an iron-beam on a crushed foot, moaning the whole time.

A ghastly red stream ran from him down the stone wall.

Firemen soon came. Crowds appeared as though out of the ground and men frantically tugged and pulled away at the senseless mass of brick and beams to reach the moans for help of the workmen dying beneath them. Soon white-faced women, silently crying, went about looking for husbands, brothers or sons.

A sudden movement of alarm and scattering of the crowd startled him, as someone pointed to a hand sticking out between chunks of brick-work on which the crowd itself was standing. After pulling away bricks, finally scarlet plaster, a mangled human being was drawn out—too late. One of the sobbing women knelt over it on the grass. And so it went all day long and far into the night.

The youth stayed for hours clinging to the iron fence that surrounded the park, too heartsick to go away. Then he went home—ill. Dreamed of it all that night and the next and the next. The horror of the scene has never entirely left his consciousness and remains to prompt him to this day.

Only outside walls were left standing. The interior columns had fallen and the whole interior construction was a gigantic rubbish heap in the basement.

The huge concrete piers in that basement, on which rested the interior cast-iron columns supporting the floors and roof, had collapsed and let the columns down. Of course that meant all the floors and interior walls as well.

Architect Jones, good and conscientious architect, had made those piers so excessively large that the contractor thought it no sin to wheel barrows full of broken brick and stone into the hearts of them. They were found rotten at the core where the columns stood. Poor Architect Jones! He was now guilty of manslaughter—tried by a jury of his peers and condemned. He never built another building. He was no kinsman, fortunately.

The University of Wisconsin had its beautiful situation on the hill by Lake Mendota, but the life of the University then was not as it is now. The herd of hungry students less by many thousands and more hungry. The buildings were few and badly furnished. Nor were the professors particularly able or distinguished. It was more like a high school today, only less sophisticated than the modern high school. It had the airs, dignitaries and dignities assumed by a university. But all values being relative, it served then as it serves now.

In love with the grand gesture and in common with the others—he got himself a black mortar-board with a beautiful red-silk tassel hanging overboard: a pair of light-gray, skin-tight pants—in vogue then: toothpick shoes. And he dressed and acted the part with his hair still rather too long for it all. An incorrigible sentimentalist.

But his heart was never in this education. It never seemed to be for him. Where was architecture in all this?

This "education" meant nothing so much to him as a vague sort of emotional distress, a sickening sense of fear—of what he could not say. The inner meaning of nothing came clear. Besides there was something embarrassing in the competitive atmosphere. Something oppressive and threatening in the life of rules and regulations. Both hampered him.

So the university training of one Frank Lloyd Wright, Freshman, Sophomore, Junior, and part-time Senior was lost like some race run under a severe handicap, a race which you know in your heart you are foredoomed to lose: a kind of competition in which you can see nobody winning anywhere. Nor quite knowing why anyone should want to win. Just for the degree? Emulation? Just to be one of the countless many who had that certificate?

Things would start but nothing would seem to happen.

It wasn't like the farm. Doctrine, it was. Perfunctory opinion administered the doctrine. He was being doctored in a big crowd and the doses never seemed to produce any visible effect at any vital spot whatever; and anyway, he didn't feel sick. Science Hall was in course of construction. So was the machine shop and chemical laboratory. He didn't get into those new buildings.

His course didn't lead him into any shop at all, although he did get a beautiful red and white field rod and a fine transit into his hands and went surveying with his classmates. And there was the testing of materials. But finally he did get to work on the buildings themselves by the way of his generous employer, Professor Conover.

At that time Science Hall was being built by a Milwaukee architect out of Professor Conover's office, the professor being superintendent of buildings for the University. So the young sophomore got a little actual contact with this construction. He was entrusted with the working out of some steel clips to join the apex of the trusses of the main tower roof. . . . They wouldn't go together and the workmen, disgusted, left them hanging up there against the sky by the few bolts that would go in.

It was dead of winter—only the iron beams of the floors were in place in the floor levels below. All was slippery with ice, but he went up there, climbing the lattice on the chords of the trusses to the very top, with nothing between him and the ground but that forest of open steel beams. Got the clips loose. Dropped them down.

That was educational?

And the office work with Professor Conover was a great good for him. As he realized then and since. That work was truly educational. But in the university, notwithstanding certain appearances, he was and remained outsider, yearning all the while for the active contact with the soil or for the tests of a free life of action—waiting for something to happen that never happened. Now he realizes that it never could have happened, for "they" were all there to see that it did not and should not happen.

Reading Goethe only made matters worse, for action, again action and more action was his urge.

The boy already wondered why "Culture"—that was what the University stood for wasn't it?—shouldn't consist in getting rid of the inappropriate in everything. Whereas "Education" as he encountered it was as inappropriate as the rubbish wheeled by the contractor into the foundation piers of the Capitol. This he couldn't have told you then, but he felt it somehow—as resentment.

But his "Classical" course whenever he compared it with the life on the farm seemed to him to be the very *practice* of the inappropriate; so any human edifice reared up on it was likely to fall down like the Capitol.

Gestures were here, fine enough but—how about *work*? Reality?

The feeling about this best period of youth, lasting three and one-half years, is not so much that it was wasted.

How foolish to say anything is wasted in the living of any life!

Were one thing different, all were different.

So what weakness to regret any incident or turning.

"Might-have-beens" are for the "Never-weres." Uncle James said that.

Nature is organic in Man's character-making as in other forms. His instinct was not to criticize her work unless he could know her method and discern her ends: thanks, for this, to the farm.

But Man's puny mind so affronts "Nature" continually! He never knows what happens to him because of his philosophy, his "wisdom" usually something *on* life and seldom *of* life.

Motoring to and from Taliesin—seeing masses of the ten or more thousand students increasingly thronging grounds and buildings of the University, overflowing University Avenue, comes the same feeling of unhappiness. Something tragic in it all: a seeming futility or betrayal? The feeling is indefinable, but deep. A resentment against the mass product? Deeper than that. A conviction of betrayal.

Small wonder that we grow "old." Educated so soon.

The College Town

FROM *American Memoir*

The small college town has something of the character, feeling, and tone, that mark a mill or a coal town. It is a one-industry town, the product of which is education. The town is an echo of the college, and its small talk and gossip are trade talk and shop talk. In this selection, Henry Seidel Canby, critic and social historian, considers town and industry.

Canby has maintained one or another connection with Yale since he graduated in 1899. He taught freshman English at the Sheffield Scientific School, helped edit The Yale Review *and still lectures from time to time on literary criticism or on writing.*

I REMEMBER first the college town. Surely it is amazing that neither history, nor sociology, nor even fiction, has given more than passing attention to the American college town, for it has had a character and a personality unlike other towns. And quite as surely, its imprint of small-town respectability, convention, and common sense is deeper upon American education than has ever been guessed. With the rarest exceptions the home of the college has been a small town, even if that town was a suburb or a section, self-contained, of a city. There were hundreds of such towns in the period of which I write, and all with a family resemblance.

Cleaner, neater than other towns, with green spaces somewhere toward the center, and white spires of Gothic towers or windowed dormitories half hid by trees, they were the little capitals of the academic states. As trading or industrial centers their life might be indistinguishable from towns or cities of a like size, but in their social consciousness there was always some recognition of peculiarity. For the heart of the community was a college. Its subtle influences were as pervasive, if less noticeable, than the quite unsubtle symbols of college life—playing fields, cafés, and collegiate clothing.

And in the early nineteen-hundreds the college town was no luncheon

450

stop for automobiles. It was secluded, even if it was a town within a city, like the Yale section of New Haven; it knew its boundaries and kept them; it was jealous of its distinctions; if it was uneasy, it was also proud. The campus and the college buildings dominated its architecture like the temple and citadel of a Greek city-state, a difficult relationship since there was always some doubt in the minds of the town folk whether the college was an asset or a parasite. The town with its college was like a women's club committee with a celebrity in tow, a credit to them but also an embarrassment and sometimes a nuisance; it was like a French village built upon a Roman camp to which tourists resort; it was like the mistress of an actors' boarding house, pleased by the notoriety but worried by the manners, or the morals, of her boarders; it was like almost anything but a town without a college. And many a college town was like a resentful mother who, expecting a quiet and manageable infant, had given birth to a Gargantua that swallowed whole streets and squares in its gigantic growing. I do not wish to be fantastic, yet only such similes will express how very unlike the rest of the United States was the college town.

New Haven, as I first knew it in the late nineties, was a decorous and beautiful town, set in the midst of a sprawling industrial city of slums, factories, and long, undistinguished avenues. The college town was old New Haven, with its Green, its bordering business streets, its campus and blocks of residences north-stretching into park and country beyond. The elm-shaded streets of this old town were lined by sedate houses which in various modes still kept the impress of the Greek revival of the early nineteenth century. Eight out of ten had a portico of wood with two Doric columns painted brown or gray or white. Down the length of shady streets these columns made a pleasant arcade, broken here and there by high brick mansions of the eighties, or a charming green-shuttered, white-walled reminder of the better proportions of a Colonial day.

It was a guarded town, very unlike the ample if ugly spaciousness of the mansarded avenues of my youth, where broad porches and open gates welcomed relatives and friends. There were no open doors in the New England college town. Behind the twin Doric columns, which might have been labeled Respectability and Reserve, two squint lights seemed always to be looking down their noses at the passer-by, fearful lest he should wish to enter. The college town, unlike the rest of America, was jealous of privacy, and doubtful of casual relationships.

Lights went out early in these bosky streets, often to be relit in upstairs studies. When the chapel bell rang ten, and the undergraduate navigating homeward across the Green filled the night with shouts and melody, the prim town pulled up its covers, shut its ears, or burrowed deeper in a book. Nights in the college town were consecrated to sleep or work.

Along these town streets, professors lived, students wandered, but also the social and professional leaders of the city sought residence, because, after all, it was the college that gave tone to the community. Academic society was therefore both town and gown, and had a double flavor which recalled in homely fashion the atmosphere of those small European courts where both prince and bishop had their following. It was not an exciting society, yet certainly it was not dull. New Haven had never forgotten that it was once a colony, all of itself, and might have been a state had it not sheltered republicans and regicides. There was a stiff, aristocratic quality in the old families, now entirely lost there as elsewhere in America. From their harsh stalks sprouted personalities of extraordinary independence, so that it was hard to tell sometimes whether decorum or eccentricity was the dominant note of the town's society. These families belonged to the college world, yet were not wholeheartedly of it. They arranged its finances, fought its lawsuits, supplied a president or a professor now and then, were mysteriously powerful sometimes in academic affairs, yet in general their attitude of respectful but slightly contemptuous toleration of learning, so characteristic of America, was tempered only by the belief that the college belonged to them and put them a cut above the aristocracies of Hartford or Springfield, and made them able to take rank even in New York. Hence the teacher, who in his money-making age lived on the edge or beyond of society, in the college town might have a definite place, though he was not society himself. Wealth and position did not so much stoop to him as restrain their privileges so that he could enter. By a self-denying ordinance, tacitly understood, the rich in the college set (and no other society counted) spent only a part of their incomes at home, eschewed butlers, denied themselves broughams, and later, for a while, automobiles, kept dues low in the clubs, and, if they did spend, put their money into that good wine and costly food which the scholar has always enjoyed. And he responded with an unexpected geniality which was sometimes grateful and sometimes lumbering, and sometimes only a courteous irony.

Thus the college was privileged socially, not only in the hand-picked sons of the cultivated or the well-to-do that came as students, but in the close contacts between the faculty and the aristocracy of the college town. But it was conditioned also by the life of a small-town community, which, no matter how good its traditions, how admirable its character, how genuine its culture, was, by definition, a little provincial, a little priggish, and very much inbred. And yet there was a raciness in this mingling of town and gown that gave its own flavor to the college society, and was some compensation for the gustier airs which blew through capitals and metropolises.

I can see now a characteristic "reception" in a great house behind the broad sweep of the elms of Hillhouse Avenue, which was to the college town of New Haven what Fifth Avenue once was to New York—a terminus of social pride. Tables were laden with heavy, mind-satisfying food, champagne bubbled on the sideboards, stiff-backed professors were trying to relax, while their wives, with the curious pursed mouth of the academic woman, showed more concern for their dignity than for the entertainment. Among them moved the grand dames of our town society, soothing vanities by a kind word, snubbing with a vacant look the strange uncouth creatures that science was bringing into the university, but not too emphatically, since one never knew nowadays who might become famous. And with them were our town eccentrics, women usually of old families, too sure of themselves to bother about social distinctions. Worse dressed than the professors' wives, they had a confident distinction of ugliness which lifted them above our small-town limitations, and they spoke the language of the academic world with understanding and tolerance, like missionaries among an Indian tribe. Trailing behind them, yet always heading back toward the champagne, were our faculty "characters"—the great hearty souls that scholarship which is not pedantry creates in its happier moods, men whose broadcloth might be shiny and spotted, their linen none too clean, yet with minds and faces of the great world, known in Europe and conscious of it, witty often, sarcastic usually, ill-mannered, inclined to lash out at this pompous bourgeois society, which nevertheless gave them their only chance to eat, drink, and be merry with their own kind. There was our famous Chaucerian scholar, Lounsbury, his sparse white beard wagging under his rapid tongue, his eyes a little bleary, an epigram worth quoting with every glass of champagne. "Why do they want to inscribe old Whitney's name on the Court House wall? All he knew was Sanskrit. What did he ever do for New Haven?" says a banker. "Do!" Lounsbury shoots back. "By Gorry! It's enough that he lived here!"

There were subtle jealousies between town and gown which could not be assigned to differences in income. The town had inherited a Yankee distrust of ministers who talked about God but made no money, and now that ministers were less and professors more it transferred this distrust with increments. It was irritated by its own deference to an institution that did not make for profits. Energy that in other communities was organizing machine tools or life insurance, here in this college community leaked away in a trickle that sometimes carried sons and heirs with it into the academic world where it was transformed into the teaching of adolescents or into books that nobody but professors read. The town derived a goodly share of its income from the rapidly increasing expenditures of the college and its students, and this, too, it resented, feeling that it was committed to an approval of what the college was doing. It endured the noisy night life of the students, the untidy boarding houses that crowded its streets, the frequent arrogance of the academic mind, but it disliked the haunting sense of inferiority which came from knowing that it was celebrated because of the college. It listened to the endless shop-talk of the faculty and pretended to take the "big men" of the undergraduate world at their face value, but it could not entirely respect, and still less understand, the creature upon which it lived and which it believed it had created. Not until the expansive twenties when alumni, enriched by the war and prosperity, upset their applecarts of gold into the college coffers, and made education, or at least the side-shows of education, a big business, was the town convinced that the college, its own college, was worthy of its birthplace. No Commencement orator was ever so persuasive as gifts in the millions and a building program that was a major industry.

And yet, as with Christians and Infidels living together in old Spain, there was more interpenetration than appeared on the surface. The college taught the town to discuss ideas; it taught also friendship and a delight in the companionship of like-minded men. The two blended in the adult life of the community, for the habit of the undergraduate fraternity persisted in dozens of little clubs of talkers which flourished throughout the town because their members had learned clubability. It was a rash hostess who gave a dinner party on Wednesday or Friday nights, their favorite meeting times. In these clubs scholar, lawyer, and business man ate, drank, and read papers explaining their jobs or their social philosophy. Ideas spread through the college town, freed from that taboo on abstractions which was the curse of the small town elsewhere in America, and many a scholar was saved from pedantry, or a paralysis of the emotions in the arid wastes of specialist theory, by his contacts with men whose daily task was the handling of men. Even the women became clubable; and indeed it was in New Haven that by happy inspiration Our Society was born, whose inestimable privilege after the meeting was to inspect every closet in their hostess's house. But it was a man's town.

Still another institution the college gave to the society of the town, the college widow. I knew two of them in their old age and profited greatly from my friendships. For the college widow had a depth and richness of emotional experience never developed in American life of that day outside of the few metropolises, and seldom there. She began at sixteen or eighteen as a ravishing beauty, the darling of freshmen; she passed on in the years of her first blooming from class to class of ardent youngsters, until, as her experience ripened, she acquired a taste, never to be satisfied by matrimony, for male admiration abstracted from its consequences; and, more subtly, for the heady stimulant of intimacy with men in their fresh and vigorous youth. By her thirties she had learned the art of eternal spring, and had become a connoisseur in the dangerous excitement of passion controlled at the breaking point, a mistress of every emotion, and an adept in the difficult task of sublimating love into friendship. The students lived out their brief college life and went on; she endured, and tradition with her, an enchantress in illusion, and a specialist in the heart. Twenty, even thirty years, might be her tether; and when suddenly on a midnight, a shock of reality, or perhaps only boredom, ended it all, she was old—but still charming and infinitely wise. To smoke a cigarette with her when cigarettes were taboo for women, and drink her coffee and liqueur, was a lesson in civilization.

Yet in fostering in its midst the sprawling infant, gray-headed but still growing, which was the college, the town sacrificed its own youth. There was childhood and maturity in a college town, but no youth in between. Youth male was absorbed into the undergraduate community and came home only on Sundays, youth female was usually sent off perforce to school or women's colleges, away from the dangerous glamour of college streets. Hence the young folk in the college town settled back into their home environment only in their mid or late twenties, and then only did social life in a community begin for them. There were no calf loves in the society of the college town, no gawkish immaturity, no giggling, no rebellious escapes. And since the young had reached the earning and marrying stage in a society where the scale of living was based upon an instructor's salary, their pleasures were necessarily simple. Relative poverty was regarded as a virtue, doing without was a pride. One walked, not rode; went to concerts rather than to the theater; danced to a piano and a cornet; gave books, not jewelry; sat down four at a table, not eight; kept married instead of toying with expensive ideas about lovers and divorce.

The results for the college town were by no means ill. The tittle-tattle of a small town had little fuel here. It was an educated society, and since it could not afford to be frivolous, and both puritan custom and economy held the passions in check, every opportunity was given to vivacity and ideas in conversation. Talk was cheap, which did not prevent it from being good. It was often stiff with convention and sometimes pedantical, yet the fun was more civilized than country-club horseplay, the wit, when any, aware of the nature of wit.

And yet it was all a little arid. The young people had come together too late. They had no sentimental memories to share, and thanks to the restrictions of what was, after all, a small town, and to the official nature of their college society, and to relative poverty, the sex in relationships was weak. Every emotion had its inhibition. Like the columns of the houses, the twin shrines in every heart were Reserve and Respectability.

The college town was thus the imperfect resultant of two worlds in a physical merger where souls and minds remained disparate. Even this understates the difficulty. The undergraduates belonged to the faction of the gown, but had themselves come in a vast majority from uncollegiate small towns, and so in ideas and attitudes toward learning were far closer to the Philistines of the streets than to the Israelites of the campus faculty. Their relations with the faculty could too often be described as passive resistance, usually with the sneaking sympathy of both parents and town. Hence there was a split in the college itself, so that in my days not a duality but a trinity —town, gown, and sweater—would have best described our community.

I have written of the college town with pleasure because I was happy there, and excited, and amused, and also cabin'd, cribb'd, confined; yet also with a very definite purpose. For it is impossible to think of the college of that day without its encircling town. This was the air the professor breathed, and which the student absorbed from his freshman year onward. For him the town often provided his first experience in adult social life. Nor in discussing the internal conflicts of the college itself which have been so decisive in shaping the type known as the college graduate, is it right to forget for a moment the influence of these nests of puritan respectability, given tone by the American aristocracy that clung to them for shelter from the make-money world outside. Here is a factor in education and in the faiths and prejudices of the educated and educator which has escaped the theorist and the statistician alike. We have forgotten that the types we analyze so readily—professors, alumni, humanists, scientists, scholars—were in their conditioning period American boys in a small college town.

Some of My Best Friends
Are Yale Men

FROM *Collected Edition of Heywood Broun*

Like the feud between the Hatfields and the McCoys, nobody knows how the Yale-Harvard feud got started—or why. Sufficient to the day is the tradition thereof.

Here Heywood Broun gives us the thinking, admittedly subjective, of a Harvard man on the subject. Broun was Harvard '10, but not by official sanction. He never received a degree because he couldn't bother to work off a "condition" in elementary French.

Broun was a passionate liberal in the days before that became a dirty word. He wrote articles and drama criticism, was one of the inner group that made the old New York World *famous for its columns, did a short stint as radio commentator, ran unsuccessfully for Congress, and founded the American Newspaper Guild. Broun was a passionate partisan against social injustice; his well-known newspaper column, "It Seems to Me," although it dealt with sports, manners, contemporary trivia and humor, was the storm center for liberal protest in the Sacco-Vanzetti case. In the heat of that great debate, Broun accused Harvard's President Lowell of having tacitly helped doom the poor fish peddler and the Italian shoemaker.*

Oh, Harvard was old Harvard
   when Yale was but a pup,
And Harvard will be Harvard
   Still when Yale has all gone up,
And if any Eli——

THIS is about as far as the old song should be carried. Perhaps it is too far. Our plea today is for something of abatement in the intensity of the rivalry between Harvard and Yale. To be sure, we realize that the plea has been made before unsuccessfully by mightier men. Indeed, it was Charles W. Eliot himself, president of Harvard, who rebuked the students when first they began to sing, "Three cheers for Harvard and down with Yale." This, he said, seemed to him hardly a proper spirit. He suggested an amendment so that the song might go, "Three cheers for Harvard and one for Yale." Such seventy-five per cent loyalty was rejected. Yale must continue to do its own cheering.

Naturally, it is not to be expected that Yale and Harvard men should meet on terms of perfect amity immediately and that the old bitterness should disappear within the time of our own generation. Such a miracle is beyond the scope of our intention. Too much has happened. Just what it was that Yale originally did to Harvard we don't profess to know. It was enough we suppose to justify the trial of the issues by combat four times a year in the major sports. Curiously enough, for a good many years Yale seemed to grow more and more right if judged in the light of these tests. But the truth is mighty and shall prevail and the righteousness of Harvard's cause began to be apparent with the coming of Percy Haughton. God, as some cynic has said, is always on the side which has the best football coach.

Our suggestion is that whatever deep wrong Yale once committed against Harvard, a process of diminution of feeling should be allowed to set in. After all, can't the men of Cambridge be broad-minded about these things and remember that nothing within the power of Yale could possibly hurt Harvard very much? Even in the days when the blue elevens were winning with great regularity there should have been consolation enough in the thought that Harvard's Greek Department still held the edge. Seemingly nobody ever thought of that. In the 1906 game a Harvard halfback named Nichols was sent in late in the game while the score was still a tie. On practically the first play he dropped a punt which led directly to a Yale touchdown and victory.

Throughout the rest of his university career he was known in college as "the man who dropped the punt." When his brother entered Harvard two years later he was promptly christened, and known for his next four years, as "the brother of the man who dropped the punt."

Isn't this a little excessive? It seems so to us, but the emphasis has not yet shifted. Only a month or so ago we were talking in New Haven before an organization of Yale graduates upon a subject so unpartisan as the American drama—though to be sure Harvard has turned out ten playwrights of note to every one from Yale—and somehow or other the talk drifted around to football. In pleading for less intensity of football feeling, we mentioned the man who dropped the punt and his brother and told how Yale had recovered the fatal fumble on Harvard's nineteen-yard line. Then, with the intention of being jocose, we remarked, "The Yale eleven with characteristic bulldog grit and courage carried the ball over the line." To our horror and amazement the audience immediately broke into applause and long cheers.

Some of my best friends are Yale men and there is no basis for the common Harvard assumption that graduates of New Haven's leading university are of necessity inferior to the breed at Cambridge. Still, there is, perhaps, just a shade of difference in the keenness of perception of wit. Practically all the Harvard anecdotes about Yale which we know are pointed and sprightly, while Yale is content with inferior and tasteless jibes, as the falsetto imitation which begins, "Fiercely fellows, sift through." Even the audience of graduates to which we referred was singularly cold to the anecdote about the difference in traditions which prevails at New Haven and at Cambridge. "When a Yale man is sick, the authorities immediately assume that he is drunk. When a Harvard man is drunk, the authorities assume that he is sick."

Nor were we successful in retelling the stirring appeal of a well-known organizer who was seeking to consolidate various alumni bodies into a vast unified employment agency for college men. "There should be," he cried, "one great clearinghouse. Then when somebody came for a man to tutor his children we could send him a Harvard man and if he needed somebody to help with the furnace, we'd have a Yale graduate for him."

Joking with undergraduates we found still more disastrous. After the last Harvard-Yale football game—score Harvard 9, Yale 0, which doesn't begin to indicate the margin of superiority of the winning team—we wrote an article of humorous intent for a New York newspaper. Naturally our job as a reporter prevented us from being partisan in our account of the game. Accordingly, in a temperate and fair-minded spirit, we set down the fact that, through the connivance of the New York press, Yale has become a professional underdog and that any Harvard victory in which the score is less than 42-0 is promptly hailed as a moral victory for Yale.

Developing this news angle for a few paragraphs, we eventually came to the unfortunate fist fight between Kempton of Yale and Gaston of Harvard which led to both men being put out of the game. It was our bad luck to see nothing but the last half-second of the encounter. As a truthful reporter we made this admission but naturally went on to add, "Of course, we assume that Kempton started it." For weeks we continued to receive letters from Yale undergraduates beginning, "My attention has been called to your article" and continuing to ask with great violence how a reporter could possibly tell who started a fight without seeing the beginning of it. Some letters of like import were from Princeton men.

Princeton is always quick to rally to the defense of Yale against Harvard.

This suggests a possible common meeting ground for Harvard and Yale. Of course they can hardly meet on the basis of a common language, for the speech of Yale is quite alien. For instance, they call their "yard" a "campus." Also, there are obvious reasons why they cannot meet as equal members in the fellowship of educated men. Since this is a nonpartisan article designed to promote good feeling it will probably be just as well not to go into this. Though football is the chief interest at New Haven, Yale men often display a surprising sensitiveness to attacks on the scholarship of their local archeologists. Nor will religion do as a unifier. Yale is evangelical and prays between the halves, while Harvard is mostly agnostic, if it isn't Unitarian. No, just one great cause can be discovered in which Harvard men and Yale men can stand shoulder to shoulder and lift their voices in a common cause. Each year some public-spirited citizen ought to hire Madison Square Garden and turn it over to all graduates and undergraduates of Harvard and Yale for a great get-together meeting in which past differences should be forgotten in one deep and full-throated shout of "To Hell with Princeton!"

All Sons of
Dear Ol' Washin'ton

FROM *College Humor*

*John Monk Saunders, in this sprightly piece on varied and inebriated
alumni of dear ol' Washington insists there ought to be some positive means
of identification for college brothers met in the odd bistros of the world.
It would seem a reasonable demand, considering.*

*Saunders was, of course, Washington—class of 1919. He followed with
a sojourn at Oxford as Rhodes Scholar, and returned to America to report
for the* Los Angeles Times *and the* New York Herald Tribune, *and to write
musical comedies and screen plays.*

Y OU," said the man, earnestly waggling his finger, "are all brothers, blood
brothers of learning, all sons of Washington. You will carry her traditions,
her ideals, her spirit with you out into the world. No matter where you go,
how high you rise or how low you fall, remember that you are sons of
Washington. You will stand by each other, cheer each other on, fight for
each other."

With that solemn objurgation ringing in my ears I went forth into the
world. Certainly I would carry the name of dear old Washington to the far
corners of the earth. If any other son of old Washington needed help I
would be right at his elbow.

My first opportunity presented himself on the Ritz Roof one evening. It
being New Year's Eve and a jocose and informal spirit being abroad, and
strangers saluting one another's wives and lady friends with Happy New
Years and everybody out for a good time, it was not a shock to find a mis-
cellaneous individual seated at our table when we returned after a round
on the floor.

461

He appeared harmless enough, albeit a bit awry-eyed, and there seemed to be little point in guiding him to his proper table, since this was probably just a whim and undoubtedly he would set out soon under his own steam.

However, he welcomed me graciously to my seat and then cocking his head knowingly at me inquired: "Aren't you Freddy Weddy?"

"No, nor Georgie Porgie."

"New Haven?"

"No."

"Where'd you go?"

"Washington," said I weakly.

"I *thought* I reco'nized you! Tha's *my* school. Good ol' Washington! *Good* ol' Washin'ton!"

Thereupon he reached under the table and helped himself to the New Year's cheer that had been thoughtfully provided for the party. Though no one had had him particularly in mind when the negus had been negotiated for.

Attempts to ascertain the direction and extent of his studies at our Alma Mater elicited only a "Good ol' Washin'ton," a phrase which he was heard to utter periodically and with increasing vehemence thereafter. He only varied once and that was when he shouted confidentially in my ear that he was dead, dead broke and would one Washin'tonian lend 'nother Washin'tonian ten dollars. He did, and the whimsical stranger and the ten dollars faded mysteriously from view.

Some time later, in the Green Cockatoo in Vienna, while I was seated at a table, buried deep in reflection, I was favored by the speculative glance of a young man nearby and eventually addressed:

" 'Merican?"

"That's right."

"Where y' from?"

"America."

"I know, but whereat?"

"The Pacific slope."

"*California!*" he exclaimed eagerly.

"No," said I happily, "Washington."

"*Wash'n'ton!*" he cried. "Are *you* from Wash'n'ton too? Well, I'll be—what do you know—well, I'm a—well, for—can you—Are *you* from Wash'n'-ton? So'm I! Good ol' Wash'n'ton!

"Jus' think of us two Washin'tony—Washin'tony—onions meetin' here clear th' other side of the worl'. 'Magine it?

" 'S a damn' lucky thing f'r me I run acrost you like this," he confided. "Don' know what I woulda done. Fact is," he said, "fact is, I'm broke. You know, 'f I hadn't run into you tonight, I couldn't 've got out of here to-night. Couldn't 've paid the check. Haw-haw-haw. 'Magine 'at?

"You got twenty-fi' bucks, ain't you? Sure. Jus' till tomorrow. Got a 'Merican 'spress check comin' in t'morrow sure."

His name, it developed, was "Smish" and he was stopping at the "Brish-tol," and the miracle of two sons of Washington meeting providentially like this cost me twenty-five dollars.

But before I gave up completely I fixed him with a stern eye.

"Young man," I said severely, "you've seen better days."

"Ah, yes," quoth he, "but not better nights."

I surrendered immediately and Smish and the twenty-five swam out of my ken forever.

A week or so later when Tracy Cole and I were standing in Madame Sacha's celebrated emporium behind the Vienna Opernhaus doing our daily dozen along with Count Salm and other playmates a slightly shopworn young man edged his way up to my elbow. Inevitably he spoke up.

"From the States?"

"Oh, quite," I said in my top-hattest manner.

"What part?"

"The West," I said panic-stricken.

His eyes brightened and a look of extreme recognition started to illu-mine his countenance.

"What college?"

I took a deep breath. "You say first!"

That was an inspiration, that answer. It saved the day then, and it has saved a few since.

I am still ready to cheer along my brothers in learning, and to fight for them, and to stand by them, but I want that there should be a more positive system of identification.

I'd Send My Son to Cornell

FROM *Our Cornell*

In this essay, Elwyn Brooks White gives some good reasons—and some very curious ones—to explain why he would send his boy to Cornell, but together they make up a picture well and lovingly remembered of four magic years. White, needless to say, is Cornell—1921.

Irwin Edman called White the finest essayist in the country, a writer who says "wise things gracefully." Besides his close association with The New Yorker—*he is not only one of that magazine's major writers and editors, but has also probably written more anonymous "Notes and Comment" than anyone else—he writes children's books which are avidly read by sophisticated adults.*

CORNELL is a fairly big institution. It has five or six thousand students counting the rabbit-hunters, and it dominates, from its high hill above Cayuga Lake, the town which lies at its feet. This physical and spiritual dominance of art over life, of gown over town, is a good thing for a boy to experience for a while. In a place like Columbia or N. Y. U. it must be obvious to the students, just from reading the papers, that the town holds the whip hand. In New York, dwellers in apartment buildings are in a position to spit out of the window and have it land on the head of a philosopher; this naturally gives the latter the wrong impression and makes him willing to compromise, or even dodge. But in Ithaca the Library tower commands the valley; learning dominates industry; and even the toboggan slide deposits the red-cheeked scholar far above the roofs of trade.

Cornell is not only big and high, it is cosmopolitan and friendly; and it is an infinitely various place. Its students do not run to type. On the Campus are found both sexes, all colors, all beliefs—from the most conservative fraternity sophomore with Republican tendencies and a contempt for the irregular, to the bloody-eyed anarchist who wants to tear the vines right off the buildings. My son will probably be a Christian, five feet nine; but he will make a great many friends in Ithaca who do not conform to that amazing standard. When I was there I knew two men from Hawaii, a girl from Johannesburg, a Cuban, a Turk, an Englishman from India, a Negro from New York, two farmers, three Swedes, a Quaker, five Southerners, a reindeer butcher, a second lieutenant, a Christian Scientist, a retired dancer, a motorcyclist, a man who had known Theda Bara, three gnomes, and a lutist. That's not counting the general run of broad-jumpers, second tenors, and veterinarians who make up the great body of the undergraduates, the same as in any school.

I suppose many parents hesitate to send a son to a coeducational school, but I think it is a good thing. At Cornell men outnumber women by four to one, or maybe five to one. This gives a male the steadying feeling that he is wearing the pants. To me the presence in my classes of a few nineteen-year-old girls was a stirring and beautiful phenomenon, rich in adventures of the mind and heart, and subtly prophetic of Man's Future. In general I think it is healthier for a college student to study the opposite sex in the flesh than in the movies: Marlene Dietrich may well be his heroine, but the girl across the aisle from him in his Money and Banking Class at least affords him a standard of comparison.

Some years ago at Cornell there was a great to-do about the coeds; a little band of supermen got together and decided that the women would have to be segregated in fairness to the football team, who seemed to be fumbling the ball a good deal. The students, both male and female, had a whirl of a time—they wrote letters to the paper, burned fiery crosses, and scattered broadsides in the early morning in front of the Library. After a while the futility of the battle began to be apparent; it was recalled by some of the quieter elements that the segregation of the ladies would be incompatible with the University's charter, which stated that anybody under the sun, with proper academic qualifications, could be a Cornellian.

There is really a great dissimilarity among coeducational schools. In some the sexes have established a rather annoying parity which is subversive to the pursuit of asceticism. But in Ithaca, although it is no sin for a man to walk across the quadrangle with a girl, he nevertheless is gnawed by the feeling that he should by rights be trying out for the soccer team.

In sending off a son, I suppose academic standing should be considered. I don't know how Cornell rates. As at other colleges, at Cornell one chooses a certain course because it happens to occur miraculously at 10 o'clock, thereby fitting in between one which occurs at 9 o'clock and one which occurs at 11. This is the universal accident of erudition—a touching quality. As at other universities, at Cornell the student is subjected to the benign influence of two or three dozen professors, of which three or four usually manage to get to first base. I know that Cornell turns out good doctors, lawyers, engineers, actors, farmers, poets, statesmen, architects, and salesmen; it seems to me its batting average is pretty high.

The amazing range of instruction available at Ithaca is itself an inspiration; for although one stays pretty much within one's narrow sphere of culture, the evidences of the broader life are all around on the Campus. The civil engineer, making his unceasing survey of the quadrangle, approaches the very steps of the Arts College; and this fills him with an awareness of the realm of pure beauty he will never enter. In return, the Arts student, tripping over a transit, is humbled by the power of exact science. Further, Cornell is a land grant institution; its Agricultural College pays homage to the State, and this flavors the whole place with the sweet breath of kine and endows it with the vitality of the soil. I'd send my son to Cornell because, passing the Vet College where dogs howl by day and by night, he will be reminded that even in the Almost Perfect State toward which his education is wafting him, all dogs will have worms and be disconsolate.

I'd send my son to Ithaca because it has the most perilous topography in sixteen counties; and because he'd find men trained by Will Strunk, Jr., who first hoped to graft me on the tree of knowledge by emphasizing the sanctity of an English sentence (of which I hope this article is full). I'd send him there to walk up Six Mile Creek in the early wetness of a recalcitrant spring; and because, returning, he might meet Uncle Pete Smith, who has a soft voice and a humble spirit. I would send him to sit in the mysterious Sunday night conclaves of a Greek-letter den, in robes that smell of other sophomores and other Sunday nights. Cornell is one of the most Grecian of the big fraternity centers—but it doesn't seem to do anybody much harm. Formerly, before Willard Straight Hall was erected as a pleasance for the independent students, there was a practical disadvantage in not belonging to a fraternity—a disadvantage which very nearly offset the splendid spiritual catharsis of living in that unholy state. Willard Straight Hall now offers all the comforts of home to everybody, and the fraternities are beginning to feel the way speakeasies felt after repeal: that there is nothing to be exclusive about any more.

I am this way and that way about fraternities. They are ostensibly founded on brotherhood, but in practice they thrive on a gentle snobbery. In spite of that, they do seem to solve, in a curiously fortuitous way, the acute problem of sleeping and eating and talking. Mine, in addition to furnishing me with friends, satisfied my proprietary instincts: I had a lawn, a bed, a dining table, a library. I was always troubled, though, by the uneasy feeling that the "independent" students, who did not conform to the arbitrary standards of dress and conversation dictated by the fraternities, were probably getting a whole lot better education; and I envied them their freedom of conscience, implicit in the word "independent."

I would send a son to Cornell because it would be impossible for him to come home frequently. When you get to Ithaca, you stay put. The ice forms early, and you buy a sheepskin coat and dig in for the winter along about the first of November. I would send him there to walk up from the *Sun* offices at quarter to six, and see the lighthouses on the Inlet; to go to Bristow Adams's house, which has been home for many students; to meet Woodford Patterson, Bull Durham, Tubby Sailor, Morris Bishop, Rym Berry; and to see the room where Martin Sampson taught—his profile strong in the light from the west window. I would send him to doze over supplementary reading in the Library; and to explore Varna, Enfield, Trumansburg, Renwick, West Danby, and the pool below the suspension bridge. And I will be disturbed if he fails to grow homesick on one of those Sunday afternoons of the first fall, when the hill drones with banjo chords and when an invisible freshman, unable to endure longer the sultriness of the Sabbath, brings life to a little head by firing off a blank.

WILLIAM MAKEPEACE THACKERAY

On University Snobs

FROM *The Book of Snobs*

William Makepeace Thackeray, Victorian novelist, had a jaundiced eye for colleges and college characters, as this selection on the varieties of college snobs demonstrates. He cut short his own university career at Trinity College, Cambridge, after a year, deciding that "the studies would be of no use" to him. Most of that short year was evenly divided between an immense amount of reading in fiction, poetry and history, that had no bearing on his university courses, and a hectic social life, fox-hunting, attending supper parties and, says one biographer, "considering his luck, gambling more than he should."

I SHOULD like to fill several volumes with accounts of various University Snobs; so fond are my reminiscences of them, and so numerous are they. I should like to speak, above all, of the wives and daughters of some of the Professor-Snobs: their amusements, habits, jealousies; their innocent artifices to entrap young men; their picnics, concerts, and evening parties. I wonder what has become of Emily Blades, daughter of Blades, the Professor of the Mandingo language? I remember her shoulders to this day, as she sat in the midst of a crowd of about seventy young gentlemen, from Corpus and Catherine Hall, entertaining them with ogles and French songs on the guitar. Are you married, fair Emily of the shoulders? What beautiful ringlets those were that used to dribble over them!—what a waist!—what a killing sea-green shot-silk gown!—what a cameo, the size of a muffin! There were thirty-six young men of the University in love at one time with Emily Blades: and no words are sufficient to describe the pity, the sorrow, the deep deep commiseration—the rage, fury, and uncharitableness, in other words—with which the Miss Trumps (daughters of Trumps, the Professor of Phlebotomy) regarded her, because she *didn't* squint, and because she *wasn't* marked with the small-pox.

As for the young University Snobs, I am getting too old, now, to speak of such very familiarly. My recollections of them lie in the far far past—almost as far back as Pelham's time.

We *then* used to consider Snobs raw-looking lads, who never missed chapel; who wore highlows and no straps; who walked two hours on the Trumpington road every day of their lives; who carried off the college scholarships, and who overrated themselves in hall. We were premature in pronouncing our verdict of youthful Snobbishness. The man without straps fulfilled his destiny and duty. He eased his old governor, the curate in Westmoreland, or helped his sisters to set up the Ladies' School. He wrote a "Dictionary," or a "Treatise on Conic Sections," as his nature and genius prompted. He got a fellowship: and then took to himself a wife, and a living. He presides over a parish now, and thinks it rather a dashing thing to belong to the "Oxford and Cambridge Club;" and his parishioners love him, and snore under his sermons. No, no, *he* is not a Snob. It is not straps that make the gentleman, or highlows that unmake him, be they ever so thick. My son, it is you who are the Snob if you lightly despise a man for doing his duty, and refuse to shake an honest man's hand because it wears a Berlin glove.

We then used to consider it not the least vulgar for a parcel of lads who had been whipped three months previous, and were not allowed more than three glasses of port at home, to sit down to pineapples and ices at each other's rooms, and fuddle themselves with champagne and claret.

One looks back to what was called a "wine-party" with a sort of wonder. Thirty lads round a table covered with bad sweetmeats, drinking bad wines, telling bad stories, singing bad songs over and over again. Milk punch—smoking—ghastly headache—frightful spectacle of dessert-table next morning, and smell of tobacco—your guardian, the clergyman, dropping in, in the midst of this—expecting to find you deep in Algebra, and discovering the gyp administering soda-water.

There were young men who despised the lads who indulged in the coarse hospitalities of wine-parties, who prided themselves in giving *recherché* little French dinners. Both wine-party-givers and dinner-givers were Snobs.

There were what used to be called "dressy" Snobs:—Jimmy, who might be seen at five o'clock elaborately rigged out, with a camellia in his button-hole, glazed boots, and fresh kid-gloves twice a day;—Jessamy, who was conspicuous for his "jewellery,"—a young donkey, glittering all over with chains, rings, and shirt-studs;—Jacky, who rode every day solemnly on the Blenheim Road, in pumps and white silk stockings, with his hair curled,—all three of whom flattered themselves they gave laws to the University about dress—all three most odious varieties of Snobs.

Sporting Snobs of course there were, and are always—those happy beings in whom Nature has implanted a love of slang; who loitered about the horsekeeper's stables, and drove the London coaches—a stage in and out—and might be seen swaggering through the courts in pink of early mornings, and indulged in dice and blind-hookey at nights, and never missed a race or a boxing-match; and rode flat-races, and kept bull-terriers. Worse Snobs even than these were poor miserable wretches who did not like hunting at all, and could not afford it, and were in mortal fear at a two-foot ditch; but who hunted because Glenlivat and Cinqbars hunted. The Billiard Snob and the Boating Snob were varieties of these, and are to be found elsewhere than in universities.

Then there were Philosophical Snobs, who used to ape statesmen at the spouting-clubs, and who believed as a fact that Government always had an eye on the University for the selection of orators for the House of Commons. There were audacious young free-thinkers, who adored nobody or nothing, except perhaps Robespierre and the Koran, and panted for the day when the pale name of priest should shrink and dwindle away before the indignation of an enlightened world.

But the worst of all University Snobs are those unfortunates who go to rack and ruin from their desire to ape their betters. Smith becomes acquainted with great people at college, and is ashamed of his father the tradesman. Jones has fine acquaintances, and lives after their fashion like a gay free-hearted fellow as he is, and ruins his father, and robs his sister's portion, and cripples his younger brother's outset in life, for the pleasure of entertaining my lord, and riding by the side of Sir John. And though it may be very good fun for Robinson to fuddle himself at home as he does at College, and to be brought home by the policeman he has just been trying to knock down—think what fun it is for the poor old soul his mother!—the half-pay captain's widow, who has been pinching herself all her life long, in order that that jolly young fellow might have a University education.

Are Collegiate Flappers a Flop?

FROM *College Humor*

Apart from the clothes and the patter, the coed apparently hasn't altered much in the thirty-odd years since this knowing appraisal was penned. The essentials seem to be unvarying. This sprightly study of O. O. McIntyre's considers the coed of the flapper days, those frenetically formative years when new patterns of collegiate behavior were being shaped—to the accompaniment of some fairly extreme experimentation.

O. O. McIntyre was one of the most popular columnists of the hectic '20s. His syndicated column of New York's doings had an estimated readership of millions.

M OST of us middle-aged birds who sit around in club lounges in valetudinarian ease testing our knee jerks and speculating on whether we will have the inevitable toupee parted in the middle or on the side have a decided contempt for the young folks of the day.

We see Joe Doakes' daughter Mary come back from four years at a tony finishing school snapping a Dunhill lighter, inhaling a cigarette to the ankles, and slithering a new Black Bottom step that is nothing less than a panic.

We hang to old traditions like the two-toed sloth to a limb. When a girl used to "go away to school" it meant she would come back fitted to teach Greek or Delsarte—what's become of that, by the way?—in the North High. Eventually she would marry the banker's son, live in a house on the hill in the River Oaks subdivision and go in for club work. And be pointed out as "the girl who went to Vassar."

Today Mary Doakes comes home to shock the preacher with a fast one about the Pullman porter and the deaf old lady, becomes known in the hot

471

joints as "Go-Go, queen of the uke" and is spoken of in whispers by Aunt Libbie Adams as being wild as a pigeon.

She can gulp six jolts of gin and thread a needle to sew up a runner. Warbles of faithless lovers and downhearted frails and seems about as helpful to her folks as a carbuncle. In a few words she knows her onions and is a red-hot sketch.

Her talk is the scrambled jargon of the Broadway wisecracking world. She is "hep" to all the latest nifties and her conversational patter has the rapid-fire manner of a machine gun.

The bashful young man with the faint down on his upper lip approaches her, feeling all feet and hands, to beg for a dance. Instead of the mid-Victorian curtsy and a modulated "That would be charming!" she flips her cigarette among the palms and cries: "Sold to the gentleman with the blond mustache."

And if he doesn't know how to "lay the leather" she jockeys him to a table, and while emptying his flask tells the poor squirt he reminds her of John Barrymore and gives him her wrong telephone number.

And the college flappers' clothes! My, my! Just the other day Aunt Het received a request for a contribution to help buy clothing for the heathen and she remarked, "Thank heavens, the flappers are coming to their senses."

Most of the girls trek home from school in a dress that wouldn't be sufficient to dust off a flute and the skirts wouldn't make a self-respecting pen wiper. At an age when the girls of grandma's day feared the coming of walnut knuckles and goat's elbows, our flappers air their knee caps in public and V their dresses about two notches below the twelfth vertebra.

The flappers may not indulge in tracing the history of Florentine art under the soft glow of the parlor lamp with grammy chaperoning between cat naps, but they have a "stewdious" mind just the same. And any one of them can tell you right off the bat how to take a half pint of shoe polish, six drops of hyoscine and a gill of ether and frost up the shaker with a concoction that will probably result in your being found on somebody's roof top next morning cutting out paper dolls and babbling the old Russian folk song *Da*.

They have the vitality of the eagle and are just as swift. You see them one morning greeting the dawn with a slight hiccup outside of a New York supper club, and at luncheon the same day you see them tearing the herring or messing up the avocado with the boy friend in the Voisin, Colony or sunken gardens of the Ritz. There they are—all merry and bright and getting ready to snap into one of those phony afternoon teas where everybody gets blotto.

Of course, the girls don't have to go to finishing schools to pick up these high-jumping ideas. And I know a college flapper who doesn't smoke, drink or dance. She has rheumatism.

So it is that most of us who used to stand out on the Flatiron Building corner on windy days have found out we don't have to any more. That's what the modern co-ed with her short skirts and sheer stockings has done for us. Hooray for education!

I can remember when Elise Dufour, the wholesale grocery people, came back from three years at a young ladies' seminary in Washington, D. C. She shocked Second Street by riding a ladies' safety bicycle wearing a divided skirt. There was talk of calling off her engagement to read from Sir Walter Scott at the monthly meeting of the Thursday Club, which incidentally met on Tuesdays.

What a laugh for these tumultuous times when girls romp home, give papa and mamma a pecking kiss, hop into the roadster to flush out a reliable bootlegger, bring home the makings and by dusk probably have papa sleeping feet up in the kitchen sink and mamma kicking up the drawing room rugs to do a Charleston.

If you haven't a little college flapper in your home you really don't know what real fun and gayety are. They are the life of any home, apartment or what have you in the way of domiciles. No meek wallflowers among these squabs. The only way they will sit against the wall is to "gin" out a dance.

They can discuss the Lesbian theme of the drama between cigarette puffs with all the bland innocence of a golden-haired child reciting her piece at a Christmas cantata. They are roguishly rouged and often buoyantly bunned and yet—

Just try to get fresh with these bambinos! You will instantly receive one of those cold, metallic laughs where the face doesn't change expression. You know the sort. The villain laughs that way just before he plunges the rapier through the hero's—wait a minute. Herman, the dictionary. Oh, here it is in the v's—viscera.

We try to frown on all their unconventional gestures. We call them— ha-ha—the "new degeneration." We laugh at their knickers. We are incensed at their cigarette smoking. Pulpiteers from their smug rostrums thunder their doom. But the world spins on.

We don't understand them and frankly they don't give a hang. They offer no alibi. They are themselves.

And out of this flapper age of high flings has come a sturdy American girl to swim the English Channel. We find them, when at their age girls carried smelling salts to keep from swooning thirty years ago, running big industrial enterprises. We find them taking their place as the best short story writers of the period. We find them capitalizing two dimples and a smile so that hard-boiled gentlemen of Hollywood must pay them from $5,000 to $20,000 a week on the screen.

We find them running motors, spinning over clouds in aeroplanes, and editing newspapers and magazines. Many of them are the very same girls who return from the boarding schools handling a cigarette carelessly and not as though it might go off.

They have nicotine-stained fingers and knees chapped from exposure. They can demolish a shaker of cocktails and go to the circus and come out and find their cars. They are secure and confident and it is going to take a lot more than our old-fashioned chortles to howl them down.

They have invaded our barber shops, they are slowly adopting our comfortable fashion of dress. The truth is as we grow ripe for the ether cone they become general nuisances.

As one who has sneered at them for many years I confess dismal failure. The more I sneer the more reckless and self-assured they become—drat 'em.

And the higher they go in business and the arts. We find them reigning capably over luxurious homes, marrying substantial men and raising healthy children.

I have come to the point where I don't know what to do with these college flappers. Except perhaps to give them another cocktail and a fresh cigarette.

EDMUND WILSON

Visiting Professor

FROM *I Thought of Daisy*

Edmund Wilson is acknowledged to be one of the most erudite and discerning of modern writers. Although he is principally a critic—one reviewer called him "a natural critic in the way some writers are natural poets"— he has written short stories, novels and a recent best-selling book on the Dead Sea Scrolls.

This selection, "A Visiting Professor," is from I Thought of Daisy, *a fictional autobiography of the '20s in which Edna St. Vincent Millay, and others of the creative writers of Wilson's Greenwich Village days, figure as characters.*

IN THE bright warm room, so alive inside the bleak November dark, before the fire burning briskly and stoutly, Professor Grosbeake's three beautiful daughters gave me tea, in their parents' absence. Among the elegant and slender spindles of the legs and rungs of the English furniture, which seemed blacker and stronger-sinewed, as if they had been brought to a sharper focus, than American mahogany—which, as in the case of the Queen Anne secretary, with its narrow shape, its dark dense grain, its close-laid shelves above, hooded with a double-loaf top, and its close-packed drawers below, diminishing in thickness toward the bottom, its air of having always contained sealed letters and legal papers, all safely and neatly locked away, seemed designed for a tighter, compacter, and more downright civilization; among the late pale autumnal flowers, the roses and the bowl of white cosmos; the white ruffle-bordered curtains against the black of the winter panes and the patches of confused pink and green made by the modest modernist paintings—Magda, Frieda, and Rosamond, themselves in fresh light frocks like the flowers, enchanted me with their loveliness and candor.

They were all very smooth and blonde; they had never bobbed their

475

hair, and Frieda and Magda wore theirs brushed abundantly down their backs, like Alice in the Alice books. Rosamond, who was older than the twins, had hers up; it was parted in the middle and tightly wound behind in a blonde and young womanly knot, so that, if one thought only of her hair, she seemed like a young German fräulein (Mrs. Grosbeake was German), whereas, if one thought of her blue eyes, her straight nose, her long oval face and her long and graceful neck, she seemed like an English girl. She served tea with nice shy manners. Rosamond was dressed in pale blue; and one of the twins, Magda, wore white, and Frieda, a kind of lilac, with stockings a kind of lavender, lighter than the frock. The twins seemed rather German than English: they had plump round cheeks and round noses, and were maturely developed for fourteen.

Frieda had golden-red hair, which gave a singular effect of richness as it came down over her purple dress; Magda was more heavily built and slower-moving and slower-thinking than her sister: she was the blondest of all—her hair was the palest, purest flaxen I had ever seen. . . .

I liked the English voices of the young Grosbeakes: they had a soft flurried way of speaking, and a maidenly innocence of timbre, quite unlike young American girls (though the twins were beginning already to acquire American slang). "I don't like this kind of crackers," said Magda. "We couldn't get the regular biscuits," Rosamond explained. "The grocer's all out of them.—I'm sorry," she went on seriously to me. "I'm afraid they're not very good!" "You always say 'biscuits,'" said Frieda, "and Magda always says 'crackers.' I think we all ought to say the same thing!" "What do you say?" queried Magda. "Sometimes I say one," said Frieda, "and sometimes I say the other. But I like 'biscuits' best!" "I think these are really crackers," said Rosamond, who did not want my feelings hurt by a discrimination in favor of "biscuits," "because they crackle so when you break them." "That's why I think 'biscuits' is better," insisted Frieda, "—because 'crackers' sounds as if they *all* crackled—but *some* biscuits just bend, you know!" "They're not biscuits," said Rosamond. "They're cakes. Won't you have some more tea?" she urged me. "No," said Frieda, "you know those little soft ones that we had in the country last summer, that you can almost bend in two!" "They were little cakes," said Rosamond.— We heard someone come in at the front door. "There's Father," Magda announced.

I could see Grosbeake taking off his black coat and his low-crowned black hat and setting his stick in the stand, before he appeared in the doorway. He had the rounded back of the scholar, a back, indeed, almost humped—of which I always used to feel that the exceptional extent to which it was bowed was an index to the degree of the difficulty of his researches. But Grosbeake, beyond this, had nothing of the physical de-

ficiency—the weak eyes or the feeble figure—ordinarily attributed to the
scholar. On the contrary, he seemed to have sprung from some tough,
ruddy-cheeked English stock which not even a lifetime of universities
could enervate or fade. Despite the fineness of his features, he had something
of Mr. Pickwick and even something of Mr. Punch. And upon an American
who had been living in New York, he produced a curious and gratifying
impression: it was as if one were surprised and rejoiced, after seeing a horde
of depersonalized masks, at finding someone who possessed a face. With
his fair cheeks flushed rosy by the cold, his salient nose and chin, his slanting
Henry VIII eyes and his look of having been carved by hand out of some
very sound kind of wood by a woodcarver of the days before machinery,
he gave the impression of being a product, by way of the generations which
had preceded him, of a constant hand-to-hand encounter with the turbu-
lence of the elements and with the occasions of human life. He wore
black English clothes and his stiff white cuffs were very white: his collar
and his cravat, and his white locks which came down over his collar, seemed
to me very old-fashioned. He always carried a thickish dark stick, with a
brass top of interlocked apes, which a brother had brought him from India.

He greeted me with his charming courtesy and peered up at me with
wise and subtle bird-lidded eyes. "I'm sorry," he explained, "not to have
been able to be here for tea. But there was a meeting of the examination
committee at precisely a quarter to five—something which would be un-
thinkable in England, you know." He lifted sparse old eyebrows in a smile.
"Rather than make the dons miss their tea, they'd allow the examination
to be prepared without adequate consultation! I had proposed holding the
meeting in a tea-room, but they didn't seem to care for the suggestion—or
to take the hint!" He spoke slowly and very deliberately, and his voice had
fine up-and-down inflections of sweetness and irony; his nostrils had inflections, too, and vibrated while he spoke.

"I'm afraid the tea's cold," said Rosamond. "I'll have some fresh made."
"No: never mind!" said Grosbeake. He stood before the fire, his hands
clasped just above his stomach. "I think we shall have snow," he announced.
"I think we shall have snow! The Dean was very sure we shouldn't—but I
believe that we shall!" I remarked that we had had no frost and that the
afternoon had been warm. "That was what the Dean pointed out," he
replied. "He even insisted on making a bet with me. He bet me a bottle of
Scotch whisky against a bottle of my sherry. I think he'll get the better of
the bargain: the sherry is very good: it was given me by a friend in the
Embassy, who had the privilege of bringing it in!"

He took the cup of tepid tea from Rosamond and sat down in an
armchair before the fire. He asked me about myself and what I had been
writing. I was ashamed to be obliged to tell him that, even while I had

been abroad, I had really not written anything—I said that my literary morale had been low, or something equally silly.

"I was just thinking," he replied, "in the Dean's room, in looking at the portraits of the college presidents there—that it may be from certain points of view as much of a misfortune to have too much character, too well-sustained a morale, as to have too little. When I looked at the early presidents, especially the seventeenth-century ones, I said to myself, 'There are men whose character has been overdeveloped!' It's a very special combination of qualities, you know, that's required for a mind capable of original work. A man mustn't have his character too vigorously developed, because he must be able to experiment with ideas. It's like going to buy a hat, you know—first you try one on and wear it for a bit to see how it goes, and then you try on another. But a man with a strongly developed character is unable to do that.—But, on the other hand, of course, he must still have character enough not simply to drift about without preferring one idea to another."

Grosbeake had a curious irony, which was always at the same time benign. It was the irony—one sees it seldom—of a mind which is at once innocent and subtle, and which has, in consequence, something divine about it: an irony without malice. He had a touch perhaps of the vanity, or rather, of the dandyism, of the modern mathematical philosopher, who finds himself provided with paradoxes at once so surprising, so attractive and so sound. I have heard him comment with his calm amusement on the mistakes of unmathematical philosophers when they attempted to invoke mathematics: "It's curious," he would say, "how peculiarly unfortunate they are in their choice of mathematical examples! They always seem to hit upon something which isn't necessarily true at all—which might as well be the other way, you know! Bradley, for example, in his *Logic,* when he wants to give an illustration of a particularly indisputable truth—something we must accept as self-evident—that, if B is to the left of C, and if A is to the left of B, then A must be to the left of C, also—when, of course, that's not true at all!—if you prolong a straight line indefinitely, you come back on the other side!" Though, when Bradley's *Logic* was written, non-Euclidean geometry could hardly have been widely known. (There may have entered, also, into Grosbeake's attitude, in this particular instance, some traditional opposition between the points of view of Cambridge and Oxford.)

But no one could have been farther than Grosbeake from the essential triviality of mind which academic arrogance or complacency so often tries to disguise. . . . Grosbeake was a modern type of sage, who taught wisdom in casual conversation and virtue only by example. I had felt his influence even in college, at a time when I as yet knew nothing of his philosophical ideas. For Grosbeake had the most comprehensive mind, at home in the most varied fields, with which I had ever come into contact. For him, philosophy was an attempt to take account of all the aspects of the universe, and to find in them coherence and a meaning; so that Grosbeake's comment on any subject had a special signifiance and value, and, despite the fact that he never made an effort to expostulate or convert, was likely to present itself long afterwards as something to be seriously considered in making up one's mind on the subject. And though he detested every sort of preaching . . . and though even the study of Ethics was inconceivable to him, he had the effect, more than any one else I had known, of making moral distinction attractive. I remember his saying once of some student, a student of whose abilities he thought well, but who, as punishment for some escapade, had had his chapel cuts taken away from him, so that he couldn't go out of town over Sundays, that it would "do him good," because he would now work during the week-ends. "So you do believe in doing people good!" someone present had caught him up. "I thought you didn't believe in that!" "That's an object," Grosbeake had replied, a little taken back, "which I believe is best promoted indirectly."

Mrs. Grosbeake came in before dinner: she was a broad, handsome, placid German woman, very thoroughly educated and very practical. One always felt that she was a kind of base upon which Grosbeake's metaphysics rested; for he was more sensitive and nervous than he appeared, and, although intellectually imperturbable, was in other ways easily disorganized.

We had dinner in the white-walled dining room—it was a solid and attractive Colonial house. The Grosbeakes had brought over their own silver, as well as their own furniture, and the pieces had always seemed to me to possess plainly discernible personalities, even physiognomies: there was a squarish silver teapot which squatted flat upon the table and had a very sharp emphatic spout that jutted straight out from the base and was balanced on the other side by a long straight high-cocked handle. And the cream pitcher, the sauce boat, and even the little salt cellars straddled sturdily on three tiny legs, like some sort of blunt-beaked beetles, or rather, it occurred to me tonight, like the snouted and pot-bellied demons of Bruegel or Callot. Even the color and substance of the food seemed to have a special richness and density, as if they had been painted in a still-life: the bread and the boiled potatoes looked particularly white and firm, the mound of currant jelly particularly lucent and red, and the beefsteak particularly vivid in its contrasts of red and brown. The Ambassador's sherry was delicious. In spite, however, of the satisfaction which Grosbeake had seemed to feel in it, his epicurean tastes were really indulged almost exclusively in the things of the intellect, so that I have heard him relish a page of Hume as if it had been a wine, whereas food and drink themselves, as well as other material comforts, he usually disregarded. Now he dominated the table, talking tranquilly and blandly; and in the presence of their father and mother, the three lovely Grosbeake girls—unlike young American girls, who usually dominate their parents—were entirely in abeyance, with only an occasional low rapid interchange between the twins, who were sitting together.

"I've been reading Sinclair Lewis's *Babbitt*," Grosbeake remarked. I asked him what he thought of it. "Oh, very good," he replied. "Though a little unfair to Babbitt, I think. Of course, I know very little about the American cities of the Middle West—I can't pretend to speak. But from the students from the West whom I've had in my courses, I get rather a different impression. They're very alert, you know—very eager to learn. And they do well: they grasp things very quickly. So I don't think that the families they come from can be quite so uniformly benighted as Lewis represents them in *Babbitt*. . . ."

I always listened with interest and respect to Grosbeake's opinions on American matters. He had studied American affairs with the attention, at once sympathetic and detached, which he applied to everything, and he often succeeded in illumining them with that uncanny divination which he displayed in all sorts of fields quite outside his special province. At that time, it had become the custom for Englishmen who visited America—we encouraged it, of course, ourselves—to edify us with generalizations about American life and institutions—generalizations often based on a round of cocktail parties in New York, or, at most, on a lecture tour. So many of the prizes in America always went to the third- and second-rate that we had become, especially since the War, a paradise for British mediocrities— poets, novelists, and universal critics, who had often great success as lecturers. They went about patronizing the Americans with a gusto and a giddy elation which suggested that they might themselves have been patronized at home; and they would sometimes tour the country from coast to coast and return again and again. It was, therefore, peculiarly gratifying for an American to discover in Grosbeake those qualities of toughness, richness, eccentricity, and independence which one had admired in English literature and history, but of which one had so often been disappointed in the English celebrities who visited us.

After dinner, we sat before the fire. Mrs. Grosbeake seemed to contribute a ground-tone of infinite repose: she made one feel that the body of humanity was invulnerably solid and sound, and that it was deep and contained many treasures which had never been brought to birth. She sat with her feet side by side, resting squarely on the floor, and she wore some sort of leather sandals, with very wide blunt toes. These sandals, like the modernist paintings (which Grosbeake had bought from a former student, in financial difficulties), were one of the odd notes of unconventionality in the tranquil conventional household; and they surprised me in the same unwarranted way as when one found Grosbeake, in certain of his writings, carrying his philosophical principles through morals into the field of political criticism and bringing an indictment against nationalism or capitalism.

I had never, as an undergraduate, read anything which Grosbeake had written, and I had never taken any of his courses. I had, however, in my senior year, sometimes gone to his house. After meeting him once or twice at teas, I had run into him one day in the hallway of one of the recitation buildings: he had recognized me and had talked to me about an article which I had just written for the college magazine. I had attacked wholesale, as a sinister conspiracy against freedom of action and thought, the policy of the English Department, the administration of the Dean's office, football mass meetings, compulsory chapel, and the custom of compelling freshmen to wear little black caps; and I was surprised and rather embarrassed by Grosbeake's expression of friendly interest. I replied almost apologetically—I had been dismayed by the rumpus I had roused—that I seemed to have laid myself open for a good deal of adverse criticism. "Ah, well," Grosbeake had reassured me, "one can't take up any position, can one? without doing that." My complaints had been made in resentment, and they had been answered with resentment by the faculty, the alumni, the editors of the college daily, the officers of the athletic association, and some of the more ardent and articulate freshmen, who insisted that they asked nothing better than to pay homage to the college tradition by continuing to wear their little black caps: it had never occurred to me, at the time, that I was engaged in doing anything so dignified as taking up a position, and I had felt that I must be careful, in the future, to conduct the controversy with more scrupulousness and sobriety, that I must remember my intellectual responsibilities. And half my bitterness and indignation against the college authorities was gone at finding an elderly and important professor willing to consider without heat what I had said.

He had invited me then to his house, and I used to go there on Sunday evenings, when the Grosbeakes received faculty and students. I rarely heard him talk about his subject, and did not understand him when he did: I had only the vaguest notion what it was. I figured him as eternally occupied with solving the same sort of problems with which I had struggled in Trigonometry and Permutations and Combinations. I did not know that those strings of puzzles were not the whole of mathematics, but merely multipled illustrations of general mathematical laws, in which no one had attempted to interest us. And still less did I realize that Grosbeake had passed beyond Mathematics proper to Symbolic Logic (it was principally the fact that we had in our faculty another of the small but infatuated band of students of Symbolic Logic—a man with whom he wished to collaborate

—which had brought him to the United States and which had kept him there so long). I did not know that Symbolic Logic was an attempt to provide a universal language for all the branches of science, and that this attempt to formulate relations common to different departments of thought was itself a deeper expression of the same genius which had given rise to Grosbeake's interest in such varied fields of human activity, and of his extraordinary instinct for tracing their inter-relations. Aside from his personal distinction and charm, it was this gift which had fascinated me: he had usually talked to me about literature, but, aside from his appreciation of poetry, plays, and novels as such—which was in itself remarkable— he had also a brilliant faculty for reading into them social and moral history and revealing their philosophic implications. . . .

I wanted to make him talk on this subject, and I inquired vaguely about the congress of a scientific association which he had attended the summer before. He told me briefly of some of its proceedings, then added, after a pause, with his bland and serious irony: "If you want to see the sort of men that the medieval church must have been made up of, you should study an assemblage of modern scientists. I thought about them last summer that they must be very like the medieval doctors. They're all more or less internationally minded, you know, and they're men of strong character and conviction—and they're all authoritarians: they subscribe to a body of dogma and they won't countenance any heresy. If a scientist has evolved an hypothesis which runs counter to the established hypothesis, they won't give it a serious hearing—if he's performed an experiment, you know, which conflicts with accepted experiments, they refuse to look at it!"

At this point of the conversation, Magda and Frieda, who had to go to bed, came in to say good night. They kissed their mother, who spoke to them in a low voice, but they hesitated about kissing their father—in the midst of solemn discourse and with a visitor present. Magda hung back by her mother's couch, but Frieda cut the knot by dashing forward, diving for his bald brow—I saw her own beautiful hair over her shoulders, like some spilling of gold by the gods—and running abruptly out of the room. "Oh, good night, my dear!" said Grosbeake.—"They have never executed any-one," he continued—Magda kissed him on the cheek, more diffidently: "Good night, my dear!—But there are other methods of suppression even more expedient and effective; for burning calls attention to the victim."

His criticism of contemporary science soon led him into metaphysics.— The entrance of those gold and white girls—the offspring, so late in life, of that old bald round-shouldered man who had spent long years in the obstinate plumbing (by means of formulas so difficult and abstract that they excluded even ideas of number, so far beyond the ordinary reaches of even scientific minds that they dismayed even mathematicians) of that mysterious reality which is at once what we find outside us and what we think about it—the entrance of Grosbeake's lovely daughters had had the effect on me of a revelation of the human vitality, the creative force of flesh and blood, which is embodied in abstract thought. It was as if my imagination had fully conceived for the first time that the logician's chain of propositions, no less than the astronomer's systems and the physicist's analysis of the invisible, was as much the ripened fruit of rich natures as the poetry of Shakespeare and Dante, or as those beautiful long-limbed children, the breed of the Kentish seas and of the forests of the Rhineland, who had brusquely embraced their father.

He talked to me about the book he was writing. . . .

What astonished me most, however, was that Grosbeake now crowned his system with a new conception of God: he brought God back into the universe of science under what appeared to me at first an unfamiliar form. For Grosbeake's God was as different as possible from the tolerant and moderate Great Spirit, the enlightened parliamentary monarch, of the modern liberal theologian. God, for Grosbeake, was the ultimate harmony implied by the aesthetic and moral values of which men were aware in the universe; and our moments of divine revelation were simply those when we realized most indubitably the necessity of this harmony and order, when we became most acutely conscious of this creative purpose of God. And it was, then, this creative purpose which, in the interest of the ultimate harmony, determined which possibilities, among the infinite possibilities of the constant flux of events—the development of the universal organism should make themselves actual.

I listened to Grosbeake with excitement. He seemed to me at that moment to justify to me those instincts and those beliefs which—suspicious of all the world and uncertain of myself most of all—I had lately come to doubt. And I was moved by what seemed to me the greatness of his mind and the boldness of his spirit amidst the modesty and mildness of his home. I mustn't keep him up, then, and tire him: Mrs. Grosbeake had already gone to bed.

I said that I must go, and he got up and brought a bowl of nuts, which we cracked in front of the fire. He told me some Victorian anecdote about Gladstone and Disraeli, whom he always called "Dizzy."

As I finally came out of the warm house into the white-framed, glass-sided porch which enclosed the front door, I felt a tinge of crispness in the air, as when the first ice-splinters web a pond, and I caught the chilly fragrance of the roses and the white and daisylike cosmos, which had been set out in vases for the night—and as I took leave of Grosbeake—gazing out through the glass at the pavement lightly dappled with leaves and the dark grass glittering with wet—my mind bemused with a vision of

God as a vast crystal fixing its symmetry from a liquefied universe—I felt a delicious delicacy of iciness, glossy fall-leaf slivers and black rain-glinting glass.

"It's beginning to snow," said Grosbeake. It was true: it was not raining, but snowing. A great flake alighted on my sleeve. "So I win my bet with the Dean," he said. "I shall have his Scotch whisky and not he my sherry!—You know, the weather's the only subject on which I really regard myself as infallible. It comes from being bred on the Kentish coast—learning about one's weather from the narrow seas! What does Dean Mosely know of the weather?—coming from an inland city like Indianapolis!"

Grosbeake stood in the outside door and regarded the large flakes with satisfaction. "Dean Mosely kept insisting," he continued, "that there were none of the signs of snow—and when he came to enumerate them, I saw that it was true: there were none of the signs. But I knew it was going to snow!"

ALEXANDER WOOLLCOTT

Colleges Large and Colleges Small

FROM *College Humor*

Alexander Woollcott was a man of many and untiring enthusiasms, and of prodigious prejudices for and against an incredible variety of things, places, people and ideas. Among his enthusiasms was Hamilton College, his alma mater, whose virtues he touted whenever occasion permitted—or could be forced. He was without doubt the most partisan and most vocal of its many distinguished alumni. Unlike most supporters of the small college, he took no defensive position on the question, deeming it unnecessary and, in any case, beneath his dignity.

Woollcott was a columnist (at one time for The New Yorker*), drama critic, newspaperman, radio personality and conversationalist. In the latter role, his caustic wit and epigrammatic utterances won him constant quotation and misquotation, which he scornfully corrected whenever he could. In fact, he was at great pains to make certain that he alone was the final authority on himself, even writing his own characterizations of himself in the third person, past tense: "He had the memory of a pachyderm and a pianola's loyalty to the same tune."*

He was the inspiration for The Man Who Came To Dinner, *and at one time played the part. Those who knew him say that the expansive character was no more than a pale copy of the original.*

IN THAT tedious and interminable debate as to the relative values of small colleges and large universities, the men from such vast factories of instruction as Chicago or Columbia really should mention oftener than they do the sheer wear and tear on the nerves of small college graduates, who always are having to explain where and what their Alma Mater is.

"Oh, you went to Hamilton College, did you?" the former say. "Let's see, that's at Colgate, isn't it?"

This ridiculous confusion is due to the circumstance that Colgate is in a town presumptuously called Hamilton, a town that happens to be some eighty miles away from the college called Hamilton, perched on a hilltop at the edge of Clinton, New York. The confusion is the more annoying because in my time we did not think much of Colgate. As my time was twenty years ago, I have not heard much about that neighboring institution of late years, so that my information available for the old Hamilton sport of jeering at Colgate is not as up-to-date as one could wish.

Indeed, within the past year I happened to have heard the name of Colgate brought up only twice in conversation. Once was a reference to an interesting undergraduate at my college who, merely because he had quietly heaved a lot of granite boulders through the sacred windows of the Administration Building, was officially persuaded to go away and not come back. Of course, he just went to Colgate, where a gesture which the Hamilton authorities had regarded as tinged with vandalism was doubtless interpreted as a mere prank of healthy animal spirits.

The other instance was when Harpo Marx, the last of the mad Marxes, expressed himself as pretty bitter because no college had ever given him an honorary degree. He suggested that I sound out Colgate on the subject and told me frankly that he was willing to go as high as fifteen dollars. So you see I have not been sufficiently in touch with that neighboring institution to speak of it with as much disparagement as I should like. . . .

Yet, if there is an irritation for the graduate of any small college in the outside world's bland ignorance of its great importance, there is an accompanying compensation in the glow which comes when it *is* recognized, a glow which no man from Harvard or Leland Stanford can ever experience. It is akin to the glow induced by two Hamilton men coming face to face in some far, unexpected corner of the world, a reunion not unlike the chance meeting of two members of some select and secret fraternity.

I remember noticing during the war that when two New Yorkers would meet in France, the meeting was of no special interest to either of them. But just let two men from Nacogdoches, Texas, or Aspen, Colorado, or Phalanx, New Jersey, run into each other in the cobbled streets of some small French village and the spark would be electric.

"From Aspen? From Aspen, Colorado? You don't say. Well, put it there, buddy!"

And off they would go arm-in-arm to the nearest *buvette*, happy as lords in the joint possession of a set of memories that few could share with them. Any graduate of a little school will know just how they felt. . . .

Perhaps I can convey a sense of its deep rooted tranquillity by telling you that in my own day at Hamilton, I lounged to classes under shade trees planted by Lafayette. Or by telling you that when I was a senior, there came up the Hill a freshman who was matriculating there because his father and his grandfather and his great-grandfather had done so before him. He was the fourth of his name in direct succession to be awakened by the sound of the chapel bell calling across the Valley of the Oriskany.

Or by telling you that my fraternity, though launched at Hamilton in 1867 at a time when some of the undergraduates still went to recitations in the blue they had worn as captains and majors in the Civil War, was nevertheless the most recently established chapter of any fraternity on the Hill and was, therefore, properly regarded by the older crowds with the question due any upstart, and the decent willingness to think that this one might amount to something when it had had time to get on its feet. At Hamilton, even D. K. E. and Psi U. are sneered at by Alpha Delta Phi and Sigma Phi, who behave just like the two old families in Boston where, as you doubtless recall, *the Lowells speak only to Cabots, and the Cabots speak only to God. . . .*

I turn to the catalogue to lift a little of the matter printed under the general heading "Situation." This caption, "Situation," does not, as you might think, foreshadow any really helpful information as to how to get one after learning all the Greek and Latin that Hamilton so firmly imparts. It refers instead to the physical posture of the college. I quote:

"The college occupies a natural plateau nine hundred feet above the sea and three hundred feet above the adjacent valley. Its campus is a park of ninety-five acres, shaded by venerable trees, with an easterly exposure overlooking the Oriskany and Mohawk Valleys. Its buildings, arranged in quadrangles, are modern and adequate and, with few exceptions, are constructed entirely of stone. The naturally healthful conditions, secured by the elevation and by air exceptionally pure and dry, are supplemented by a private water supply from spring fed reservoirs above the college and by an extensive system of sanitation constructed in accordance with the best modern practice, and officially approved by the state authorities."

But what does that tell you of the beauty of the chapel spire, the gold of its weather vane touched by the slanting red of the setting sun, its open windows pouring out the plaintive choral sweetness of the *Ave Maria?* It does not tell you of verandahs from which, when the air is clear, you can see the foothills of the Adirondacks, a bad forty miles away. As you look across the valley, there is a pretty checkerboard of green sheep meadows, cozy villages, yellowing wheat, chattering brooks, lovely as the Rhineland, "fair as the Garden of the Lord."

It tells you nothing of the miraculous Christmas card the hill becomes in its mid-winter cloak of snow, when the gingko and the spruces swoon under their icing, and the whole community turns to sleds as the Hollanders turn to skates—the wild banshee wail of "Road! Roa—d!" mingling oddly with the curses of the fractured as they are borne off to the bonesetter.

Once I met a man who had paid a visit to every college and university in the world. He was a collector of impressions, and this hobby of his must have cut into his spare time considerably. He said that of them all only one was more beautiful than Hamilton. That was Upsala, in Sweden. I wiped out a thousand ancient grudges in replying, "Upsala? Upsala? I never heard of it." . . .

Perhaps one can come closer to a man's real estimate of any college by asking him two questions. Would he, if he had five million dollars to give away, present it to that college? And would he send his son there?

I have taken these questions home and tried them over on my own set of opinions about Hamilton College. Brooding on the question of that highly hypothetical five million dollars, I think I would as soon give it to Hamilton as to any other existing college.

That decision may seem somewhat less than loyal and impulsive. Its lack of warmth can probably be traced to a suspicion that the Hamilton curriculum, like all college curricula that I know anything about, is a mere accidental hodgepodge of courses taught because they always have been taught; lazy, automatic leftovers of old forgotten expediencies. I even suspect that there is no more (and no less) reason for teaching Latin or calculus, for instance, than for teaching ceramics.

With five million dollars to blow, I would rather put it into a school established by a man who would at least challenge the validity of every single item in the traditional college curriculum, who would, indeed, map out his highhanded use of the undergraduate's priceless time as if there never had been a college since Noah offered to humanity its most recent chance to start afresh.

I would get H. G. Wells to come over and plan the course of study, select the faculty and linger long enough to preach the first baccalaureate sermon, if (and this, too, would have to be critically pondered) any. In presenting five million dollars to such an experiment, one would feel less as if one were lazily pouring a fortune into a sieve.

But backing hastily out of such deep water in the nick of time to avoid total immersion, I turn to other questions. Would I send my even more hypothetical son (on whom admittedly I have not even made a good start) to Hamilton College? I can only reply that if I had one and ventured to tell him to which college he must go, I hope the sturdy and presumably handsome lad would also have a strong enough sense of his own sovereignty to tell me to mind my own business.

If, however, he were disposed to consult me in the matter, I would tell him frankly that I could no more conceive myself as having gone to another college than I could conceive myself as having had another mother. I would admit to him that I could no more describe the Hill to him than I could describe my mother's face.

But I think I would assure him that in my own wanderings over the face of the earth, I had come upon no more charming place in which to spend four years. "Now four years, my boy," I would remark, "are not to be sneezed at." And I would go on to say to him that a mortal who falls into the miserly habit of regarding any four years as a mere preparation for another four is a little too much like the man who saves all his money so he can have a high old time when he is eighty.

"My son," I would say, *"Carpe Diem."*

For thus does my college days Latin come back, with the tingle of a recent soda water.

The Coeds Were Real—
The Boys Were Shadows

FROM *College Humor*

🔖 *The late Bernard De Voto—brave man—wrote this article while he was teaching English at Northwestern. It created something of a stir. But then, there were few things De Voto wrote that didn't. He was a man of belligerent certainties, whether he wrote of coeds or of Mormonism, or of the condition of contemporary American literature. Among his other activities—mostly writing—he taught at Harvard in the '30s, then, for two years, was editor of* The Saturday Review of Literature. *Subsequently, he conducted "The Easy Chair" for* Harper's Magazine *until his death. Whatever he was doing, De Voto was, as one commentator put it, "a gadfly to all manner of intellectual softies."*

THERE was, I found, a neurosis at Northwestern. Also, there was something, at first nebulous and baffling, that set me thinking of Ernest Hocking standing remote above us in Emerson Hall and, in the voice of a lover, setting before us philosophies that had had their moment two thousand years ago, and had gone their way into the limbo of men's hopes. Let me particularize.

It was autumn of 1922 when I went there, and the neurosis was already old. Early that fall the football team and a third of the undergraduates traveled to Urbana for the Illinois game. Insult awaited them there. From store front and lamp post, from fraternity house and trolley car hung banners painted to greet the visitors. "Welcome, sisters," the banners said, and "Northwestern for its pretty girls," and "Hail, Northwestern, the finest girls' school in the Middle West." And many other opprobrious devices. In its recesses of despair the neurosis burned and throbbed. If heaven had been merciful, the girls' school team would have walloped the contemners and exalted the humble, but heaven was realistic. Illinois won by some incalculable score, and the girls' school went homeward, mourning.

Thereupon the neurosis passed into an active phase. First there were mass meetings, secret, compulsory. Only males could enter them, and if anyone looked like a reporter he was barred at the door. Inside athletes, fraternity officials, professors, deans, Prexy himself danced and bellowed and exhorted. The theme was: there must be more men at Northwestern, and men must be tougher there.

The mass meeting rash lasted for weeks, and meanwhile alumni went out into the sticks resolutely. The campus responded. He who wore a tie was first scorned, then threatened, and finally ducked in the lake. Corduroys and stagged shirts became the uniform of loyalty. Those who could kept a symbolic stubble on their jowls. In the quaint local manner someone declared it proper to "start a tradition," and it was set down in the books as traditional that no Northwestern man took a girl to any athletic contest. To do so would, presumably, interfere with the whole duty of man, to help that team. And again, another spontaneously generated tradition. The athlete was pictured as resenting the softer man's prerogative of spending an evening with a girl; therefore, necking was restricted to certain nights a week, to help that team.

Happily, Tom Robinson's swimming teams gleamed through the darkness. Regularly, methodically, they won Big Ten championships, intercollegiate championships, national championships. So that the neurosis, faced by routine disaster everywhere else, could always allay itself with the waters of the tank. But baseball, basketball, track, wrestling, cross-country and all other diversions gave us only the ignominious ninth or tenth place to which we were accustomed. Football was worst of all. Everywhere the alumni—and the luncheon clubs of Evanston—were active. A stream of hard-muscled lads poured into the campus and out to the field house. But fruitlessly.

My second autumn the team did more disastrously than my first, for then some halfback had run ninety yards to a touchdown against Minnesota, but this year particularly no one ran any distance against anyone. The third autumn was no better, though by now even the commercially-minded downtown campus had caught the neurosis. They went forth to battle, these teams, but they always died. The campus was wholly evangelical. More men and maler men! More men and hairier chests for Northwestern! The corduroys were greasier, the stagged shirts more dissolute. The neurosis had germinated a religion, an exaltation. The student body hardly noticed the weekly martyrdom, so intent, so prayerful were they. looking forward to the day of compensation. Not now, not today, not next week, perhaps not next year, but some time!

Long since, I had understood why I remembered Ernest Hocking in the dimness of Emerson Hall, dealing gently with the vanished idealisms of mankind. For here before me was Heraclitus. It was not today's defeat that counted at Northwestern, not the ignominy of the real, not that which was. No, the neurosis had blotted out ignominy and shame and reality. Only what was to be had any meaning. It was not Being. It was Becoming. This understanding was to make clear to me far more about Northwestern than the football neurosis.

That, indeed, relaxed and for a splendid moment disappeared, as neuroses will. The fourth autumn desperation had its first fruits. The team won a Conference game, and then so vengefully assaulted Notre Dame that Rockne had to send in his first-string backfield to win the game, and at last reached out and touched the stars. A cloudburst fell on Soldiers' Field the day Michigan came, and somehow, in four inches of water, Northwestern won three to two against a team that would have scored much more if the ground had been dry. The boys burned down an abandoned fraternity house, and cut lengths from the first hose, and battered a few policemen. Prexy reproved them and they cheered him, seeing his eyelid droop.

Then the skies lightened toward daybreak and the trustees laid the cornerstone of a million dollar stadium, hoping that this would generate the ultimate energy. It did. The next year, by beating the weakest four teams in the Conference while Michigan was beating the strongest four, the team achieved the gold footballs that temporarily sublimated the neurosis. For a moment the flux of things paused in symmetry. For a moment Becoming ceased and Being was achieved. But by that time I was following the clew of Heraclitus through more subtle mysteries of Northwestern.

Being a bachelor and, in years, not much older than the students I taught, I had begun by associating intimately with the undergraduate men. I spent my time at their dormitories and fraternity houses. I went with them to movies and restaurants and speakeasies. I joined their bull sessions and their poker games. For a while. They were likable boys, companionable boys—but only boys. Visits to other colleges showed me that at the other Conference schools boys grew up into men, young men of course, but past adolescence and well past puberty. Maturity was assumed elsewhere, yet I could not find it on our campus. I missed it, and with it most of what had been glamorous in college.

Where were the generous, preposterous, passionate midnight arguments that enlarged the soul? Arguments that reinvented God and re-created the universe a dozen times an evening. Where were the hot lusts for knowledge, sprung from a roommate's air of superiority, or a drowsing professor, or some obscure, probably lascivious allusion in a text? Where were the sparks that set youth championing anarchy or socialism or Rosicrucianism or decadence or astrology? I do not say they were not there, but only that they were not visible. The boys who were not yet young men had driven them under cover. The individual did not appear; the man who experimented with absinthe or table tapping, who expressed a preference for golf or Sanscrit over homecoming and indulged it without shame, who wore spats because he wanted to or last year's suit because he couldn't afford a new one, who went walking at sunrise because that was his whim or indulged himself with the ladies of the street corner because that was his whim also. There was no individual; or, rather, none was unwary enough to show himself. The tribe had no toleration of individuality.

For all boys were tribal, and Northwestern men were boys. The dreadful Philistinism of adolescence was on them, and overlaying it was a Philistinism more discouraging still. . . . From the first, the women of the campus were a reassurance. Whatever of glamour the men missed, the co-eds had. The men were Philistine, herd-minded, immature. The co-eds were liberal, individual, grown up. The men had lost entirely the sense of adventure, and in its place had only a formalism that made one's heart gray. The co-eds lived an adventure, and it was a joyful one. Here were enthusiasm and open-mindedness and sophistication and the will to have those intangible accompaniments of college that I have mentioned.

Sophistication! That, I think, was the first, most obvious difference. They seemed so much older than the little boys, so much more of the world. The varied evidence of this was on every hand. I first realized it, I think, when I noticed that if my courses in literature brought up a sexual topic, the men blushed or sniggered while the co-eds treated it as a matter of course. But they were not sophisticated in biological calmness only, but in more worldly ways. They were skeptical. They were tolerant. They were realistic. They were eccentric in that they varied from the norm, whereas the men approached it. They were also gay and delightful and in all things praiseworthy.

Oh, they had their absurdities. Sorority worship is, if possible, even sillier than fraternity awe, and I must confess that these charming girls gabbled like idiots when being true to the star and dagger was talked about. And yet, between the solemnity of a boy telling you why loyalty to Sigma Chi half suffocates him, and a girl hymning the immortal loveliness of Kappa Kappa Gamma there is a significant difference. The realistic basis of social importance is never mentioned in the pæons to Sigma Chi. It is frankly conceded in the salutations to Kappa Kappa Gamma, and that is wholesome.

These delightful girls, too, had created at Northwestern as imbecile an "activity" as was ever conceived (save only the Purple Key). I refer to what were called the literary societies, Alethenai, Anonian, Laurean and others. Yet these, too, had a leaven of good sense and realism. No member of Purple Key ever realized that his organization was absurd: no member of Alethenai ever pretended that her organization was literary. With a sanity that redeemed the original absurdity, they all frankly admitted that the literary societies were purely social. That was the tonic realism that the men lacked. That was sophistication, amusement, the worldly sense.

And with these two absurdities, redeemed by their realism, I have exhausted the indictment against Northwestern women. For the rest they were admirable. I remember them as an earnest assurance that youth in the Midland is not wholly Philistine, an assurance that the college is doing its proper work. They had the wit to dress as they liked, which the men did not, and I here acknowledge the charm that resulted. They bowed not down in Rimmon's house, and when they passed the commerce school there was no genuflection. They resisted the regimentation of orthodoxy. They welcomed innovation and individualism. No bunk from the authorities or the alumni imposed upon them. They went the way they had chosen and when a regulation opposed them, ignored it: and when a convention or taboo rose up, laughed it out of sight. Nor did they, as the boys did, regard the faculty as perhaps dull but certainly infallible. . . . For it is the essence of my theme that here, among the women, was everything that Northwestern seemed elsewhere deprived of. They were what youth should be. They were eager and determined and enthusiastic and cool-minded, sane when sanity was desirable, mad when madness was a virtue. For them there was the ancient possibility of wisdom, the ancient possibility of adventurousness and delight in life. They were real; the boys were shadows.

Away, now, from Northwestern, I remember them as incredibly slangy and self-possessed, witty, satirical, underdressed. They tend, in my mind, to become a composite of laughter, bright scarfs and beige stockings. The stockings are, in fact, worth more than perfunctory attention, not alone because they were charming. Those knees, exhibited with such nonchalance, such matter-of-fact carelessness, signified freedom and realism and self-respect. She showed her knees, this composite Northwestern co-ed, and thought nothing of it. No doubt she delighted in them, but not disproportionately. Knees were gay, but life was adventurous. That was the essence; she preserved, and at Northwestern monopolized, the eagerness and arrogance of youth that have immemorially signified college. Currents ran deeply in the earth, tides rose in the sea, and winds were blowing in from beyond the world—and she would find out about them, valuing them more than a cost accounting sheet from Wieboldt Hall or a culture hero of the future who might some day score on Michigan. . . .

If I had a son of college years, would I send him to Northwestern? The answer to such a question may well be: I am a Harvard man. But ignoring that obligation, what I have written ought to indicate my answer. I would send no son of mine to Northwestern. But a daughter? That, assuredly, is another question. I think of those girls, and of how much of the reality of education they achieve there, in spite of the shadow aforesaid, in spite of the stampede toward commerce, in spite of the careful orthodoxy that is encouraged. Yes, if I thought well of my daughter, I would send her to Northwestern.

I Invent
My Way Through College

FROM *My Boyhood and Youth*

John Muir was America's greatest conservationist and a founder of our national park system. He spent most of his life "on a glorious botanical and geological excursion" in the University of the Wilderness, as he called it—the Sierras, Yosemite, the Alaskan mountains.

Muir was born in Scotland, came to America in 1848 with his parents when he was ten, and grew up in a rural log cabin in Wisconsin. With the gift of curiosity he combined imagination and inventive hands. In his early youth, he invented a series of ingenious devices, some of which he brought for display to the Madison State Fair. Thence, he found his way to the University of Wisconsin. By selling "bedsteads that set the sleepers on their feet in the morning" and other equally bizarre and intriguing gadgets, and by supplementing his earnings with summer work as a farm laborer, he paid his way through college.

I WAS looking around in the mean time to find out where I should go to seek my fortune. An inventor at the Fair, by the name of Wiard, was exhibiting an iceboat he had invented to run on the upper Mississippi from Prairie du Chien to St. Paul during the winter months, explaining how useful it would be thus to make a highway of the river while it was closed to ordinary navigation by ice. After he saw my inventions he offered me a place in his foundry and machine-shop in Prairie du Chien and promised to assist me all he could. So I made up my mind to accept his offer and rode with him to Prairie du Chien in his iceboat, which was mounted on a flat car. I soon found, however, that he was seldom at home and that I was not likely to learn much at his small shop. I found a place where I could work for my board and devote my spare hours to mechanical drawing, geometry, and physics, making but little headway, however, although the Pelton family, for whom I worked, were very kind. I made up my mind after a few months' stay in Prairie du Chien to return to Madison, hoping that in some way I might be able to gain an education.

At Madison I raised a few dollars by making and selling a few of those bedsteads that set the sleepers on their feet in the morning,—inserting in the footboard the works of an ordinary clock that could be bought for a dollar. I also made a few dollars addressing circulars in an insurance office, while at the same time I was paying my board by taking care of a pair of horses and going errands. This is of no great interest except that I was thus winning my bread while hoping that something would turn up that might enable me to make money enough to enter the State University. This was my ambition, and it never wavered no matter what I was doing. No University, it seemed to me, could be more admirably situated, and as I sauntered about it, charmed with its fine lawns and trees and beautiful lakes, and saw the students going and coming with their books, and occasionally practising with a theodolite in measuring distances, I thought that if I could only join them it would be the greatest joy of life. I was desperately hungry and thirsty for knowledge and willing to endure anything to get it.

One day I chanced to meet a student who had noticed my inventions at the Fair and now recognized me. And when I said, "You are fortunate fellows to be allowed to study in this beautiful place. I wish I could join you." "Well, why don't you?" he asked. "I haven't money enough," I said. "Oh, as to money," he reassuringly explained, "very little is required. I presume you're able to enter the Freshman class, and you can board yourself as quite a number of us do at a cost of about a dollar a week. The baker and milkman come every day. You can live on bread and milk." Well, I thought, maybe I have money enough for at least one beginning term. Anyhow I couldn't help trying.

With fear and trembling, overladen with ignorance, I called on Professor Stirling, the Dean of the Faculty, who was then Acting President, presented my case, and told him how far I had got on with my studies at home, and that I hadn't been to school since leaving Scotland at the age of eleven years, excepting one short term of a couple of months at a district school, because I could not be spared from the farm work. After hearing my story, the kind professor welcomed me to the glorious University—next, it seemed to me, to the Kingdom of Heaven. After a few weeks in the preparatory department I entered the Freshman class. In Latin I found that one of the books in use I had already studied in Scotland. So, after an interruption of a dozen years, I began my Latin over again where I had left off; and, strange to say, most of it came back to me, especially the grammar which I had committed to memory at the Dunbar Grammar School.

During the four years that I was in the University, I earned enough in the harvest-fields during the long summer vacations to carry me through the balance of each year, working very hard, cutting with a cradle four acres of wheat a day, and helping to put it in the shock. But, having to buy books and paying, I think, thirty-two dollars a year for instruction, and occasionally buying acids and retorts, glass tubing, bell-glasses, flasks, etc., I had to cut down expenses for board now and then to half a dollar a week.

One winter I taught school ten miles north of Madison, earning much-needed money at the rate of twenty dollars a month, "boarding round," and keeping up my University work by studying at night. As I was not then well enough off to own a watch, I used one of my hickory clocks, not only for keeping time, but for starting the school fire in the cold mornings, and regulating class-times. I carried it out on my shoulder to the old log schoolhouse, and set it to work on a little shelf nailed to one of the knotty, bulging logs. The winter was very cold, and I had to go to the schoolhouse and start the fire about eight o'clock to warm it before the arrival of the scholars. This was a rather trying job, and one that my clock might easily be made to do. Therefore, after supper one evening I told the head of the family with whom I was boarding that if he would give me a candle I would go back to the schoolhouse and make arrangements for lighting the fire at eight o'clock, without my having to be present until time to open the school at nine. He said, "Oh! young man, you have some curious things in the school-room, but I don't think you can do that." I said, "Oh, yes! It's easy," and in hardly more than an hour the simple job was completed. I had only to place a teaspoonful of powdered chlorate of potash and sugar on the stove-hearth near a few shavings and kindling, and at the required time make the clock, through a simple arrangement, touch the inflammable mixture with a drop of sulphuric acid. Every evening after school was dismissed, I shoveled out what was left of the fire into the snow, put in a little kindling, filled up the big box stove with heavy oak wood, placed the lighting arrangement on the hearth, and set the clock to drop the acid at the hour of eight; all this requiring only a few minutes.

The first morning after I had made this simple arrangement I invited the doubting farmer to watch the old squat schoolhouse from a window that overlooked it, to see if a good smoke did not rise from the stovepipe. Sure enough, on the minute, he saw a tall column curling gracefully up through the frosty air, but instead of congratulating me on my success he solemnly shook his head and said in a hollow, lugubrious voice, "Young man, you will be setting fire to the schoolhouse." All winter long that faithful clock fire never failed, and by the time I got to the schoolhouse the stove was usually red-hot.

At the beginning of the long summer vacations I returned to the Hickory Hill farm to earn the means in the harvest-fields to continue my University course, walking all the way to save railroad fares. And although I cradled four acres of wheat a day, I made the long, hard, sweaty day's work still longer and harder by keeping up my study of plants. At the noon hour I collected a large handful, put them in water to keep them fresh, and after supper got to work on them and sat up till after midnight, analyzing and classifying, thus leaving only four hours for sleep; and by the end of the first year, after taking up botany, I knew the principal flowering plants of the region.

I received my first lesson in botany from a student by the name of Griswold, who is now County Judge of the County of Waukesha, Wisconsin. In the University he was often laughed at on account of his anxiety to instruct others, and his frequently saying with fine emphasis, "Imparting instruction is my greatest enjoyment." One memorable day in June, when I was standing on the stone steps of the north dormitory, Mr. Griswold joined me and at once began to teach. He reached up, plucked a flower from an overspreading branch of a locust tree, and, handing it to me, said, "Muir, do you know what family this tree belongs to?"

"No," I said, "I don't know anything about botany."

"Well, no matter," said he, "what is it like?"

"It's like a pea flower," I replied.

"That's right. You're right," he said, "it belongs to the Pea Family."

"But how can that be," I objected, "when the pea is a weak, clinging, straggling herb, and the locust a big, thorny hardwood tree?"

"Yes, that is true," he replied, "as to the difference in size, but it is also true that in all their essential characters they are alike, and therefore they must belong to one and the same family. Just look at the peculiar form of the locust flower; you see that the upper petal, called the banner, is broad and erect, and so is the upper petal of the pea flower; the two lower petals, called the wings, are outspread and wing-shaped; so are those of the pea; and the two petals below the wings are united on their edges, curve upward, and form what is called the keel, and so you see are the corresponding petals of the pea flower. And now look at the stamens and pistils. You see that nine of the ten stamens have their filaments united into a sheath around the pistil, but the tenth stamen has its filament free. These are very marked characters, are they not? And, strange to say, you will find them the same in the tree and in the vine. Now look at the ovules or seeds of the locust, and you will see that they are arranged in a pod or legume like those of the pea. And look at the leaves. You see the leaf of the locust is made up of several leaflets, and so also is the leaf of the pea. Now taste the locust leaf."

I did so and found that it tasted like the leaf of the pea. Nature has used the same seasoning for both, though one is a straggling vine, the other a big tree.

"Now, surely you cannot imagine that all these similar characters are mere coincidences. Do they not rather go to show that the Creator in making the pea vine and locust tree had the same idea in mind, and that plants are not classified arbitrarily? Man has nothing to do with their classification. Nature has attended to all that, giving essential unity with boundless variety, so that the botanist has only to examine plants to learn the harmony of their relations."

This fine lesson charmed me and sent me flying to the woods and meadows in wild enthusiasm. Like everybody else I was always fond of flowers, attracted by their external beauty and purity. Now my eyes were opened to their inner beauty, all alike revealing glorious traces of the thoughts of God, and leading on and on into the infinite cosmos. I wandered away at every opportunity, making long excursions round the lakes, gathering specimens and keeping them fresh in a bucket in my room to study at night after my regular class tasks were learned; for my eyes never closed on the plant glory I had seen.

Nevertheless, I still indulged my love of mechanical inventions. I invented a desk in which the books I had to study were arranged in order at the beginning of each term. I also made a bed which set me on my feet every morning at the hour determined on, and in dark winter mornings just as the bed set me on the floor it lighted a lamp. Then, after the minutes allowed for dressing had elapsed, a click was heard and the first book to be studied was pushed up from a rack below the top of the desk, thrown open, and allowed to remain there the number of minutes required. Then the machinery closed the book and allowed it to drop back into its stall, then moved the rack forward and threw up the next in order, and so on, all the day being divided according to the times of recitation, and time required and allotted to each study. Besides this, I thought it would be a fine thing in the summer-time when the sun rose early, to dispense with the clock-controlled bed machinery, and make use of sunbeams instead. This I did simply by taking a lens out of my small spy-glass, fixing it on a frame on the sill of my bedroom window, and pointing it to the sunrise; the sunbeams focused on a thread burned it through, allowing the bed machinery to put me on my feet. When I wished to arise at any given time after sunrise, I had only to turn the pivoted frame that held the lens the requisite number of degrees or minutes. Thus I took Emerson's advice and hitched my dumping-wagon bed to a star.

I also invented a machine to make visible the growth of plants and the action of the sunlight, a very delicate contrivance, enclosed in glass. Besides this I invented a barometer and a lot of novel scientific apparatus. My room was regarded as a sort of show place by the professors, who oftentimes brought visitors to it on Saturdays and holidays. And when, some eighteen years after I had left the University, I was sauntering over the campus in time of vacation, and spoke to a man who seemed to be taking some charge of the grounds, he informed me that he was the janitor; and when I inquired what had become of Pat, the janitor in my time, and a favorite with the students, he replied that Pat was still alive and well, but now too old to do much work. And when I pointed to the dormitory room that I long ago occupied, he said: "Oh! then I know who you are," and mentioned my name. "How comes it that you know my name?" I inquired. He explained that "Pat always pointed out that room to newcomers and told long stories about the wonders that used to be in it." So long had the memory of my little inventions survived.

Although I was four years at the University, I did not take the regular course of studies, but instead picked out what I thought would be most useful to me, particularly chemistry, which opened a new world, and mathematics and physics, a little Greek and Latin, botany and geology. I was far from satisfied with what I had learned, and should have stayed longer. Anyhow I wandered away on a glorious botanical and geological excursion, which has lasted nearly fifty years and is not yet completed, always happy and free, poor and rich, without thought of a diploma or of making a name, urged on and on through endless, inspiring, Godful beauty.

From the top of a hill on the north side of Lake Mendota I gained a last wistful, lingering view of the beautiful University grounds and buildings where I had spent so many hungry and happy and hopeful days. There with streaming eyes I bade my blessed Alma Mater farewell. But I was only leaving one University for another, the Wisconsin University for the University of the Wilderness.

The Convivial
Sons of Dartmouth

FROM *College Humor*

Gene Markey's wistful lament for the good old convivial days at Dartmouth is more moving when we realize that it was penned during the days of prohibition.

Prolific, popular and a versatile master of the communication arts, Markey has written novels, plays, motion pictures and short stories. He has also achieved a reputation as the only Dartmouth man ever to have married three movie stars, having been the husband of Joan Bennett, Hedy Lamar and Myrna Loy—successively, of course.

Old Eleazor Wheelock was a very pious man,
He went into the wilderness to teach the Indi-an,
With a Gradus and Parnassus,
A bible and a drum
And five hundred gallons of New England rum!

Chorus

Fill the bowl up, fill the bowl up,
Drink to Eleazor—
And his primitive Alcazar,
Where he mixed drinks for the heathen
In the goodness of his so-ul!

So RUNS the old chant, wherein Dartmouth College lifts a mug to toast its founder. In the middle of the eighteenth century the Reverend Eleazor Wheelock established in the fastnesses of the White Mountains

502

of New Hampshire a school for Indians. There are too many Indians at Dartmouth now, although this statement might be challenged by the constables who have witnessed Dartmouth football revels in New York and Boston.

In this arid age there is, one assumes, very little of drinking at Dartmouth, but tradition, dating from Parson Wheelock's original "five hundred gallons of New England rum" has always favored an alcoholic content of something more than one-half of one per cent. Richard Hovey, most permanent of Dartmouth poets, exalted the flowing bowl in his *Hanover Winter Song*:

> *Ho, a song by the fire!*
> *(Pass the pipes, fill the bowl!)*
> *Ho, a song by the fire!*
> *—With a Skoal. . . .*

The rousing chorus ends in a manner that calls for a glee club to do it justice:

> *And the cup is at the lip*
> *In the pledge of fellowship.*
> *Skoal!*

Throughout, the Dartmouth legend is pleasantly scented with the fragrance of the grape. It is a matter of record that Daniel Webster, our least obscure alumnus, for whom Time has woven a crown of laurel and vine leaves, dwelt, while an undergraduate at Hanover, in a neighborhood known as "Rum Hollow." *Eheu! Fugaces.* The old Dartmouth has given way to the new, and the flagon has been supplanted by the teacup. Which may or which may not be for the best. But Dartmouth is still a man's college, and those of us who remember gayer days upon its green campus can only surmise that Sir Thomas Lipton will never become such a popular college idol as was that stout fellow, Sir Johnnie Walker. . . . You can wring a sigh out of the most hard-hearted alumnus by reminding him of those dear departed days when a mail order to the taverns of Springfield, Greenfield or Bellows Falls would bring by the next express a camouflaged keg of beer, addressed usually to "John Smith." (During the beer season there were almost as many John Smiths in college as there are daily upon the hotel registers of New York.) Then, some time during the day, "Smith" would call for his weighty package, bear it from the station, often under the scrutiny of official eyes, and secrete it in some grotto, cloaked in ice.

A soft starlit spring night. Up the railroad track proceeds a merry band of minnesingers, following on the heels of an athlete bearing the keg upon his shoulders. (He has been specially invited for this purpose.) They reach a remote spot in the hills, and the Atlas of the party sets up the keg. A fire is built, and by its rosy glow, amid an admiring chorus, the keg is tapped. A geyser of fragrant foam spurts into the air—then tin cups are filled, and *prosits* drunk. Bags of pretzels appear, the fire burns brighter, and the night is cleft with song and merriment. From neighboring hillsides flare other beacons, where other kegs are being festively milked. Out of the darkness emerge occasional visitors, privileged seniors, with tin cups strapped to their belts. They are hailed according to their talents. A gifted entertainer may be welcome at half a dozen keg parties in an evening, if he be capable of mounting a rock and delivering a ribald oration, or rendering such popular sagas as *The Shooting of Dan McGrew,* or *The Lady Known as Lou.* Ah, bemoaned the old grad, those were nights!

F. SCOTT FITZGERALD

We'd Never
Be Quite So Young Any More

FROM *Afternoon of an Author*

It is the long spring before the First World War that F. Scott Fitzgerald recalls in this essay—Princeton in 1917—when not only the college, but the whole of the world, seemed to be splitting, breaking up, as he watched it. He left Princeton to join the army. Here is a quieter, older Fitzgerald looking back on his world and, more poignantly, on his generation grown old.

Perhaps no one man has ever so potently stood as spokesman for his generation as did Fitzgerald. In part, this is the fruit of his skill as writer and observer. But it must also be attributed to the fact that he was not only the clear-seeing author. He was also—in many aspects of his charming, bitter-sweet, reckless, destroyed life—his own most typical and convincing character. The generation, of course, was variously described as lost, and of The Jazz Age. Its heyday was in the booming '20s. Despite the undertone of tragedy and waste which characterized it, it has won—as no other period has done—a warm and nostalgic regard for its insouciant defiance and its gaiety. Fitzgerald's books and stories have the capacity to inspire this nostalgic feeling even in those readers who know nothing first hand about flappers, speakeasies, the incredible novelty of bobbed hair and short skirts, and a dominating mystique in which a bootlegger could seem a hero.

IN PREPARATORY school and up to the middle of sophomore year in college, it worried me that I wasn't going and hadn't gone to Yale. Was I missing a great American secret? There was a gloss upon Yale that Princeton lacked; Princeton's flannels hadn't been pressed for a week, its hair always blew a little in the wind. Nothing was ever carried through at Princeton with the same perfection as the Yale Junior Prom or the elections to their senior societies. From the ragged squabble of club elections with its scars of snobbishness and adolescent heartbreak, to the enigma that faced you at the end of senior year as to what Princeton *was* and what, bunk and cant aside, it really stood for, it never presented itself with Yale's hard, neat, fascinating brightness. Only when you tried to tear part of your past out of your heart, as I once did, were you aware of its power of arousing a deep and imperishable love.

Princeton men take Princeton for granted and resent any attempt at analysis. As early as 1899 Jesse Lynch Williams was anathematized for reporting that Princeton wine helped to make the minutes golden. If the Princetonian had wanted to assert in sturdy chorus that his college was the true flower of American democracy, was deliberately and passionately American's norm in ideals of conduct and success, he would have gone to Yale. His brother and many of the men from his school went there. Contrariwise he chooses Princeton because at seventeen the furies that whip on American youth have become too coercive for his taste. He wants something quieter, mellower and less exigent. He sees himself being caught up into a wild competition that will lead him headlong into New Haven and dump him pell-mell out into the world. The series of badges which reward the winner of each sprint are no doubt desirable, but he seeks the taste of pleasant pastures and a moment to breathe deep and ruminate before he goes into the clamorous struggle of American life. He finds at Princeton other men like himself and thus is begotten Princeton's scoffing and mildly ironic attitude toward Yale. . . .

Princeton is in the flat midlands of New Jersey, rising, a green Phoenix, out of the ugliest country in the world. Sordid Trenton sweats and festers a few miles south; northward are Elizabeth and the Erie Railroad and the suburban slums of New York; westward the dreary upper purlieus of the Delaware River. But around Princeton, shielding her, is a ring of silence— certified milk dairies, great estate with peacocks and deer parks, pleasant farms and woodlands which we paced off and mapped down in the spring of 1917 in preparation for the war. The busy East has already dropped away when the branch train rattles familiarly from the junction. Two tall spires and then suddenly all around you spreads out the loveliest riot of Gothic architecture in America, battlement linked on to battlement, hall to hall, arch-broken, vine-covered—luxuriant and lovely over two square miles of green grass. Here is no monotony, no feeling that it was all built yesterday at the whim of last week's millionaire; Nassau Hall was already thirty years old when Hessian bullets pierced its sides.

Alfred Noyes has compared Princeton to Oxford. To me the two are sharply different. Princeton is thinner and fresher, at once less profound and more elusive. For all its past, Nassau Hall stands there hollow and barren, not like a mother who has borne sons and wears the scars of her travail but like a patient old nurse, skeptical and affectionate with these foster children who, as Americans, can belong to no place under the sun.

In my romantic days I tried to conjure up the Princeton of Aaron Burr, Philip Freneau, James Madison and Light Horse Harry Lee, to tie on, so to speak, to the eighteenth century, to the history of man. But the chain parted at the Civil War, always the broken link in the continuity of American life. Colonial Princeton was, after all, a small denominational college. The Princeton I knew and belonged to grew from President McCosh's great shadow in the seventies, grew with the great *post bellum* fortunes of New York and Philadelphia to include coaching parties and keg parties and the later American conscience and Booth Tarkington's Triangle Club and Wilson's cloistered plans for an educational utopia. Bound up with it somewhere was the rise of American football.

For at Princeton, as at Yale, football became, back in the nineties, a sort of symbol. Symbol of what? Of the eternal violence of American life? Of the eternal immaturity of the race? The failure of a culture within the walls? Who knows? It became something at first satisfactory, then essential and beautiful. It became, long before the insatiable millions took it, with Gertrude Ederle and Mrs. Snyder, to its heart, the most intense and dramatic spectacle since the Olympic games. The death of Johnny Poe with the Black Watch in Flanders starts the cymbals crashing for me, plucks the strings of nervous violins as no adventure of the mind that Princeton ever offered. A year ago in the Champs Elysées I passed a slender, dark-haired young man with an indolent characteristic walk. Something stopped inside me; I turned and looked after him. It was the romantic Buzz Law whom I had last seen one cold fall twilight in 1915, kicking from behind his goal line with a bloody bandage round his head.

After the beauty of its towers and the drama of its arenas, the widely known feature of Princeton is its "clientele."

A large proportion of such gilded youth as will absorb an education drifts to Princeton. Goulds, Rockefellers, Harrimans, Morgans, Fricks, Firestones, Perkinses, Pynes, McCormicks, Wanamakers, Cudahys and duPonts light there for a season, well or less well regarded. The names of Pell, Biddle, Van Rensselaer, Stuyvesant, Schuyler and Cooke titillate second generation mammas and papas with a social row to hoe in Philadelphia or New York. An average class is composed of three dozen boys from such Midas academies as St. Paul's, St. Mark's, St. George's, Pomfret and Groton, a hundred and fifty more from Lawrenceville, Hotchkiss, Exeter, Andover and Hill, and perhaps another two hundred from less widely known preparatory schools. The remaining twenty per cent enter from the high schools and these last furnish a large proportion of the eventual leaders. For them the business of getting to Princeton has been more arduous, financially as well as scholastically. They are trained and eager for the fray.

In my time, a decade ago, the mid-winter examinations in freshman year meant a great winnowing. The duller athletes, the rich boys of thicker skulls than their forbears, fell in droves by the wayside. Often they had attained the gates at twenty or twenty-one and with the aid of a tutoring school only to find the first test too hard. They were usually a pleasant fifty or sixty, those first flunk-outs. . . . Priggishness sits ill on Princeton. It was typified in my day by the Polity Club. This was a group that once a fortnight sat gravely at the feet of Mr. Schwab or Judge Gary or some other parel-like spirit imported for the occasion. Had these inspired plutocrats disclosed trade secrets or even remained on the key of brisk business cynicism the occasion might have retained dignity, but the Polity Club were treated to the warmed over straw soup of the house organ and the production picnic, with a few hot sops thrown in about "future leaders of men." Looking through a copy of the latest year book I do not find the Polity Club at all. Perhaps it now serves worthier purposes. . . .

Princeton's sacred tradition is the honor system, a method of pledging that to the amazement of outsiders actually works, with consequent elimination of suspicion and supervision. It is handed over as something humanly precious to the freshmen within a week of their entrance. Personally I have never seen or heard of a Princeton man cheating in an examination, though I am told a few such cases have been mercilessly and summarily dealt with. I can think of a dozen times when a page of notes glanced at in a wash room would have made the difference between failure and success for me, but I can't recall any moral struggles in the matter. It simply doesn't occur to you, any more than it would occur to you to rifle your roommate's pocketbook. . . .

Vivid lights played on the whole colorful picture during the winter and early spring of 1917, just before the war. . . . Everything around us seemed to be breaking up. These were the great days; battle was on the horizon; nothing was ever going to be the same again and nothing mattered. And for the next two years nothing did matter. Five per cent of my class, twenty-one boys, were killed in the war.

That spring I remember late nights at the Nassau Inn with Bill Coan, the proctor, waiting outside to hale selected specimens before the dean next morning. I remember the long afternoons of military drill on the soccer fields, side by side perhaps with an instructor of the morning. We used to snicker at Professor Wardlow Miles' attempts to reconcile the snap of the drill manual with his own precise and pedantic English. There were no snickers two years later when he returned from France with a leg missing and his breast bright with decorations. A thousand boys cheered him to his home. I remember the last June night when, with two-thirds of us in uniform, our class sang its final song on the steps of Nassau Hall and some of us wept because we knew we'd never be quite so young any more as we had been here. And I seem to remember a host of more intimate things that are now as blurred and dim as our cigarette smoke or the ivy on Nassau Hall that last night. . . .

Looking back over a decade one sees the ideal of a university become a myth, a vision, a meadow lark among the smoke stacks. Yet perhaps it is there at Princeton, only more elusive than under the skies of the Prussian Rhineland or Oxfordshire; or perhaps some men come upon it suddenly and possess it, while others wander forever outside. Even these seek in vain through middle age for any corner of the republic that preserves so much of what is fair, gracious, charming and honorable in American life.

THE EDITOR
AND HIS BOOK

Auguste Comte Spectorsky *was born in Paris on August 13, 1910, the child of American parents who had gone abroad for an indefinite stay. Until he was four years old he spoke only French and considers himself a refugee of the First World War, this event having precipitated his family's return to America. He went to school in New York City and was graduated from New York University with a Science degree in 1934. His first sale as a writer was to The New Yorker which, he says, was "a sheer accident that filled me with a baseless courage for which I am grateful." He subsequently went to work for the magazine and later joined the staff of The Chicago Sun as assistant to the literary editor. For the Sun he wrote a thrice-weekly book column and then set up the first Sunday book supplement published outside of New York City. After six years in Chicago he returned to New York to work as Associate Eastern Story Editor for 20th Century-Fox Films and subsequently joined Street & Smith, serving in various capacities on various of the S&S publications. After editing the now-defunct Park East, he became a senior editor for NBC-TV. He currently is Associate Publisher of Playboy Magazine and Vice-President of the HMH Publishing Company, which is the magazine's parent organization. His writings have appeared in many magazines, including The New Yorker, Harper's Bazaar, Mademoiselle, College English, Collier's, Cosmopolitan, This Week and Reader's Digest. His previous books are:* Invitation to Skiing *(Simon & Schuster, 1947),* The New Invitation to Skiing *(Simon & Schuster, 1948) and* The Exurbanites *(Lippincott, 1955) and the following anthologies: the Mid-West section of* North East South West *(Howell-Soskin, 1945),* Man Into Beast *(Doubleday, 1948),* The Book of the Sea *(Appleton, 1954),* The Book of the Mountains *(Appleton, 1955),* The Book of the Sky *(Appleton, 1956), and* The Book of the Earth *(Appleton, 1957). He is also the author of a pamphlet,* The Future For Books In America *(Chicago Sun Publishing Company, 1945).*

The College Years *(Hawthorn, 1958) was designed by Ernst Reichl. The type was set by Pyramid Composition Company, New York City, and the book was printed and bound by Montauk Book Manufacturing Company, New York City. The titles and initial letters are Bulmer, a type face designed in 1790 by William Martin for William Bulmer and the Shakespeare Press, London. The body type was set on the Linotype in Baskerville, a modern rendering of the types cut in 1760 by John Baskerville, of Birmingham, England.*

A HAWTHORN BOOK

A Prospect of the Colledges in Cambridge in New England

VIEW OF COLLEGE IN 1739.

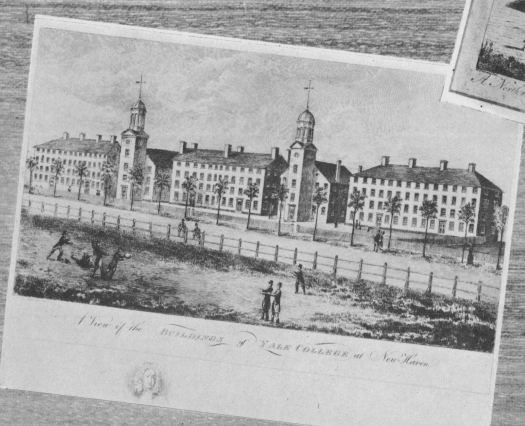

View of the BUILDINGS of YALE COLLEGE at New Haven